100
MATHS
LESSONS

YEAR 5

Published by Scholastic Ltd,
Villiers House,
Clarendon Avenue,
Leamington Spa,
Warwickshire CV32 5PR

© **2000 Scholastic Ltd**
Text © Lucy Simonds 2000
6789 456789

SERIES CONSULTANT
Ann Montague-Smith

AUTHOR
Lucy Simonds

EDITOR
Joel Lane

ASSISTANT EDITORS
Roanne Davis
David Sandford

SERIES DESIGNER
Joy White

DESIGNERS
Paul Cheshire
Mark Udall

COVER PHOTOGRAPH
Kim Oliver

ILLUSTRATIONS
Ray and Corinne Burrows

British Library Cataloguing-in-Publication Data
A catalogue record for this book is available from the British Library.

ISBN 0-439-01697-5

ACKNOWLEDGEMENTS

The publishers wish to thank:
The Controller of HMSO and the DfEE for the use of extracts from *The National Numeracy Strategy: Framework for Teaching Mathematics* © March 1999, Crown Copyright (1999, DfEE, Her Majesty's Stationery Office).
Galt Educational and NES Arnold Educational Supplies for kindly loaning the equipment used on the front cover.

CONTENTS

INTRODUCTION

100 Maths Lessons is a series of year-specific teachers' resource books for Reception to Year 6 that provide a core of support material for the teaching of mathematics within the National Numeracy Strategy *Framework for Teaching Mathematics* (March 1999), and within the structure of the 'dedicated mathematics lesson'. Each book offers three terms of medium-term planning grids, teaching objectives and lesson plans. At least 100 maths lessons are given in detail, with outlines for all the others needed to provide support for teachers for a whole year of maths teaching. Photocopiable activity pages and resources are included to support the learning, and regular assessment is built into the structure of the book with assessment activity pages which can be kept as evidence of attainment.

The activities in this book are designed to encourage pupils to develop mental strategies, to use paper and pencil methods appropriately, and to use and apply their mathematics in realistic tasks. There is a strong emphasis upon encouraging pupils to explain to each other the mathematics that they have used, the strategies that they employed and to compare these with each other to determine efficiency of method.

Each **100 Maths Lessons** book provides support across all the mathematics topics and learning objectives specified for a particular year group. However, the pages of the books have been hole-punched and perforated, so that they can be removed and placed in teachers' own resource files, where they can be interleaved with complementary materials from the school's existing schemes. This makes the integration of favourite material into this series very easy.

These books are intended as a support for the dedicated mathematics lesson for the school mathematics co-ordinator, teachers and trainee teachers. The series of books can be used as the basis of planning, teaching and assessment for the whole school, from Reception to Year 6. These resources can be adapted for use by the whole school for single-aged classes, mixed-age classes, single- and mixed-ability groups and for team planning across a year or a key stage. There is sufficient detail in the differentiated group activities within the 100 lesson plans to offer adequate guidance to classroom assistants working with a group.

The content of these activities is appropriate for and adaptable to the requirements of Primary 6 in Scottish schools. In schools which decide not to adopt the National Numeracy Strategy, choose activities to match your planning.

USING THIS BOOK

THE MATERIALS

This book provides at least 100 maths lesson plans for Year 5, and further activity ideas to support all other dedicated maths lessons required during the year. Each maths lesson plan contains ideas for developing pupils' oral and mental maths, a detailed explanation of the main part of the lesson, ideas for differentiated activities and suggestions for the plenary session. The book follows the Year 5 planning grid given in the National Numeracy Strategy *Framework for Teaching Mathematics* (March 1999) and so for each teaching section, whether one, two or three units of work, there are detailed lessons plans and objectives together with outline content for the other lessons. These materials should be regarded as a core for developing your own personalised folder for the year. More detail on planning and managing all aspects of the National Numeracy Strategy can be found in the *Framework for Teaching Mathematics* (March 1999).

ADAPTING AND PERSONALISING THE MATERIALS

The materials are based upon the 'Teaching programme and planning grid' for Year 5 from the National Numeracy Strategy *Framework for Teaching Mathematics* (March 1999). What follows is a suggested method of using this book to its full potential, but bear in mind that you may need to make adjustments to these materials in order to meet the learning needs of the pupils in your class.

● Separate the pages of the book and place them in an A4 ring binder.

● Check that the activities are of a suitable level for your pupils and agree with colleagues who teach higher and lower years that the entry level is a good match. If not, you can use materials from the *100 Maths Lessons* books for the previous or subsequent year as appropriate, or adapt lessons from within this book.

● Add your own favourite materials in the relevant places.

● If your school uses a published scheme, insert suitable teacher and pupil resources into your file to supplement these materials.

PREPARING A SCHEME OF WORK

All schools are required to write detailed schemes of work, and this series has been designed to facilitate this process. The termly **Planning grids** given in these books (see page 20 for example) are provided at the beginning of the work for each term and list all the learning objectives, referenced to the National Numeracy Strategy.

ORGANISATION

The **Organisation chart** outlines the key activities for each part of each maths lesson and can be used as a weekly plan, but could be adjusted according to the needs of the class.

LEARNING OUTCOMES	ORAL AND MENTAL STARTER	MAIN TEACHING ACTIVITY	PLENARY
LESSON 1 ● Read and write whole numbers in figures and words, and know what each digit represents. ● Develop calculator skills and use a calculator effectively.	GUESS MY NUMBER: Guess a number from facts about it.	COMBINING THOUSANDS: Use tens charts and arrow cards to combine numbers to make a given number.	Put given numbers into a calculator and compare with a partner.
LESSON 2 ● Read and write whole numbers in figures, and know what each digit represents. ● Understand the vocabulary of comparing and ordering numbers, including symbols such as <, >, =. Give one or more numbers lying between two given numbers. Order a set of integers less than 1 million.	MYSTERY NUMBERS: Compare the sizes of numbers made by arranging a set of digits in different ways.	REARRANGING THE DIGITS: Rearrange numeral cards to make bigger or smaller numbers.	Discuss how to rearrange digits to make the largest number. See how many different numbers can be made with 3 digits, 4 digits and so on.
LESSON 3 ● **Multiply or divide any integer up to 10 000 by 10 or 100 and understand the effect** (eg $9900 \div 10$, $2060 \div 100$). ● Develop calculator skills and use a calculator effectively. ● Read and write whole numbers in figures and know what each digit represents.	FAST TIMES: Multiplication facts, responding as a class or in groups.	CALCULATOR PLACES: Use a calculator to multiply and divide a given number by 10 or 100. Discuss what you notice.	Discuss the effect of multiplying by 10 or 100. What might be the effect of multiplying by 1000?

ORAL AND MENTAL SKILLS Recognise multiples of 2, 3, 5 and 10 (Y3 revision). Recognise odd and even numbers (Y3 revision). Read and write whole numbers in figures and know what each digit represents. **Know by heart multiplication facts for 2, 3, 4, 5 and 10 times tables.** Use known facts and place value to multiply integers including 10 and 100.

LESSON PLANS

After the Organisation chart comes a short section detailing which lessons are shown as full lesson plans and which are extensions of what has already been taught in a previous lesson. Some of these will be shown in grid form.

DETAILED LESSON PLANS
Each detailed lesson plan is written to the following headings:

Resources
Provides a list of what equipment you need for that lesson.

Preparation
Outlines any advance preparation needed before the lesson begins, such as making resources or photocopying worksheets.

Learning outcomes
These are based upon the objectives in the 'Teaching programme: Year 5' from the *Framework for Teaching Mathematics*. All the objectives are covered at least once in this book. Key objectives for Year 5 are highlighted in bold as they are in the *Framework for Teaching Mathematics*. If a lesson does not cover an objective in its entirety, then only the portion which is intended to be covered is listed in the 'Learning outcomes' (or any of the grids provided).

The specific objectives for the **Oral and mental starter** and **Main teaching activity** are listed separately.

Vocabulary
The National Numeracy Strategy *Mathematical Vocabulary* booklet has been used to provide the vocabulary lists. New or specific vocabulary to be used during the lesson is listed. Use this vocabulary with the whole class so that all the children have a chance to hear it and begin to understand it. Encourage pupils to use the vocabulary orally, when asking or answering questions, so that they develop understanding of its mathematical meaning. Where flashcards are suggested these can be made by printing out onto card the appropriate sections from the CD-ROM which should have accompanied your school's copy of the *Mathematical Vocabulary* booklet.

Oral and mental starter
This is designed to occupy the first 5–10 minutes of the lesson, but the duration of the work is not critical. This section contains activity suggestions to develop oral and mental work to be used with the whole class and is based on what has already been taught. Some suggestions for differentiated questioning are included to show how all the children can benefit. The detail in the lesson plan will help you to; provide a variety of sequentially planned, short oral and mental activities throughout the week; use a good range of open and closed questions; encourage all children to take part; target differentiated questions to individuals, pairs or small groups.

Main teaching activity
This sets out what to do in the whole class teaching session and should last for about 40 minutes. In some lessons much of the time will be spent in whole-class, interactive teaching. In others, the whole-class session will be shorter, with differentiated activities for groups, pairs or individuals. The detailed lesson plan will help you to organise this part of the lesson appropriately.

Differentiation
This section suggests activities for differentiated group, paired or individual work for the more and less able children within the class. These activities will take the form of reinforcement, enrichment or extension, and many will provide challenges to encourage pupils to use and apply their mathematics.

Plenary
This session is a chance to bring the children together again for a 10-minute whole-class session. This offers opportunities to assess pupils' progress, identify and confront misconceptions, summarise key facts learnt, compare strategies used, make links to other topics and plan for the next topic.

EXTENSION LESSON PLANS
These provide activities which extend those already covered. They are less detailed, as they are based on one of the previous lessons for that week.

OUTLINE LESSON PLANS
These contain brief descriptions, as grids, of further lessons. These extend the scope of the book to give sufficient material for a year's work. Since they develop work already introduced, there are no vocabulary suggestions as the same range of words will be needed as in the previous, related lesson(s). For example:

RESOURCES	Calculators.
LEARNING OUTCOMES	**ORAL AND MENTAL STARTER** ● **Know by heart all multiplication facts for tables up to 10×10.** ● Use known facts and place value to multiply mentally. **MAIN TEACHING ACTIVITY** ● **Multiply and divide any positive integer up to 10 000 by 10 or 100 (eg 9900 ÷ 10, 2060 ÷ 100) and understand the effect.** ● Develop calculator skills and use a calculator effectively. ● Read and write whole numbers in figures and know what each digit represents.
ORAL AND MENTAL STARTER	FAST TIMES: Quick-fire questions in a series – respond as a group, eg 2 × 10, 2 × 100, 2 × 1000; 2 × 2, 2 × 20, 2 × 200, 2 × 2000; 3 × 10, and so on. Encourage children to answer as a group; tell them that no-one's voice should be heard above the others.
MAIN TEACHING ACTIVITY	CALCULATOR PLACES: Read out numbers with 3, 4 and 5 digits. Ask the children to put each number into their calculator and multiply it by 10 and 100. Ask them to input multiples of 100 and then divide them by 10 and 100. Discuss what they notice. Emphasise the numbers all moving one place to the left or right. Children choose numbers to multiply by 10 and 100 and multiples of 10 to divide by 10 and 100 without a calculator.
DIFFERENTIATION	More able: investigate how to divide numbers by 20. Less able: restrict to 1-digit or 2-digit numbers and division by 10 of 3-digit multiples of 10.
PLENARY	Go over the effect of multiplying by 10 or 100, encouraging the idea of moving the digits one or two places to the left, rather than adding a nought. What do the pupils think might be the effect of multiplying by 1000?

USING THE LESSON PLANS
The plans are designed so that you can work through them in order if you wish. However, you may prefer to choose the lessons that are appropriate for your pupils and combine these with your favourite activities from other sources. By placing the pages of this book into a ring binder you can easily incorporate your own supplementary materials.

WEEKLY PLANNING
If you wish to use the ready-prepared plans, follow the **Organisation chart** which appears at the beginning of each unit or block of units of work.

If you prefer to plan your week using some of the lesson plans in the book adding some activities you have chosen yourself, then make some photocopies of the blank **Weekly planning chart** on page 12 of this book (or your school weekly planning sheet). These can then be completed with details of all the activities which you intend to use, those chosen from this book and those which you have taken from other sources. A weekly plan should include objectives for the oral and mental starters and the main teaching activities (these could be written by each lesson or written on the back of the chart and cross-referenced).

MIXED-AGE CLASSES
If you have a mixed-age class, you will probably need to use the materials from more than one book in this series. You will find the blank **Weekly planning chart** on page 12 a useful planning tool, as you can combine planning from two books onto this chart, enabling you to keep track of all the relevant learning outcomes.

BLANK WEEKLY PLANNING CHART

Make photocopies of this chart, complete a copy on a weekly basis and keep this in your planning file. You may prefer to enlarge the chart to A3.

Week beginning: 6/9/99

Learning objectives for oral and mental skills	Recognise multiples of 2, 3, 5 and 10. Recognise odd and even numbers. Read and write whole numbers in figures and know what each digit represents. Know by heart multiplication facts for 2, 3, 4, 5 and 10x tables. Use known facts and place value to multiply integers, including by 10 and 100.				
	Oral and mental starter	Main teaching activity	Differentiation	Plenary	Resources
M o n d a y	1, 2, GUESS MY NUMBER: Say 'I am thinking of a number' and give number facts. Can the pupils guess the number?	BUILDING NUMBERS: Point to nos. on place value chart. Pupils read them out. Build up 4-digit numbers, read them with arrow cards and write them on the board. Increase to 5- and 6-digit numbers. Pupils pick numeral cards, make 6-digit numbers and write them in numerals and words.	Less able: concentrate on 4- and 5-digit numbers. More able: make numbers with 7 digits and beyond.	Read out numbers; pupils use calculators to input them, then compare with partner. Discuss as class what display should show.	Digit cards, place value chart, arrow cards, calculators.

CLASSROOM ORGANISATION

WHOLE-CLASS TEACHING

During a whole-class session it is important that all the children can see you, the board or flip chart and their table top. In many classrooms space is at a premium, so it is worth spending time considering how the furniture can best be arranged. If you have a carpeted area for whole-class work, think about whether the lesson you are planning to teach would work well with the children seated on the carpet, or whether they would be better placed at their tables – especially if you want them to manipulate apparatus, such as interlocking cubes, or if they need to spread out numeral cards in front of them.

GROUP WORK

Again, it is important that the pupils sit so that they can see you, and the board or flip chart if necessary. While they are working in groups you may wish to ask whole-class questions, or remind pupils of how much time is left to complete their task, so eye contact will help to ensure that everyone is listening.

WORKING WITH OTHER ADULTS

If you have classroom helpers, brief them before the lesson starts on which group you would like them to work with, the purpose of the task, the vocabulary they should be helping to develop, and give some examples of the type of questions they should be asking. Check that all the resources needed are available or, if not, that the helper knows where to find them. You may want to ask a classroom helper to work with just one or two pupils; perhaps they are finding the work difficult, or have been absent and this is an opportunity to catch up on missed work. Whatever the reason, always ensure that the helper is well briefed before the lesson starts, and allow a few minutes after the lesson has finished to discuss any specific observations which the helper would like to make.

CHILDREN WITH SPECIAL EDUCATIONAL NEEDS

Include children with special educational needs in the whole-class work. If you have a classroom helper or support assistant, ask them to sit beside the pupils with special needs to provide support. This could include repeating the questions quietly or encouraging them to use individual resources (such as counting apparatus, a

number line or number cards) to find the answer. During differentiated questioning, ensure that some questions are specifically focused for these pupils and encourage them to answer appropriately.

To assist all pupils in reading new vocabulary, and particularly to help those with reading difficulties, make flash cards for the specific mathematics vocabulary which will be used in a series of lessons and encourage the children to read these.

Pupils who are partially sighted or deaf will need to sit close to you, so take this into account when considering the layout of the classroom for maths lessons. Those with emotional or behavioural difficulties will benefit from the structure and routines of the daily maths lesson and, where possible, from the support of a helper who can encourage on-task working. For children who are learning English as an additional language, speak more slowly, repeat instructions and provide visual clues on worksheets or puzzle cards. For pupils who have an Individual Education Plan (IEP) with mathematics as an area of learning difficulty, use other books from this series to find activities of an appropriate level which can be linked to the work of the rest of the class.

HOMEWORK

For Year 5 pupils it is recommended that homework is given regularly on a weekly or twice-weekly basis. These activities might be designed to be shared with a parent or carer, or could include simple puzzles or maths games and occasionally may be of a more formal nature to consolidate work done in class. A homework diary which is completed by home and school is a useful tool for logging what the homework is and how the pupil responded. Use a range of different types of tasks for homework.

Choose favourite shared homework activities and send these home regularly. Suitable material may be found in *IMPACT Maths Homework* (Key Stage 2 titles) and *Mental Maths Homework for 10 year olds,* all written by The IMPACT Project (published by Scholastic).

Suggest a game to be played at home, 'Bingo' for example, which will help the children to learn some number facts.

RESOURCES

PHOTOCOPIABLE SHEETS

These support the work and can be resource pages or activity sheets. They are marked with the photocopiable symbol. Some sheets have many applications and are used throughout the book – these appear at the end of this Introduction on pages 12–18. Others can be found at the end of the relevant units.

RESOURCE SHEETS

These include numeral cards and arrow cards, and can be found on pages 12–18. It is a good idea to make enough of these at the start of the year for each pupil to have at least one set. You may wish to ask for help from parents and friends of the school to make these resources. Photocopy the pages onto card, then cut out and laminate as required.

For the numeral cards, consider whether to use different coloured card so that the children can put them away more easily, using the colour of their set as an aid. These cards can be stored in small polythene bags or tins so that the pupils can keep their resources in their own desks or trays. Alternatively, store these with a rubber band around each set and give them out at the beginning of the lesson. Store class sets of arrow cards in marked boxes.

ACTIVITY SHEETS

These are located at the end of the relevant units, and relate to specific activities. They may offer practical activities, more traditional worksheets or games. Photocopy the pages onto A4 paper for the pupils.

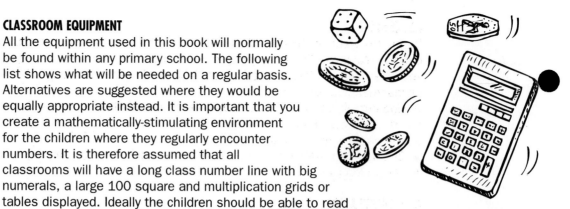

CLASSROOM EQUIPMENT

All the equipment used in this book will normally be found within any primary school. The following list shows what will be needed on a regular basis. Alternatives are suggested where they would be equally appropriate instead. It is important that you create a mathematically-stimulating environment for the children where they regularly encounter numbers. It is therefore assumed that all classrooms will have a long class number line with big numerals, a large 100 square and multiplication grids or tables displayed. Ideally the children should be able to read all the numbers easily from their seats. A chalk board and chalk, or flip chart and marker pens, are essential for interactive whole-class sessions. You will also need:

- A 'washing line' strung across the room, with sets of different numbers to peg on, for example: one place decimals, multiples of 1–10 and negative numbers
- 2-digit number cards
- counting stick: a metre length of wood, divided into ten alternately-coloured sections (some metre rulers are marked in this way)
- counters
- measuring apparatus including rulers, tape measures, trundle wheels, metre sticks, scales, measuring jugs and masses
- shape apparatus: for example shape tiles, 3D shapes, feely bag
- coins, preferably real
- dice: both 0–9 (dots and numerals) and blank
- LOGO
- data handling software such as *Find it* or *Flexidata*
- lots of interlocking cubes, such as Multilink
- calculators
- stop watch.

USING INFORMATION AND COMMUNICATION TECHNOLOGY

Make use of your favourite mathematical games software as a paired or small group activity if it links to the learning objective of the lesson. Some of the activities in this book use maths software such as Logo.

PUBLICATIONS

Oral and mental starter
Developing Mental Maths with 9–11 year olds
by Tamara Bibby

Main teaching activity
Maths Focus Kit 4
Various authors
Practising Mental Maths with 10 year olds
by Jon Kurta
Quick Mental Maths for 10 year olds
by William Hartley

Homework
IMPACT Maths Homework (Key Stage 2)
by the IMPACT Project
Mental Maths Homework for 10 year olds
by Kate Frood
Quick Mental Maths for 10 year olds
by William Hartley

Assessment
Maths Focus Kit 4
Scholastic Portfolio Assessment: Maths (KS2)
by Ian Gardner and Jean Edwards

ASSESSMENT

During the week at the end of each half term, an assessment period of two lessons is built into the planning. This gives you the opportunity to make medium-term assessments of the key objectives for Year 5 listed in the National Numeracy Strategy. The aim of these assessments is to:

● Find out what progress each pupil has made; what he or she knows, understands and can do; whether he or she can apply and use their mathematics in context and whether he or she has any weaknesses.

● Give you information on which to base feedback to pupils and their parents or carers. It will also help you to plan work for the next few weeks.

ASSESSMENT ADVICE

This is placed just before the assessment activity photocopiable sheets. Here you will find information on the aspects of mathematics which are to be assessed; some assessment activities for oral and mental starters which can be used with the whole class, some which can be used with groups, pairs and individuals, and advice on using the photocopiable assessment tasks provided.

ASSESSMENT ACTIVITIES

These activities have been designed so that you can observe pupils at work and ask questions. Explain the purpose of the activity to them before they begin, as this will help them to demonstrate to you the things that you want to observe, such as clear recording, discussion of which strategy they used, why they used it, and so on. Target small groups for a specific activity and period of time and work with them, observing how individuals respond to the activity. You may find it useful to have a notebook handy to make informal notes on observations and discussions.

If you have a classroom helper, he or she can also be involved in the assessment process. Explain the purpose of the assessment, what to do, and what to look for. After the lesson has finished make time to discuss observations and keep notes on individual pupils' achievements and weaknesses.

ASSESSMENT PHOTOCOPIABLE SHEETS

There are two photocopiable sheets for each half term assessment period. Each sheet has specific assessment criteria written at the bottom. Photocopy the pages for individual pupils to complete while you observe others undertaking the assessment activities.

Mark the completed sheets, then give pupils feedback on their strengths and set targets for improvement in their areas of weaknesses. The sheets can be kept in a portfolio as part of the evidence of the children's achievement.

CLASS ASSESSMENT RECORDING SHEET

This can be found on page 13. It lists the key objectives for Year 5 from the National Numeracy Strategy *Framework for Teaching Mathematics* (March 1999). Photocopy the sheet, enlarge it to A3, and record individuals' progress on it. By the end of the year, after six assessment sessions and a year of lessons, you will have a wealth of assessment evidence to pass on to the children's next teacher.

Each half-termly assessment offers opportunities to assess some of the relevant key objectives that have been taught. Those that are not assessed then will be assessed later in the year. Use your assessment records and informal assessment to decide whether to re-assess a child or whether it is appropriate to leave out a specific assessment objective which has already been learnt.

Weekly planning chart

(Photo-enlarge to A3.)

Week beginning:

Learning objectives
for oral and mental
skills:

	Oral and mental starter	Main teaching activity	Differentiation	Plenary	Resources
Monday					
Tuesday					
Wednesday					
Thursday					
Friday					

Year 5: class assessment record sheet

Key objectives: Year 5	Name														
Multiply and divide any positive integer up to 10 000 by 10 or 100 and understand the effect.															
Order a given set of positive and negative integers.															
Use decimal notation for tenths and hundredths.															
Round a number with one or two decimal places to the nearest integer.															
Relate fractions to division and to their decimal representations.															
Calculate mentally a difference such as 8006 – 2993.															
Carry out column addition and subtraction of positive integers less than 10 000.															
Know by heart all multiplication facts up to 10 × 10.															
Carry out short multiplication and division of a three-digit integer by a single-digit integer.															
Carry out long multiplication and division of a three-digit integer by a single digit integer.															
Carry out long multiplication of a two-digit integer by a two-digit integer.															
Understand area measured in square centimetres (cm²); understand and use the formula in words 'length × breadth' for the area of a rectangle.															
Recognise perpendicular and parallel lines, and properties of rectangles.															
Use all four operations to solve simple word problems involving numbers and quantities, including time; explain methods and reasoning.															

Photocopiable A: Numeral cards (0 to 9)

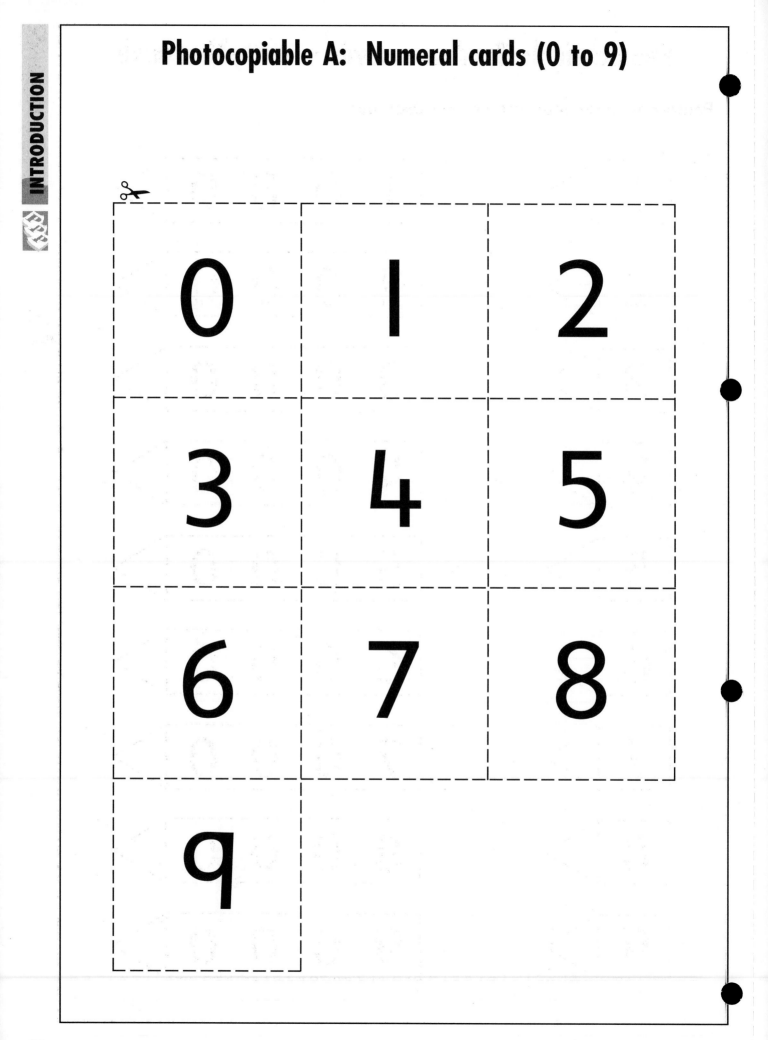

Photocopiable A: Numeral cards (0 to 9)

Photocopiable B: Arrow cards – units/thousands

Photocopy these onto card and cut them out.

1	1 0 0 0
2	2 0 0 0
3	3 0 0 0
4	4 0 0 0
5	5 0 0 0
6	6 0 0 0
7	7 0 0 0
8	8 0 0 0
9	9 0 0 0

Photocopiable C: Arrow cards – tens/hundreds

Photocopy these onto card and cut them out.

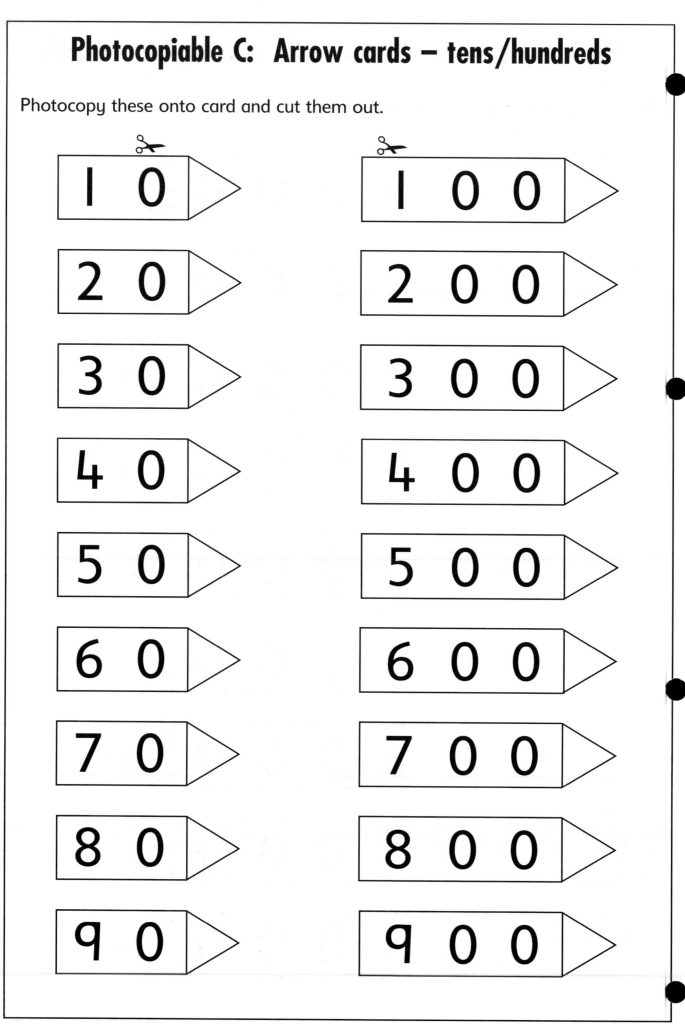

Photocopiable D: Arrow cards – tens of thousands

Photocopy these onto card and cut them out.

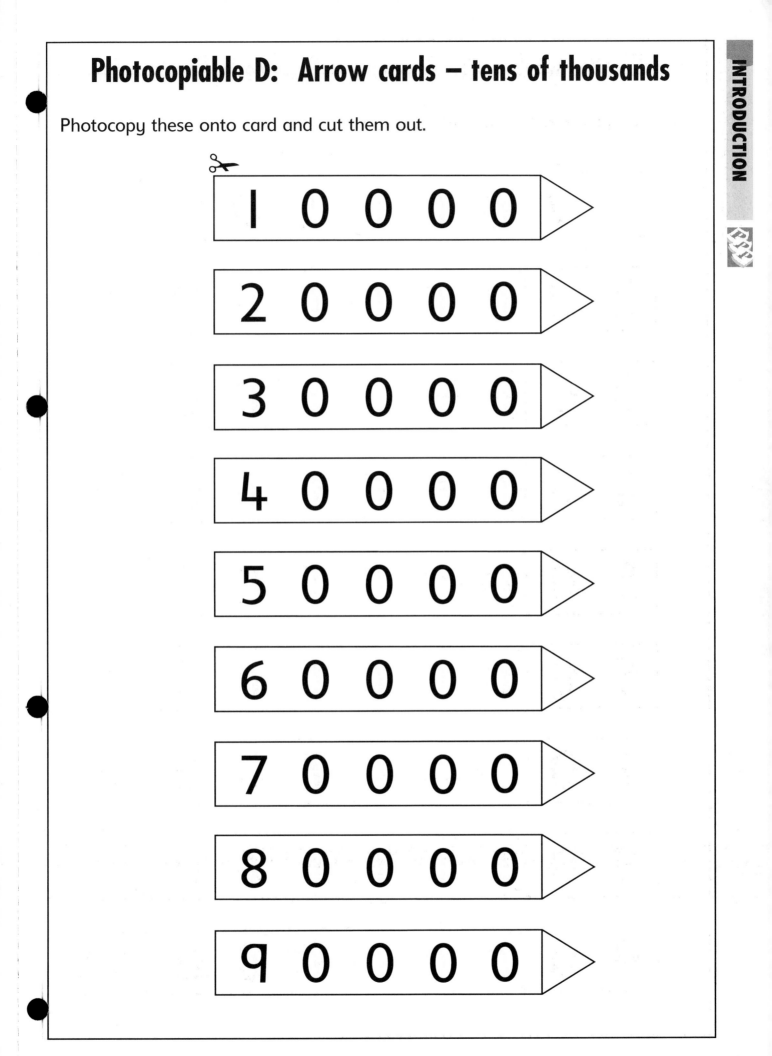

Photocopiable E: Arrow cards – hundreds of thousands

Photocopy these onto card and cut them out.

1 0 0 0 0 0

2 0 0 0 0 0

3 0 0 0 0 0

4 0 0 0 0 0

5 0 0 0 0 0

6 0 0 0 0 0

7 0 0 0 0 0

8 0 0 0 0 0

9 0 0 0 0 0

TERM 1

This term, children work with numbers up to 1 million. They extend their skills with all four operations, using expanded written layouts before moving on to the standard written method, and continue to develop mental strategies. The teaching of calculator skills is introduced, and children apply these skills to solving problems involving all four operations in a range of contexts. Work with fractions is extended to mixed numbers, equivalent fractions and finding fractions of numbers and quantities. Children are introduced to the concept of ratio. Work in 'Shape and space' will focus on: properties of triangles and rectangles; recognising, estimating and naming types of angle; visualising 3-D shapes from 2-D drawings. In 'Measures', the emphasis is on length and time, including measuring and drawing lines to the nearest millimetre and understanding 24-hour clock notation. In 'Handling data', children solve a problem by representing and interpreting data.

TERM 1 PLANNING GRID

Oral and mental: Recognise multiples of 2, 3, 5 and 10. Recognise odd and even numbers. Read and write whole numbers in figures and know what each digit represents. Know by heart multiplication facts for 2, 3, 4, 5 and 10 times tables. Use known facts and place value to multiply integers including 10 and 100. Derive quickly or continue to derive quickly: division facts corresponding to tables up to 10 × 10; doubles of all whole numbers 1 to 100 and all corresponding halves. Estimate by approximating (round to the nearest 10 or 100), then check result. Recognise multiples of 2, 3, 4, 5, 6, 7, 8, 9 to the 10th multiple. **Relate fractions to division**, and use division to find simple fractions, of numbers and quantities. Change an improper fraction to a mixed number (eg change $^{13}/_{10}$ to $1^3/_{10}$). Solve simple problems using ideas of ratio and proportion ('one for every...' and 'one in every...'). Recognise and extend number sequences formed by counting from any number in steps of a constant size.

UNIT	TOPIC	OBJECTIVES: CHILDREN WILL BE TAUGHT TO...
1	Place value, ordering and rounding Using a calculator	● Read and write whole numbers in figures and know what each digit represents. Use the vocabulary of comparing and ordering numbers, including symbols such as <, >, =; give one or more numbers lying between two given numbers; order a set of integers less than 1 million. ● **Multiply or divide any integer up to 10,000 by 10 or 100 and understand the effect (eg 9900 ÷ 10, 2060 ÷ 100).** ● Develop calculator skills and use a calculator effectively.
2–3	Understanding × and ÷ Mental calculation strategies (× and ÷) Pencil and paper procedures (× and ÷) Money and 'real life' problems Making decisions and checking results, including using a calculator	● Understand the effect of and relationships between the four operations, and the principles (not the names) of the arithmetic laws as they apply to multiplication. Begin to use brackets. ● **Know by heart all multiplication facts up to 10 × 10.** ● Derive quickly or continue to derive quickly: division facts corresponding to tables up to 10 × 10; doubles of all whole numbers 1 to 100, and the corresponding halves. ● Use doubling or halving, starting from known facts. ● Partition, eg 47 × 6 = (40 × 6) + (7 × 6). ● Approximate first. Use informal pencil and paper methods to support, record or explain multiplications and divisions. ● **Extend written methods to: short multiplication of HTU by U.** ● **Use all four operations to solve simple word problems involving numbers** based on 'real life' or money, using one or more steps. ● Choose and use appropriate number operations to solve problems. ● Check with the inverse operation when using a calculator. ● Develop calculator skills and use a calculator effectively.
4–5	Fractions, decimals and percentages Using a calculator Ratio and proportion	● Use fraction notation, including mixed numbers, and the vocabulary numerator and denominator. ● **Relate fractions to division**, and use division to find simple fractions, of numbers and quantities. ● Recognise when two simple fractions are equivalent, including relating hundredths to tenths. ● Change an improper fraction to a mixed number (eg change $^{13}/_{10}$ to $1^3/_{10}$). ● Order a set of fractions such as 2, $2^3/_4$, $1^3/_4$, $2^1/_2$, $1^1/_2$. ● Find what to add to a mixed number to make a whole number. ● Develop calculator skills and use a calculator effectively. ● Solve simple problems using ideas of ratio and proportion ('one for every...' and 'one in every...').
6	Handling data Using a calculator	● Solve a problem by representing and interpreting data in tables, charts, graphs and diagrams, for example: bar line charts, vertical axis labelled in 2s, 5s, 10s, 20s, 100s, first where intermediate points have no meaning (eg scores on a dice rolled 50 times), then where they may have meaning (eg room temperature over time). ● Develop calculator skills and use a calculator effectively.
7	Assess and review	See the key objectives listed on the relevant pages.

Oral and mental: Know by heart all multiplication facts up to 10 × 10. Derive quickly or continue to derive quickly: division facts corresponding to tables up to 10 × 10; doubles of all whole numbers 1 to 100 (eg 78 × 2); all two-digit pairs that total 100 (eg 43 + 57). Describe and visualise 2D shapes. Use, read and write standard metric units (km, m, cm, mm) including their abbreviations, and relationships between them. Recognise multiples of 6, 7, 8, 9 to the 10th multiple. Recognise odd and even numbers. Use units of time; read the time on a 24-hour digital clock and use 24-hour clock notation, such as 19:53. Continue to know by heart addition and subtraction facts for all numbers to 20. Use known number facts and place value: to add or subtract mentally including any pair of two-digit numbers; to multiply mentally. Round any integer up to 1000 to the nearest 10 or 100. Estimate by approximating (round to the nearest 10 or 100), then check result. Recognise and extend number sequences formed by counting from any number in steps of constant size, extending beyond zero when counting back (eg count on in steps of 25 to 1000).

UNIT	TOPIC	OBJECTIVES: CHILDREN WILL BE TAUGHT TO...
8–10	Shape and space Reasoning about shapes Measures, including problems Money and 'real life' problems	● **Recognise properties of rectangles.** ● Understand and use angle measure in degrees. ● Identify, estimate and order acute and obtuse angles. ● Classify triangles (isosceles, equilateral, scalene) using criteria such as equal sides, equal angles, lines of symmetry. ● Make shapes with increasing accuracy. ● Visualise 3-D shapes from 2-D drawings and identify different nets for an open cube. ● Solve mathematical problems or puzzles, recognise and explain patterns and relationships, generalise and predict. ● Use, read and write standard metric units (km, m, cm, mm) including their abbreviations, and relationships between them. ● Know imperial units (mile). ● Measure and draw lines to the nearest millimetre. ● Record estimates and reading from scales to a suitable degree of accuracy. ● **Use all four operations to solve simple word problems involving numbers and quantities** based on 'real life' and measures **(including time).** ● Use units of time; read the time on a 24-hour digital clock and use 24-hour clock notation, such as 19:53. Use timetables.
11	Mental calculation strategies (+ and –) Pencil and paper procedures (+ and –) Money and 'real life' problems Making decisions and checking results, including using a calculator	● Add several numbers (eg four or five single-digit numbers, or multiples of 10 such as 40 + 50 + 80). ● Partition into H T and U adding the most significant digits first. ● Find differences by counting up through the next multiple of 10, 100 or 1000, eg **calculate mentally a difference such as 8006 – 2993.** ● Use informal pencil and paper methods to support, record or explain additions. ● **Extend written methods to: column addition of two** or more **integers less than 10 000.** ● **Use all four operations to solve simple word problems involving numbers and quantities** based on 'real life' or money, using one or more steps. ● Choose and use appropriate number operations to solve problems and appropriate ways of calculating: mental, mental with jottings, pencil and paper, calculator. ● Estimate by approximating (round to the nearest 10 or 100), then check result. ● Use knowledge of sums of odd/even numbers. ● Check the sum of several numbers by adding in the reverse order. ● Check with an equivalent calculation. ● Check with the inverse operation when using a calculator. ● Develop calculator skills effectively.
12	Properties of numbers Reasoning about numbers	● Recognise and extend number sequences formed by counting from any number in steps of constant size, extending beyond zero when counting back, eg count on in steps of 25 to 1000, and then back. ● Make general statements about odd or even numbers, including the outcome of sums or differences. ● Solve mathematical problems or puzzles, recognise and explain patterns and relationships, generalise and predict; suggest extensions asking 'What if...?' ● Make and investigate a general statement about familiar numbers by finding examples that satisfy it. Explain a generalised relationship in words.
13	Assess and review	See the key objectives listed on the relevant pages.

UNIT 1

ORGANISATION (3 LESSONS)

	LEARNING OUTCOMES	ORAL AND MENTAL STARTER	MAIN TEACHING ACTIVITY	PLENARY
LESSON 1	● Read and write whole numbers in figures and words and know what each digit represents. ● Develop calculator skills and use a calculator effectively.	GUESS MY NUMBER: Guess a number from facts about it.	COMBINING THOUSANDS: Use tens charts and arrow cards to combine digits to make a given number.	Put given numbers into a calculator and compare with a partner.
LESSON 2	● Read and write whole numbers in figures and know what each digit represents. ● Understand the vocabulary of comparing and ordering numbers, including symbols such as <, >, =; give one or more numbers lying between two given numbers; order a set of integers less than 1 million.	MYSTERY NUMBERS: Compare the sizes of numbers made by arranging a set of digits in different ways.	REARRANGING THE DIGITS: Rearrange numeral cards to make bigger or smaller numbers.	Discuss how to rearrange digits to make the largest number. See how many different numbers can be made with 3 digits, 4 digits and so on.
LESSON 3	● Multiply or divide any integer up to 10 000 by 10 or 100 and understand the effect (eg 9900 ÷ 10, 2060 ÷ 100). ● Develop calculator skills and use a calculator effectively. ● Read and write whole numbers in figures and know what each digit represents.	FAST TIMES: Multiplication facts, responding as a class or in groups.	CALCULATOR PLACES: Use a calculator to multiply and divide a given number by 10 or 100. Discuss what you notice.	Discuss the effect of multiplying by 10 or 100. What might be the effect of multiplying by 1000?

ORAL AND MENTAL SKILLS: Recognise multiples of 2, 3, 5 and 10 (Y3 revision). Recognise odd and even numbers (Y3 revision). Read and write whole numbers in figures and know what each digit represents. Know by heart multiplication facts for 2, 3, 4, 5 and 10 times tables. Use known facts and place value to multiply integers including 10 and 100.

Lessons 1 and 2 are shown in detail. Lesson 3 develops the content of Lesson 2.

LESSON 1

RESOURCES
Numeral cards (photocopiable page 14); number words cards; a place value chart (photocopiable page 24); arrow cards (a set, up to 900 000 for each pair of pupils); calculators; OHP (if available).

PREPARATION
Copy the place value chart (photocopiable page 24) onto acetate if available, or alternatively copy onto A1 paper. Clearly display number words on cards: one, two... eleven, twelve... twenty, thirty... hundred, thousand and so on. These may be printed from the NNS *Mathematical Vocabulary* CD-ROM, if available.

LEARNING OUTCOMES

ORAL AND MENTAL STARTER
● Recognise multiples of 2, 3, 5 and 10.
● Recognise odd and even numbers.

MAIN TEACHING ACTIVITY
● Read and write whole numbers in figures and words and know what each digit represents.
● Develop calculator skills and use a calculator effectively.

VOCABULARY
Units, tens, hundreds, thousands, ten thousands, hundred thousands, million, represent, column.

ORAL AND MENTAL STARTER

GUESS MY NUMBER: Ask the children to sit at their tables with their numeral cards spread out face up in front of them. Using number facts (including tables facts), ask pupils to guess the number you are thinking of and show the answer using the cards. For example: *I am thinking of a number less than 10, it is a multiple of 3 and it is even* (6). *I am thinking of a number, it is a multiple of 3 and of 5, and it is between 10 and 20* (15). After each answer, ask pupils to explain (in full sentences) how they worked it out.

MAIN TEACHING ACTIVITY

COMBINING THOUSANDS: Explain that this lesson is about reading and writing large numbers. Ask the children to read out the numbers you point to on the place value chart. Point to 10, 50, 300, 4000, 7000, 20 000 and so on. Then point to numbers that, as the children read them, give the combined number: point to 300, then 20, then 4. Pupils should say 'Three hundred and twenty-four'. Repeat with a four-digit number. Now point to each part of a 5-digit number: 50 000, 3000, 600, 90, 1. Ask pupils to read out each part; point to 50 000 and 3000 quickly, so that they read the two together (as 'Fifty-three thousand'). Repeat with the same numbers and repeat the whole number to the class. Ask a pupil to write that number in digits on the board. Do the class agree? Ask a pupil to pick the arrow card that shows fifty thousand; ask another pupil to pick the arrow card for three thousand; continue until all the cards have been picked to form the number 53 691. Put the cards together, and compare the number with that written on the board. Is it the same? Ask the class to read the number together. Repeat with a 6-digit number.

Ask the children to work in pairs. Pick cards to make a 6-digit number. Work together to use arrow cards to build up this number. Children should write the number in digits and words in their books. Display the correct number vocabulary to help them.

DIFFERENTIATION

More able: Go on to 7-digit numbers and beyond.
Less able: Concentrate on 4-digit, then 5-digit numbers.

PLENARY

Give each child a calculator. Ask them to put in the number *one thousand and twenty-four*. They can compare with partners. Discuss as a class what the calculator displays show. Repeat with other numbers, going up to 6 digits.

RESOURCES

For teacher: Washing line; pegs; blank cards.
For children: A set of numeral cards per pair.

PREPARATION

Hang pegs on a washing line so that all the children will be able to see and reach it.

VOCABULARY

Less than, greater than, in between, worth, sign, position.

LEARNING OUTCOMES

ORAL AND MENTAL STARTER
● Read and write whole numbers in figures and know what each digit represents.
MAIN TEACHING ACTIVITY
● Read and write whole numbers in figures and know what each digit represents.
● Use the vocabulary of comparing and ordering numbers, including symbols such as <, >, =; give one or more numbers lying between two given numbers; order a set of integers less than 1 million.

ORAL AND MENTAL STARTER

MYSTERY NUMBERS: Write a 3-digit number secretly on a piece of paper. Write the digits that make up the number on the board. Ask a child to write a number using these digits on the board. Read the number together as a class. Tell the children how many of the digits are in the correct position to make the mystery number, and whether the mystery number is bigger or smaller than the number written. Continue until the class have discovered the mystery number. Repeat with 4-digit and 5-digit numbers.

MAIN TEACHING ACTIVITY

REARRANGING THE DIGITS: Use a 5-digit number from the Oral and mental starter. Ask the pupils to rearrange the digits to make the largest number they can. Ask the class to read out the number. Write it on a card and peg it on the right-hand end of the line. Now ask them to rearrange the digits again to make the smallest number they can. Write the two numbers on the board, the smaller first, with a space between them, and ask which sign should go between the numbers: < or >. Read the number sentence as a class, pointing to each part. Write the smaller number on a card and peg it on the left-hand end of the line. Ask the pupils to rearrange the digits again to make a number that lies between the two numbers shown. Write this number on a card and ask a child to peg it at an appropriate place on the line. Do the class think this is the correct place? Why? Write the middle number and the smallest number on the board and ask which sign should go between them. Repeat with other numbers until there are six numbers on the line.

Ask pupils to work in pairs to pick six numeral cards and use them to make the largest and the smallest number they can, then three numbers that lie in between the first two. They should write all five numbers in order, from smallest to largest, in their maths book.

DIFFERENTIATION

More able: Find exactly how many different numbers they can make with 4 or 5 digits.
Less able: Do the paired activity with 4-digit or 5-digit numbers.

PLENARY

Write a number with 3 different digits on the board. Ask pupils to rearrange the digits to make the smallest and largest possible numbers. How many different numbers can they make? How many with 4 digits? How many with 5 digits? Is there a pattern? (3 digits – 6 numbers, 4 digits – 24 numbers, 5 digits – 120 numbers.)

LEARNING OUTCOMES	**ORAL AND MENTAL STARTER** ● Know by heart multiplication facts for 2, 3, 4, 5 and 10 times tables. ● Use known facts and place value to multiply integers, including by 10 and 100. **MAIN TEACHING ACTIVITY** ● Multiply and divide any positive integer up to 10 000 by 10 or 100 (eg 9900 ÷ 10, 2060 ÷ 100) and understand the effect. ● Develop calculator skills and use a calculator effectively. ● Read and write whole numbers in figures and know what each digit represents.
RESOURCES	Calculators.
ORAL AND MENTAL STARTER	FAST TIMES: Quick-fire questions in a series – respond as a group, eg 2 × 10, 2 × 100, 2 × 1000; 2 × 2, 2 × 20, 2 × 200, 2 × 2000; 3 × 10, and so on. Encourage children to answer as a group; tell them that no-one's voice should be heard above the others.
MAIN TEACHING ACTIVITY	CALCULATOR PLACES: Read out numbers with 3, 4 and 5 digits. Ask the children to put each number into their calculator and multiply it by 10 and 100. Ask them to input multiples of 100 and then divide them by 10 and 100. Discuss what they notice. Emphasise the numbers all moving one place to the left or right. Children choose numbers to multiply by 10 and 100 and multiples of 10 to divide by 10 and 100 without a calculator.
DIFFERENTIATION	More able: Investigate how to divide numbers by 20. Less able: Restrict to 1-digit or 2-digit numbers and division by 10 of 3-digit multiples of 10.
PLENARY	Go over the effect of multiplying by 10 or 100. Encourage the idea of moving the digits one or two places to the left, rather than adding a nought. Ask: *What would be the effect of multiplying by 1000?*

Place value chart

1	2	3	4	5	6	7	8	9
10	20	30	40	50	60	70	80	90
100	200	300	400	500	600	700	800	900
1000	2000	3000	4000	5000	6000	7000	8000	9000
10000	20000	30000	40000	50000	60000	70000	80000	90000
100000	200000	300000	400000	500000	600000	700000	800000	900000
1000000	2000000	3000000	4000000	5000000	6000000	7000000	8000000	9000000

UNITS 2-3

ORGANISATION (10 LESSONS)

	LEARNING OUTCOMES	ORAL AND MENTAL STARTER	MAIN TEACHING ACTIVITY	PLENARY
LESSON 1	● **Know by heart all multiplication facts up to 10 × 10.** ● Understand the effect of and relationships between the four operations, and the principles (not the names) of the arithmetic laws as they apply to multiplication.	ORDERING MULTIPLES: Put multiples of 2, 3, 5 or 10 in order on a number line.	FILL THE GRID: Complete a multiplication grid by making connections. Roll a dice to set multiplication problems.	Use the grid to respond to questions about multiplication and division facts.
LESSON 2	● Derive quickly or continue to derive quickly division facts corresponding to tables up to 10 × 10.	MULTIPLICATION FACTS: Hold up numeral cards to answer multiplication questions.	DIVISION FACTS: Use a completed multiplication grid to find division facts.	Missing number problem, eg __ ÷ __ = 3
LESSON 3	● Use doubling or halving, starting from known facts. For example: double/halve any two-digit number by doubling/halving the tens first. ● Derive quickly or continue to derive quickly doubles of all whole numbers 1 to 100 and the corresponding halves.	DOUBLES 1 TO 20: Say the doubles of numbers 1 to 20 and the corresponding halves.	DOUBLE QUICK: Use arrow cards to partition numbers, double the tens and the units, then recombine.	Halve numbers, halving the most significant digit first.
LESSON 4	● Understand the effect and principles of the arithmetic laws as they apply to multiplication. Begin to use brackets. ● **Know by heart all multiplication facts up to 10 × 10.** Partition, eg 47 × 6 = (40 × 6) + (7 × 6). ● Approximate first. Use informal pencil and paper methods to support, record or explain multiplications.	MULTIPLICATION AND DIVISION BINGO: Cross out numbers from a list if they are answers to problems.	PARTITION AND MULTIPLY: Make estimates. Partition numbers to multiply by a single-digit number.	Introduce partitioning of 3-digit numbers and multiplying by a single-digit number.
LESSON 5	● Use doubling or halving, starting from known facts. For example: double one number and halve the other. ● Develop calculator skills and use a calculator effectively.	DOUBLING ROUND THE ROOM: Double 2-digit numbers.	DOUBLE AND HALVE: Use calculators to work out related problems, eg 24 × 12, 96 × 3. Explore doubling and halving as a strategy.	Check which numbers are/ are not appropriate for this method.
LESSON 6 +7	● **Extend written methods to short multiplication of HTU by U.** ● Check with the inverse operation when using a calculator.	MULTIPLYING 10s: by single-digit numbers. Chant answers in groups. ESTIMATING ANSWERS: to TU × U in groups.	EXPANDED MULTIPLICATION: Go from informal written method to beginnings of expanded method. Develop expanded written method. Extend to HTU × U.	Check using a calculator. Decide which multiplications are correct.
LESSON 8	● Approximate first. Use informal pencil and paper methods to support, record or explain divisions.	DIVISION FACTS: Respond to quick questions using numeral cards.	PARTITION DIVISION: Divide 2-digit no.s by partitioning. Find remainders.	Extend to 3-digit numbers.
LESSON 9 +10	● **Use all four operations to solve simple word problems involving numbers** based on 'real life' or money, using one or more steps. ● Choose and use appropriate number operations to solve problems.	WHAT'S THE QUESTION?: Find multiplication and division questions for given answers. WORD PROBLEMS BINGO: Adapt from Lesson 4 above.	WORD PROBLEMS: Solve word problems using multiplication and division vocabulary. Solve one- and two-step word problems.	Introduce two-step problems. Go over some of the problems.

ORAL AND MENTAL SKILLS: Recognise multiples of 2, 3, 5 and 10 (Year 4 revision). **Know by heart all multiplication facts up to 10 × 10**. Derive quickly or continue to derive quickly: division facts corresponding to tables up to 10 × 10; doubles of all whole numbers 1 to 100, and the corresponding halves. Estimate by approximating (round to the nearest 10 or 100) then check result.

Lessons 1, 3, 4, 6, 8 and 9 are shown in detail. Lessons 2, 5, 7 and 10 follow on from what has already been taught.

RESOURCES

A blank multiplication grid (poster size or on acetate); a washing line and pegs; cards showing multiples of 2, 3, 5 and 10 to the 10th multiple.

X	1	2	3	4
1				
2				
3				
4				

PREPARATION

Prepare a large blank 10 × 10 multiplication grid (see figure right) on paper or acetate. Hang up a washing line so all pupils can see it and peg up the multiples of 2 in a random order.

LEARNING OUTCOMES

ORAL AND MENTAL STARTER
● Recognise multiples of 2, 3, 5 and 10.
MAIN TEACHING ACTIVITY
● **Know by heart all multiplication facts up to 10 × 10.**
● Understand the effect of and relationships between the four operations and the principles (not the names) of the arithmetic laws as they apply to multiplication.

ORAL AND MENTAL STARTER

ORDERING MULTIPLES: Tell the children to sit facing you and the washing line. Tell them that the multiples of 2 are on the line. Ask questions to help them put the multiples in order: *Which is the first multiple of 2? Which multiple of 2 is 6?* Move the numbers appropriately until they are in order. Chant the sequence as a class. Repeat with multiples of 3, 5 and 10.

MAIN TEACHING ACTIVITY

FILL THE GRID: Look at the multiplication grid. Tell the children that they are going to complete this grid by making connections. Fill in the row of multiples of 2. Point to the column of multiples of 2 and complete that. Explain that if we know 2 × 5 we also know 5 × 2. Now tell the children that they are going to complete the 4× row. Explain that to make the 4× table, you double the 2× table. Point to the 2 × 3 square and say: *If we know that 2 × 3 is 6, 4 × 3 must be double that.* Complete the 4× row by relating it to the 2× row, then complete the 4× column. Fill in the 8× table by doubling the 4× table. Complete the 3× table using multiples from the Oral and mental starter, then ask the children to complete the 6× table by doubling the 3s. Fill in the corresponding column after completing each row. Now complete the 5× table using multiples, then complete 10× by using doubles of 5s and children's knowledge of 10s. Complete 9× by subtracting the relevant amount from the 10s, eg 9 × 8 = (10 × 8) − 8. Fill in the remaining space (7 × 7).

Use the table to answer questions. Write 6 × 7 on the board. Say: *Look at the 6× row, 7 columns across.* Ask children to come up and show how to find the answer on the table. Ask them where else 42 appears on the table.

The children roll two 10-sided dice to generate pairs of multiplications (eg 3 × 8 and 8 × 3), then answer them. Complete ten of these.

DIFFERENTIATION

More able: Use number cards 4–12 to generate multiplications.
Less able: Use two 6-sided dice for this.

VOCABULARY

Multiply, divide, how many lots of, times, multiple.

PLENARY

Ask multiplication and division questions using a range of vocabulary: *What is 4 lots of 7? How many 6s in 30? What do you multiply 7 by to get 56?* Encourage use of the multiplication grid to find answers.

LEARNING OUTCOMES	**ORAL AND MENTAL STARTER** ● **Know by heart all multiplication facts up to 10 × 10.** **MAIN TEACHING ACTIVITY** ● Derive quickly or continue to derive quickly division facts corresponding to tables up to 10 × 10.
RESOURCES	Completed multiplication grid from Lesson 1; 10-sided dice; 6-sided dice; numeral cards (one set per pupil); number cards 4–12.
ORAL AND MENTAL STARTER	MULTIPLICATION FACTS: Ask multiplication questions – children hold up numeral cards to show answers.
MAIN TEACHING ACTIVITY	DIVISION FACTS: Write a multiplication on the board, eg 4 × 6 =; ask the children to complete it using the multiplication grid. Then write 24 ÷ 6 = and ask for the answer. Repeat with other multiplications, finding the corresponding division facts. Pupils work in pairs. Each rolls two 10-sided dice ten times and writes a multiplication fact for each pair of numbers. They swap sheets to write the ten corresponding division facts.
DIFFERENTIATION	More able: Generate multiplications using number cards 4–12. Less able: Use two 6-sided dice for this.
PLENARY	How many ways can the class complete a 'missing number' problem, eg __ ÷ __ = 3?

RESOURCES

Arrow cards up to 99; number cards 1–20 and even numbers 2–40; Blu-Tack; a stopwatch; photocopiable page 33.

PREPARATION

Use Blu-Tack to stick the number cards 1–20 on one half of the board and the even number cards 2–40 on the other half.

VOCABULARY

Double, halve, partition, significant digit, altogether, worth.

LEARNING OUTCOMES

ORAL AND MENTAL STARTER
● Derive quickly or continue to derive quickly: doubles of all whole numbers 1 to 20 and all corresponding halves.
MAIN TEACHING ACTIVITY
● Use doubling or halving, starting from known facts. For example: double/halve any two-digit number by doubling/halving the tens first.
● Derive quickly or continue to derive quickly: doubles of all whole numbers 1 to 100 and all corresponding halves.

ORAL AND MENTAL STARTER

DOUBLES 1 TO 20: Using the number cards that have been stuck to the board, tell the children that you are going to find out how fast they can double all the numbers. Point to children to give answers. *Double 6 is...* and so on. When all the numbers have been doubled, ask which were more difficult to double and why. Cover up the original numbers and time the class: how quickly can all the doubles be halved?

MAIN TEACHING ACTIVITY

DOUBLE QUICK: Explain that this lesson is about doubling 2-digit numbers. Ask a child to suggest a 2-digit number, eg 47. Write it on the board. *Which digit is worth more? How much is the 4 worth?* Ask a child to make the number 47 using arrow cards. Partition the number and show that it is 40 and 7. Write '40 and 7' on the board. *We are going to double the number that is worth more first. What is double 40?* Write '80' on the board. *What is double 7?* Write '14' on the board. *We have doubled 40 and we have doubled 7. How much is that altogether?* Repeat with other 2-digit numbers, including some over 50. Encourage the children to work them out in their heads.

Give out photocopiable page 33. The children join numbers to their doubles and write in the doubles of the numbers that are unmatched.

DIFFERENTIATION

More able: Pick up 2-digit number cards and write down the double of each number. How many can they do in 5 minutes? Check them with a partner.
Less able: Use number cards (multiples of 5 to 50, multiples of 10 to 100) to match multiples of 5 to their doubles.

PLENARY

Write 54 on the board. *If we wanted to halve this number, how would we do it?* Encourage children to halve the most significant digit first: *Half of 50 is... Half of 4 is... So half of 54 is...* Repeat with other numbers.

RESOURCES

Numeral cards; paper; pencils; 2-digit number cards (20–25, 30–35).

PREPARATION

Shuffle two sets of 0–9 numeral cards together. Write ten questions with answers 1–10, eg How many lots of 4 in 28? What do you multiply by 5 to get 15?

LEARNING OUTCOMES

ORAL AND MENTAL STARTER
● **Know by heart all multiplication facts up to 10 × 10.**
● Derive quickly or continue to derive quickly: division facts corresponding to tables up to 10 × 10.

MAIN TEACHING ACTIVITY
● Understand the effect of and the principles (not the names) of the arithmetic laws as they apply to multiplication. Begin to use brackets.
● **Know by heart all multiplication facts up to 10 × 10.**
● Partition, eg $47 \times 6 = (40 \times 6) + (7 \times 6)$.
● Approximate first; use informal pencil and paper methods to support, record or explain multiplications.

ORAL AND MENTAL STARTER

MULTIPLICATION AND DIVISION BINGO: Ask the children to write 5 different numbers between 1 and 20 (inclusive) spread out on a sheet of paper. Ask questions about multiplication facts to 10 × 10 and related division facts. After each question, check that everyone knows the answer. Those who have that number on their paper should cross it out. Ask several children to explain their method. Repeat with other questions until someone has crossed out all 5 numbers.

MAIN TEACHING ACTIVITY

PARTITION AND MULTIPLY: Explain that this lesson is about multiplying a 2-digit number by a single-digit number. Write a multiplication on the board, eg 38 × 3 =. Point to it and ask the children to read it out. *What does it mean? What do you think the answer might be approximately?* Encourage them to round 38 to 40 and multiply by 3. Explain that to make the multiplication easier, it is useful to partition the two-digit number in to two smaller multiplications: $38 \times 3 = (30 \times 3) + (8 \times 3)$.

x	30	8	
3	90	24	= 114

Explain the reason for the brackets. Use a grid to partition 38 (see figure above).

Generate another 2-digit × 1-digit multiplication using numeral cards. Repeat the process. Ask the children to explain how they calculated their answers, eg *How did you multiply 56 by 4?*

Give the children some numeral cards. Ask them to pick 3 digits to form a 2-digit × 1-digit multiplication, then carry out the calculation using the grid method. Repeat.

DIFFERENTIATION

More able: Rearrange the digits chosen to find the largest product possible. Make generalisations about the arrangement of the digits.

Less able: Use number cards 20–25 and 30–35, and numeral cards 2–5. Pick a 2-digit number card and a single digit to generate each multiplication.

PLENARY

Write 134 × 3 on the board. *How could we use a grid to calculate the answer?* Draw a grid on the board and work through it as a class. Repeat with another 3-digit example.

LESSON 5

LEARNING OUTCOMES	**ORAL AND MENTAL STARTER** ● Derive quickly or continue to derive quickly: doubles of all whole numbers 1 to 50 and all corresponding halves. **MAIN TEACHING ACTIVITY** ● Use doubling or halving, starting from known facts. ● Develop calculator skills and use a calculator effectively.
RESOURCES	Dice; calculators; 2-digit number cards to 30; photocopiable page 34.
ORAL AND MENTAL STARTER	DOUBLING ROUND THE ROOM: Divide class into 5 or 6 groups. The first group rolls two dice to generate a 2-digit starting number. The next group doubles it, next group doubles it again and so on. Continue until a group says a number over 100 and loses a 'life'. The first group to lose 3 lives is out. Carry on until one group is left.
MAIN TEACHING ACTIVITY	DOUBLE AND HALVE: Tell the children they are going to use doubling and halving to help them multiply 2-digit numbers. Write 24 × 16. Underneath write 48 × 8, then 96 × 4 under that, and so on. Give each pair of children a calculator to work out the answers. What do they notice? (they are all the same.) What do they notice about the pattern? (double one number, halve the other.) Explain that this is a useful method for finding answers. Use the method with other examples. The children complete photocopiable page 34.
DIFFERENTIATION	More able: Write their own multiplications. Which can be solved best using this method? Less able: Choose 2-digit number cards below 30 and multiply by 8.
PLENARY	Decide which numbers this method works for. Would it be appropriate for multiplying by an odd number?

LESSON 6 +7

RESOURCES

Numeral cards (one set per child); pencils and paper; Blu-Tack; calculators; 10-sided dice.

PREPARATION

Shuffle two sets of 0–9 numeral cards together.

LEARNING OUTCOMES

ORAL AND MENTAL STARTER

● **Know by heart all multiplication facts up to 10 × 10.**
● Estimate by approximating (round to the nearest 10 or 100) then check result.

MAIN TEACHING ACTIVITY
● **Extend written methods to short multiplication of HTU by U.**
● Check with the inverse operation when using a calculator.

ORAL AND MENTAL STARTER

MULTIPLYING 10s: Divide the class into three groups. Give each group a multiplication to do. They must respond orally as a group, so that no one voice is heard above the others. Give the groups connected multiplications, eg 4×6, 4×60, 40×60. Start with a different group each time. Write the answers on the board. Discuss the connections.

MAIN TEACHING ACTIVITY

EXPANDED MULTIPLICATION: Explain that this lesson is about using a written method for multiplication (This lesson will link mental to written calculation by doing partitioning vertically). Pick numeral cards to make a 2-digit by 1-digit multiplication. Write it horizontally, eg 43×6, and then vertically:

$$\begin{array}{r} 43 \\ \times\ \ 6 \\ \hline 18 \\ 240 \\ \hline 258 \end{array}$$

Tell the children that they are going to multiply the least significant digit by 6 first. Point to 43. *Which is the least significant digit? What is 6×3?* Write 18 underneath $\times$ 6. *What are we going to multiply by 6 now? What is 6×40?* Write 240 underneath 18. Point to the 18: *This is six lots of 3.* Point to 240: *This is 6 lots of 40. What do we need to do to find 6 lots of 43? What is 240 and 18?* Write the answer underneath: 258. Repeat with another set of digits.
    Choose three more digits. Write the multiplication vertically. Ask the children to multiply the least significant digit first.
    The children can pick numeral cards to generate ten further 2-digit by 1-digit multiplications.

DIFFERENTIATION

More able: How many different products can they make using the same 3 digits?
Less able: Do several examples, writing out each stage (as in long multiplication).

PLENARY

Ask several pupils to give their multiplications and the answers. Write them on the board. Explain that they are going to check using a calculator and inverse operations. *If we divide the answer by the digit which the original number was multiplied by, the number shown on the calculator should be the same number that we started with.* Encourage the children to check the multiplications on the board by division.

LESSON 7

For the **Oral and mental starter**, four groups play ESTIMATING ANSWERS: Group 1's target number is 100, Group 2's 200 and so on. They roll three dice and arrange the digits into a TU $\times$ U. If the answer can be rounded to their target number, they score a point. Continue until one group has 3 points. For the **Main teaching activity**, extend Lesson 6 to cover HTU $\times$ U. Demonstrate with a vertical multiplication on the board, then let the children use numeral cards to generate further examples. More able children can look for a generalisation about the position and size of the digits to make the largest possible product. Less able children can work with TU $\times$ U examples. For the **Plenary**, write some HTU $\times$ U questions and answers on the board, the children decide which answers may be correct and which cannot be.

LESSON 8

RESOURCES

Number cards 50–80 and a 6-sided dice (for teacher demo and one set per three children); numeral cards (one set per child); multiplication grids.

PREPARATION

Give each child a set of numeral cards.

VOCABULARY

Divide, how many lots of in, groups of.

LEARNING OUTCOMES

ORAL AND MENTAL STARTER

● Derive quickly or continue to derive quickly division facts corresponding to tables up to 10×10.

MAIN TEACHING ACTIVITY

● Approximate first. Use informal pencil and paper methods to support, record or explain divisions.

ORAL AND MENTAL STARTER

DIVISION FACTS: Ask quick division questions related to table facts to 10×10, eg *How many 5s in 35? What is 36 divided by 9? How many lots of 4 in 32?* The children hold up numeral cards to show the answers. Discuss methods after each question: *How did you do it? Did anyone do it a different way?*

MAIN TEACHING ACTIVITY

PARTITION DIVISION: Explain to the class that they are going to look at ways to divide larger numbers mentally. Pick a number card (eg 62) and roll the dice (eg 4). Write $62 \div 4$ on the board. *First we are going to use things that we already know. We know that there are ten 4s in 40.* Write $40 \div 4 = 10$. *We still need to work out how many 4s are in what is left. There is 22 left. How many 4s in 22?* Write $22 \div 4 = 5$. *What is the remainder?* Write r2 next to 5. Point to the $40 \div 4$ and $22 \div 4$. *There are ten 4s in 40, and five 4s in 22 with 2 left over. How many 4s are in 62?* Write 15r2 next to $62 \div 4$.

Repeat with other numbers, encouraging pupils to think about and use known facts (eg there are ten 5s in 50). Encourage approximation by asking questions such as: *Will there be more than ten 5s in 62? How do you know?*

Work in threes. The first child picks a number card, rolls the dice (if 1 or 2 is rolled, roll again) and writes down a division. The second child uses a known fact to perform the first part of the division and writes it down (eg $30 \div 3 = 10$). The third child writes down what is left of the number being divided and divides it by the number rolled. Finally, the first child completes the division. Repeat, swapping roles.

DIFFERENTIATION

More able: Pick a 2-digit number card and add 100 to the number. Roll a 10-sided dice to generate the divisor.
Less able: Work with number cards 30–50, referring to multiplication grids.

PLENARY

Extend the work: Write $124 \div 5 =$ on the board. *There are ten 5s in 50. How many 5s in 100?* Write $100 \div 5 = 20$. *How much is left over?* Write $24 \div 5 =$. *How many 5s in 24?* Write 4r4 next to the = sign. *How many 5s in 124 altogether?* Write 24r4 next to the original division. Repeat with other 3-digit numbers.

RESOURCES
Photocopiable page 35.

PREPARATION
Write these word problems on the board so that the class will be able to read them:
There are 36 children in a class sitting in groups of 6. How many groups of 6 are there?
There are 7 tables in a class. 4 children sit at each table. How many children are there?
In each box of eggs there are 6 eggs. Simon buys 7 boxes. How many eggs is that?
Another time, Simon needs 26 eggs for his recipe. How many boxes will he have to buy?

VOCABULARY
How many lots of, shared, altogether, each.

LEARNING OUTCOMES
ORAL AND MENTAL STARTER
● **Know by heart all multiplication facts up to 10 × 10.**
● Derive quickly division facts corresponding to tables up to 10 × 10.
MAIN TEACHING ACTIVITY
● **Use all four operations to solve word problems involving numbers** based on 'real life' or money, using one or more steps.
● Choose and use appropriate number operations to solve problems.

ORAL AND MENTAL STARTER
WHAT'S THE QUESTION? Write five numbers between 1 and 20 on the board. Ask pupils to give you questions involving multiplication or division to make each answer. Build up a range of questions for each answer, including word problems.

MAIN TEACHING ACTIVITY
WORD PROBLEMS: Explain that this lesson will be about solving multiplication and division problems – the pupils will have to decide which operation to perform. Read the first one together. *What does the problem tell us? How many children are there?* Write 36 on the board. *They are in groups of 6. We need to find out how many groups of 6 there are. Are we going to multiply 36 by 6 or divide 36 by 6? How do you know?* Write ÷ 6 = next to 36. *How are you going to calculate the answer?* (Use a tables grid, count up in sixes, recall)

Read and work through each of the other problems, asking pupils to decide whether they need to multiply or divide. On the last problem, make sure they understand why they need to round the answer up to 5 boxes, not down to 4.

The children work through photocopiable page 35.

DIFFERENTIATION
More able: Write their own pair of problems, one multiplication and one division. Swap them with a partner to solve.
Less able: Indicate whether each problem on the sheet is multiplication or division.

PLENARY
Introduce some two-step problems, eg *I buy 4 packs of pencils for £1.25 each. How much change do I get from £10?* Talk through the stages: *What will need to be done first? Why?* Work through another example, eg *I have a bag with 32 sweets in, and buy a packet of 18 sweets. I share the sweets out equally with my 4 friends. How many do we each get?*

LESSON 10
For the **Oral and mental starter**, play WORD PROBLEMS BINGO: Children write down five numbers between 1 and 10, then cross them off as they answer questions such as *I buy five CDs, all the same price for a total of £40. How much was each CD?* Discuss methods. For the **Main teaching activity**, extend Lesson 9: Discuss some word problems for multiplications and divisions, then ask the children to write their own problems and solve them. More able children can write two-step problems; less able children can concentrate on multiplication. In the **Plenary**, solve some of the children's word problems as a class.

Doubles

Join the numbers to their doubles.

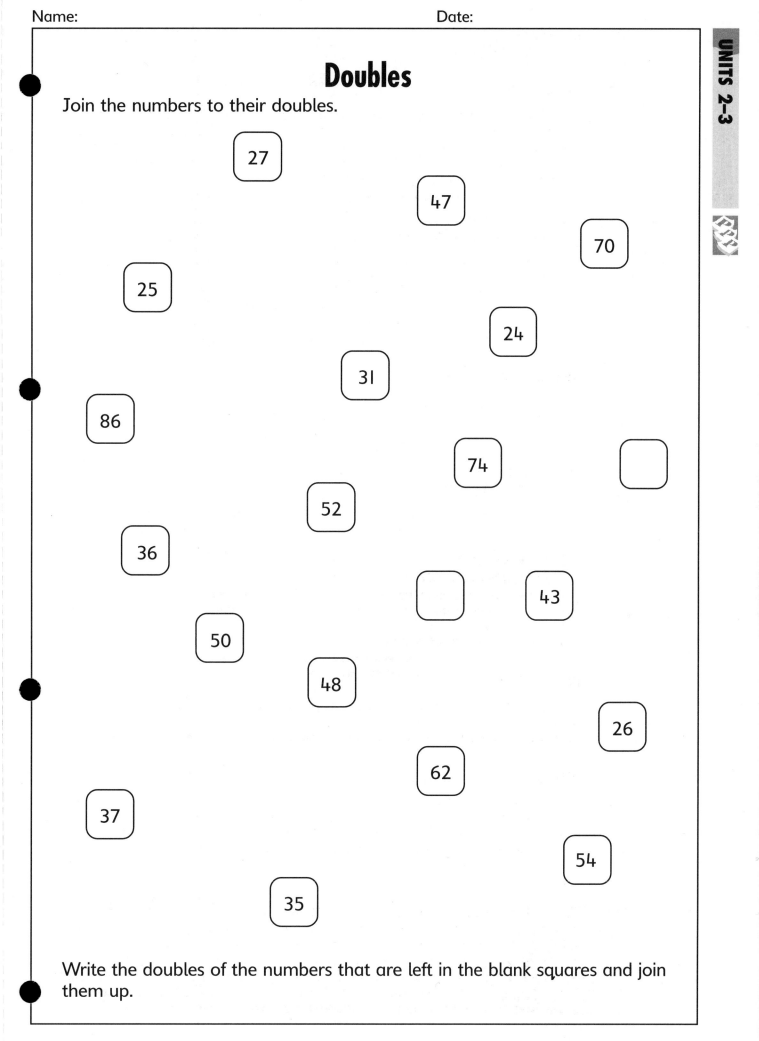

UNITS 2–3

Write the doubles of the numbers that are left in the blank squares and join them up.

Multiplication

Work out the answers to these multiplications by doubling one side and halving the other.

$32 \times 12 =$

$42 \times 8 =$

$54 \times 8 =$

$26 \times 16 =$

$38 \times 12 =$

$36 \times 16 =$

$32 \times 24 =$

$34 \times 32 =$

Write some multiplications of your own. Calculate the answers by doubling one side and halving the other. Which numbers is this method easiest to use with?

Multiplication and division

For each problem, decide whether it is multiplication or division. Write the correct sign in the box, then calculate the answer.

For example: In a school, there are 32 children in each class and 5 classes. How many children are there altogether?

$\boxed{\times}$ $\boxed{32 \times 5 = 160}$

1. In a class of 35 children, the children sit in groups of 5. How many groups are there?

2. There are 24 pencils in a box. The headmaster buys 6 of these boxes. How many pencils is that?

3. James gets £5 pocket money a week. He saves £1.50. How much does he save over 6 weeks?

4. A box holds 6 cakes. How many boxes would be needed to hold 48 cakes?

5. The children sit in rows of 8. There are 4 rows in the class. How many places are there?

6. In assembly, children sit in rows of 10. There are 100 children in the school. How may rows do they fill?

7. 24 friends take a journey to the seaside. If a car holds 4 people, how many cars will they need to take all the people?

UNITS 4-5

ORGANISATION (10 LESSONS)

	LEARNING OUTCOMES	ORAL AND MENTAL STARTER	MAIN TEACHING ACTIVITY	PLENARY
LESSON 1	● Use fraction notation and the vocabulary numerator and denominator.	MATCHING ANSWERS: Divide 2-digit by 1-digit numbers mentally. Which pairs give the same answer?	FRACTIONS OF SHAPES: Fold and cut shapes to use fraction notation. Develop idea of non-unitary fractions.	Find how many of a given unitary fraction are in a whole.
LESSON 2	● Use fraction notation, including mixed numbers, and the vocabulary numerator and denominator. ● **Relate fractions to division**, and use division to find simple fractions of numbers and quantities.	HALVES ROUND THE ROOM: Halve a number repeatedly to reach an odd number.	MIXED NUMBERS: Match shapes to numbers.	Divide given numbers into equal parts.
LESSON 3	● **Relate fractions to division**, and use division to find simple fractions of numbers and quantities.	NUMERAL CARDS: Use numeral cards to answer questions relating to fractions.	FRACTIONS AMOUNTS: Find fractions of numbers and quantities, including some non-unitary. Relate to division.	Answer questions such as: *Which is more, ¼ of 12 or ½ of 8?*
LESSON 4	● Recognise when two simple fractions are equivalent. ● Develop calculator skills and use a calculator effectively.	FRACTIONS BINGO: Cross out numbers that answer fraction questions.	MATCHING FRACTIONS: Match equivalent fractions, using a calculator and shapes.	Complete a grid of equivalent fractions.
LESSON 5	● Recognise when two simple fractions are equivalent, including relating hundredths to tenths (eg $^{70}/_{100} = ^{7}/_{10}$). ● Develop calculator skills and use a calculator effectively.	ORDERING TENTHS: Order tenths on a number line; also ½, ¼ and ¾.	EQUIVALENT FRACTIONS: Express common fractions in hundredths. Match equivalent fractions.	Order fractions in hundredths on a number line.
LESSON 6 +7	● Change an improper fraction to a mixed number (eg change $^{13}/_{10}$ to $1^{3}/_{10}$). ● Order a set of fractions such as 2, $2^{3}/_{4}$, $1^{3}/_{4}$, $2^{1}/_{2}$, $1^{1}/_{2}$, and position them on a number line.	FRACTION GRID: Roll dice to generate an answer. Find a question to match. IMPROPER FRACTIONS: Match improper fraction to equivalent mixed number.	CHANGE THE FRACTION: Use pictorial representations of mixed numbers (folded cards). Order mixed numbers on a number line.	Change fractions to mixed numbers and order on a number line. Hold up numeral card to show part of fraction to be added to make an integer.
LESSON 8 +9	● Solve simple problems using ideas of ratio and proportion ('one for every...' and 'one in every...').	WHAT'S THE QUESTION?: Roll a dice to generate an answer; think of a division question to match. FRACTION PROBLEMS: Use division facts to find answers.	INTRODUCTION TO RATIO: Use coloured counters to represent ratio. Use interlocking cubes to show ratios.	Use different sorting criteria to look at ratio. Make 'towers' to show different ratios.
LESSON 10	● Solve simple problems using ideas of ratio and proportion ('one for every...' and 'one in every...').	RATIO RACE: Roll dice to generate a ratio. Build a corresponding tower quickly.	RATIO PROBLEMS: Solve simple ratio problems in a real-life context.	Check and consolidate written work.

Lessons 1, 3, 4, 6, 8 and 10 are shown in detail. Lessons 2, 5, 7 and 9 follow on from what has already been taught.

LESSON 1

RESOURCES

Card, scissors, shape templates.

PREPARATION

Cut some large regular shapes from card – rectangle, square, circle, hexagon.

VOCABULARY

Fraction, divide, equal, parts, half, quarter, third, fifth, sixth, eighth, tenth, notation, numerator, denominator.

LEARNING OUTCOMES

ORAL AND MENTAL STARTER
● Derive quickly or continue to derive quickly division facts corresponding to tables up to 10 × 10.

MAIN TEACHING ACTIVITY
● Use fraction notation and the vocabulary numerator and denominator.

ORAL AND MENTAL STARTER

MATCHING ANSWERS: Write twelve 2-digit by 1-digit divisions on the board that make six different answers. Give the children a few minutes to look at them, then ask each group to find a pair of divisions that give the same answer. On the next round, can they think of another division that will give the same target answer as the pair they chose? Discuss the methods used.

MAIN TEACHING ACTIVITY

FRACTIONS OF SHAPES: Explain that the children are going to find out how to read and write fractions. Write ½ on the board. Ask pupils what this says. What does it mean? Hold up a shape cut from card and ask a pupil to show half of the shape. Stress the importance of the shape being folded into two equal-sized parts. *The number at the bottom, the denominator, tells us how many equal parts something has been divided into. The number at the top, the numerator, tells us how many of those parts there are.* Take another shape and ask a pupil to fold the shape into quarters. Write ¼ on the board. Stress that each part must be equal in size to the others. *Is this folded into quarters?* Ask a child to come and cut out one quarter. *If we take one quarter away, how many quarters are left?* Repeat the whole process with sixths and eighths.

The children draw their own shapes, using templates, and shade in a part to show a given fraction: $^1/_2$, $^1/_3$, $^1/_4$, $^1/_5$, $^1/_6$, $^1/_8$, $^1/_{10}$, $^2/_3$ or $^3/_4$.

DIFFERENTIATION

More able: Pick numeral cards to generate non-unitary fractions – lower card as numerator, higher card as denominator.
Less able: Shade in unitary fractions on shapes already divided up.

PLENARY

Draw a shape on the board. Divide it into two. Ask: *How many halves in a whole one? How many halves in two whole ones? How many sixths in a whole one? How many sixths in two whole ones? Three whole ones? How did you work it out?* Repeat with other fractions.

LESSON 2

LEARNING OUTCOMES	**ORAL AND MENTAL STARTER** ● Derive quickly or continue to derive quickly corresponding halves of doubles of whole numbers 1–50. **MAIN TEACHING ACTIVITY** ● Use fraction notation, including mixed numbers, and the vocabulary numerator and denominator. ● **Relate fractions to division**, and use division to find simple fractions of numbers and quantities.
RESOURCES	2-digit even number cards; photocopiable page 44; dice; shapes drawn on squared paper.
ORAL AND MENTAL STARTER	HALVES ROUND THE ROOM: Divide the class into 4 or 5 teams. First team pick a number from a set of 2-digit even number cards and read it out. Next team halve it and say the answer as a team; next team halve it again if they can, and so on. First team to say an odd number answer scores a point and takes the next starting number. Which is the first team to score 3 points?
MAIN TEACHING ACTIVITY	MIXED NUMBERS: Write $1\frac{1}{2}$ on the board. Point to each part and read it: *one and a half.* Write other mixed numbers on the board and ask pupils to read them, eg $2\frac{1}{4}$, $3\frac{2}{5}$. Draw a square and half of a congruent square on the board. Point to them and say: *There are one and a half squares here.* Write $1\frac{3}{4}$ on the board. *What would one and three quarter circles look like?* Ask a child to draw them on the board. Repeat with other mixed numbers. Pupils complete photocopiable page 44.
DIFFERENTIATION	More able: Roll 3 dice to make a mixed number. Smallest number is the whole number, middle number is the numerator, highest number is the denominator. Draw shapes and shade them to represent the fraction rolled. Less able: Shade in given shapes divided into an appropriate number of equal parts (eg 2 squares divided into quarters – shade in $1\frac{1}{4}$).
PLENARY	Write division facts on the board, eg $12 \div 4 = 3$. Relate to fractions, eg *What is a quarter of 12?* Or $15 \div 5 = 3$; *What is one fifth of 15? What do you notice?*

LESSON 3

RESOURCES

Numeral cards 0–9; counters; Blu-Tack.

PREPARATION

Give a set of 0–9 numeral cards to each child. Ask the children to lay them out in order on the table in front of them. Blu-Tack 9 counters in a line on the board.

VOCABULARY

Divide, half, quarter, third, fifth, sixth, tenth, equal.

LEARNING OUTCOMES

ORAL AND MENTAL STARTER
● **Relate fractions to division**, and use division to find simple fractions of numbers and quantities.

MAIN TEACHING ACTIVITY
● **Relate fractions to division**, and use division to find simple fractions of numbers and quantities.

ORAL AND MENTAL STARTER

NUMERAL CARDS: Ask questions relating to previous work on fractions, eg *How many fifths in a whole one? What is a quarter of 12?* Pupils hold up numeral cards to show the answers. Encourage them to explain their methods.

MAIN TEACHING ACTIVITY

FRACTION AMOUNTS: Tell the children they are going to find out how to calculate a fraction of a number. *How do we work out half of a number?* Take various suggestions, but focus on the idea of splitting the number into two equal parts. *How do we calculate a quarter of a number?* Pupils may suggest halving a half; if so, ask how many equal parts the number will be divided into. Write on the board: *To find half of a number ÷ 2. To find quarter of a number ÷ 4.* Point to and read out each statement. *How could we find a third of a number?* Write ÷3. Ask questions related to $1/3$, eg *What is $1/3$ of 15?* Find other fractions of numbers, eg *What would we divide a number by to find $1/6$?*

Split the counters on the board into groups of 3. *If I divide the counters into 3 groups of equal size, each group is $1/3$ of 9. How many counters would there be in $2/3$ of nine?* Emphasise that there must be 6. Demonstrate with other numbers of counters, finding $2/3$ and $3/4$.

Ask the children to find $1/2$, $1/3$, $1/4$, then $2/3$ and $3/4$ of numbers that are multiples of 2, 3 and 4; 12, 24, 36 etc. The numbers and fractions could be written on the board. Pupils can use counters if necessary. They should record their work, eg $1/2$ of 12 = 6.

DIFFERENTIATION

More able: Pick a 2-digit number and decide whether it can be divided exactly by 3; if so, find $1/3$ and $2/3$ of the number. Can it be divided exactly by 4? If so, find $1/4$ and $3/4$ of it. Record results as above.

Less able: Using 12 counters, find out how many in half, how many in a third, how many in a quarter. Repeat with 24 counters. Record results using pictures or numbers.

PLENARY

Write some pairs of fraction problems on the board, eg $1/4$ of 12 and $1/2$ of 8. Pupils work in pairs to decide which of each pair gives the greater answer. After a few minutes discuss.

RESOURCES

Calculators; shape templates; scissors; paper.

PREPARATION

Cut out some large shapes (circles, squares, rectangles) from paper.

VOCABULARY

Half, quarter, third, fifth, sixth, eighth, tenth, equal, equivalent, same, numerator, denominator.

LEARNING OUTCOMES

ORAL AND MENTAL STARTER
● **Relate fractions to division**, and use division to find simple fractions of numbers and quantities.
MAIN TEACHING ACTIVITY
● Recognise when two simple fractions are equivalent.
● Develop calculator skills and use a calculator effectively.

ORAL AND MENTAL STARTER

FRACTIONS BINGO: The children write 5 different numbers between 1 and 10 (inclusive), spread out on a piece of paper. Ask fraction questions, eg *What is one third of 12? How many fifths in a whole one?* Children who have the answer on their piece of paper can cross it out. Discuss methods. Continue until someone has crossed out all the numbers.

MAIN TEACHING ACTIVITY

MATCHING FRACTIONS: Explain that this lesson is about fractions that are equal to one another, or equivalent. Ask a child to fold a circle in half and open it out. Ask another child to fold another circle of the same size into quarters and open it out. Ask the class: *How many quarters in one half?* Write on the board: $1/2 = 2/4$. Compare a folded eighth of a circle with a quarter and a half. *What do you notice about the relationship between the numerator and the denominator when the fraction is equivalent to a half?* Ask for other examples of fractions equivalent to a half. Repeat with a quarter.

Say that we can check equivalence using a calculator. *How would you put one half into a calculator?* (1 ÷ 2) Ask a child to put one half into the calculator. Ask another child to input two quarters. Discuss what they notice. Repeat with the whole class putting 1 ÷ 4 then 2 ÷ 8 in to their calculators.

Repeat the above: start by folding a square into thirds and sixths, then fold a rectangle into fifths and tenths.

Children work in pairs on a given unitary fraction (eg $^1/_4$), folding the shape, shading in the correct amount and labelling it. Then they fold another of the same shape to show (in this case) $^2/_8$. They should do at least three examples, using the same shape so that direct comparison can be made.

DIFFERENTIATION

More able: Do the activity starting with non-unitary fractions.
Less able: Start by looking at fractions equivalent to $^1/_2$ before moving on.

PLENARY

Draw a grid on the board with headings as shown (see figure right). Include rows for $^1/_2$, $^1/_3$, $^1/_4$, $^1/_5$, $^1/_6$, $^1/_8$, $^1/_{10}$, $^2/_3$ and $^3/_4$. Write one fraction in an appropriate column for each row, but avoid writing them in size order. Ask questions to fill in the grid with the class.

Simplest form	equivalent	equivalent
$\frac{1}{2}$		
	$\frac{2}{8}$	
$\frac{1}{6}$		

LEARNING OUTCOMES	**ORAL AND MENTAL STARTER** ● Order simple fractions: for example, decide whether fractions such as $^3/_8$ or $^7/_{10}$ are greater or less than $^1/_2$. **MAIN TEACHING ACTIVITY** ● Recognise when two simple fractions are equivalent, including relating hundredths to tenths (eg $^{70}/_{100} = ^7/_{10}$). ● Develop calculator skills and use a calculator effectively.
RESOURCES	String; pegs; cards with 0, 1, tenths between 0 and 1, $^1/_2$, $^1/_4$, $^3/_4$ and equivalent hundredths; a blank hundred square (enlarged or on acetate); photocopiable page 45.
ORAL AND MENTAL STARTER	ORDERING TENTHS: Put up a string number line. Say: *0 is at this end and 1 is at the other end. Where would you put five tenths on this number line? Why?* Consult the rest of the class: do they agree that it has been put in the correct place? Repeat with $^1/_{10}$ to $^9/_{10}$, asking children to peg the numbers in the appropriate places. Also include $^1/_4$, $^1/_2$ and $^3/_4$.
MAIN TEACHING ACTIVITY	EQUIVALENT FRACTIONS: Put up a blank hundred square. Ask: *If we coloured in half of these squares, how many would that be? How could we write that?* Ask a child to write it on the board: $^{50}/_{100}$. *What about $^1/_{10}$? How did you work it out?* Repeat with other fractions hung on the number line. Check on a calculator that 50 divided by 100 is the same as 1 divided by 2. Children play a game of matching pairs, using cards from photocopiable page 45.
DIFFERENTIATION	More able: Make own additional pairs of cards, using other equivalent fractions known. Less able: Use only tenths cards and their equivalent hundredths.
PLENARY	Place some hundredths cards on the number line by responses to questions.

LESSON 5

LESSON 6 +7

RESOURCES

10- and 6-sided dice; strips of card; board markers in two different colours; 2-digit number cards; small cards; large cards; Blu-tack; marker pens.

PREPARATION

Draw a 4 × 4 grid on the board and write a fraction question in each space, eg $1/3$ of 9, $3/4$ of 8. The answers must lie between 1 and 6 (inclusive). Cut strips of card, approximately 5cm × 50cm.

LEARNING OUTCOMES

ORAL AND MENTAL STARTER
● **Relate fractions to division**, and use division to find simple fractions of numbers and quantities.

MAIN TEACHING ACTIVITY
● Change an improper fraction to a mixed number (eg change $13/10$ to $13/10$).
Order a set of fractions such as 2, $23/4$, $13/4$, $21/2$, $11/2$.

VOCABULARY

Improper fraction, mixed number, half, quarter, third, fifth, sixth, eighth, tenth, equal, equivalent, numerator, denominator.

ORAL AND MENTAL STARTER

FRACTION GRID: Divide the class into two teams. Ask a player from team A to roll the dice. Team A then look for a question in the grid that matches the answer they have rolled; if they find one, they put a cross through it in their chosen colour. Team B then has a turn. Continue until a team gets three in a line. If you run out of questions, count up the crosses to decide who has won.

MAIN TEACHING ACTIVITY

CHANGE THE FRACTION: Tell the children that this lesson is about writing improper fractions as mixed numbers. Explain that an improper fraction is one where the numerator is a larger number than the denominator (eg $22/7$), and that a mixed number is made up of a whole number and a fraction (eg $13/4$). Fold two strips of card into eight. Shade in the whole of one piece of card and three parts (eighths) of the second piece. Ask the class: *How many eighths are shaded?* Write $11/8$ on the board. Hold up the first piece of card: *This is one whole.* Hold up the second piece: *Three eighths.* Write $= 13/8$. Repeat with other fractions and strips of card.

Write $8/5$ on the board. Ask a child to read this out. *How many fifths in a whole one? If five fifths is one whole one,* (write 1) *how many more fifths are there in this fraction?* Write $13/5$ on the board.

Generate an improper fraction by rolling two 10-sided dice. Write the larger number over the smaller one, then convert to a mixed number. Do several examples, then let the children do at least 10.

DIFFERENTIATION

More able: Use number cards 10–20 and a 10-sided dice to generate an improper fraction, then convert it to a mixed number.
Less able: Use shapes, eg 2 squares divided into quarters – shade five quarters to make 1 whole square and $1/4$ square.

PLENARY

Write the fractions $1/4$, $2/4$, $3/4$... up to $12/4$ randomly on the board. Point to each one and change it to a mixed number. Write each answer clearly on the board. Discuss how else some of them (eg $12/4$) might be written. Draw a number line on the board; write 0 at one end and 3 at the other. Ask questions to help the children order the fractions on the line. Discuss the order.

LESSON 7

For the **Oral and mental starter**, IMPROPER FRACTIONS, make 10 pairs of cards showing improper fractions and the equivalent mixed fractions. Stick each card face down on the board with Blu-tack, then divide the class into two and play a matching game (Pelmanism). For the **Main teaching activity**, CHANGE THE FRACTION, ask children to place mixed numbers from Lesson 6 (with denominators 2, 3 and 4) on a blank number line labelled 0– 3, then 0–5. Write numbers on the board for children to place on their own 0–5 number line. More able children can place numbers with eighths; less able children can start with halves, then try quarters. For the **Plenary**, children holding large cards with mixed numbers (from 1 to 10) can be ordered by the class.

LESSON 8 +9

RESOURCES

Large counters made from card (6 red, 6 green); Blu-Tack; squared paper; coloured pens (two colours for each child); a 1–6 dice per pair; photocopiable page 47; interlocking cubes; 6-sided and 10-sided dice; numeral cards (one set per child).

PREPARATION

Make the counters from card.

VOCABULARY
Ratio, parts, for every.

LEARNING OUTCOMES

ORAL AND MENTAL STARTER

● Derive quickly or continue to derive quickly division facts corresponding to tables up to 10 × 10.

MAIN TEACHING ACTIVITY

● Solve simple problems using ideas of ratio and proportion ('one for every...' and 'one in every...').

ORAL AND MENTAL STARTER

WHAT'S THE QUESTION?: Divide the class into groups of 4–6. Roll a dice to generate a number (eg 4), then ask each group to say a division with that answer (eg 40 ÷ 10 =, 16 ÷ 4 =). Write each division on the board. Ask children to explain their methods and reasoning. Continue until each group has had the opportunity to go first.

MAIN TEACHING ACTIVITY

INTRODUCTION TO RATIO: Tell the children that they are going to find out about ratio. Ratio is used to make comparisons. Put 1 red counter and 2 green counters on the board. Point to them. *In this pattern, for every red counter there are 2 green counters. If I put another red counter down, how many more green counters will I need to add to keep the ratio the same – 2 green for every 1 red?* Repeat with different ratios, encouraging the class to say the relevant ratio (eg '3 green for every 1 red').

Pupils roll dice to generate ratios, eg 3 to 5, then colour in squares to show the ratio (3 one colour and 5 another) and write it down (eg '3 green for every 5 red').

DIFFERENTIATION

More able: Write both ratio, ie *green:red is 3:5*, and proportion, eg $^3/_8$ *are green*, $^5/_8$ *red*. Less able: Work with a group to check that they know how to draw and write the ratios.

PLENARY

Ask 2 children with dark hair and one with fair hair (if appropriate) to come to the front. *How many dark-haired children are there for every fair-haired child in this group?* Repeat using different criteria and different children. Select 2 children wearing black shoes and 4 children wearing trainers (if appropriate). *How many children with trainers are there for every child wearing shoes in this group?* Group these children 2 to 1 if necessary to emphasise the ratio.

LESSON 9

For the **Oral and mental starter**, FRACTION PROBLEMS, children hold up numeral cards to answer fraction questions (including two-step word problems such as *I have 9 counters. 2/3 are red and the rest are green. How many are green?)* For the **Main teaching activity**, extend Lesson 8, INTRODUCTION TO RATIO: use interlocking cubes to demonstrate ratios, including some simplification (eg 4 yellow, 2 red can be 4:2 or 2:1). Make towers and break them apart. The children complete photocopiable page 47. More able children can generate ratios using dice and write down those which can be simplified; less able children can make towers to show given ratios. For the **Plenary**, ask groups to hold up towers showing given ratios.

RESOURCES

Photocopiable page 48; interlocking cubes; 6-sided dice.

PREPARATION

Draw a glass divided into five parts (see figure below) on the board. Put some interlocking cubes on each table.

LEARNING OUTCOMES

ORAL AND MENTAL STARTER
● Solve simple problems using ideas of ratio and proportion ('one for every...' and 'one in every...').
MAIN TEACHING ACTIVITY
● Solve simple problems using ideas of ratio and proportion ('one for every...' and 'one in every...').

VOCABULARY

Ratio, for every, parts.

ORAL AND MENTAL STARTER

RATIO RACE: Roll two dice to generate ratios (eg 1:5). Groups hold up a tower with the correct ratio of colours. Discuss different responses, eg why some groups might hold up 1:3 to show 2:6.

MAIN TEACHING ACTIVITY

RATIO PROBLEMS: Tell the children that they are going to solve simple problems involving ratios. Point to the glass drawing. Explain that a particular brand of orange squash needs to be mixed 1 part squash to 4 parts water. *How might we show that in this glass?* Ask a child to come and shade in the correct parts of the glass. *If I had 4 glasses, how many parts water would that be altogether? How did you work it out?* Change the ratio to 2 parts orange squash to 3 parts water. *If I am mixing a jug using this ratio and I use 10 parts orange squash, how much water will I use?* Ask similar questions using different ratios.

The children go on to complete photocopiable page 48.

DIFFERENTIATION

More able: Complete the sheet, then write some problems of their own for others to solve.
Less able: Complete drawings of glasses, given simpler questions such as *If the ratio of water to orange is 2:1; how much water and orange will be needed for 2 glasses?*

PLENARY

Go over the children's answers. Encourage them to explain their methods. Pose questions in a different context: *In a recipe, 2 eggs are needed for every 100g of flour. How many eggs are needed for 400g of flour?*

Mixed numbers

Write the mixed number to show how much has been shaded:

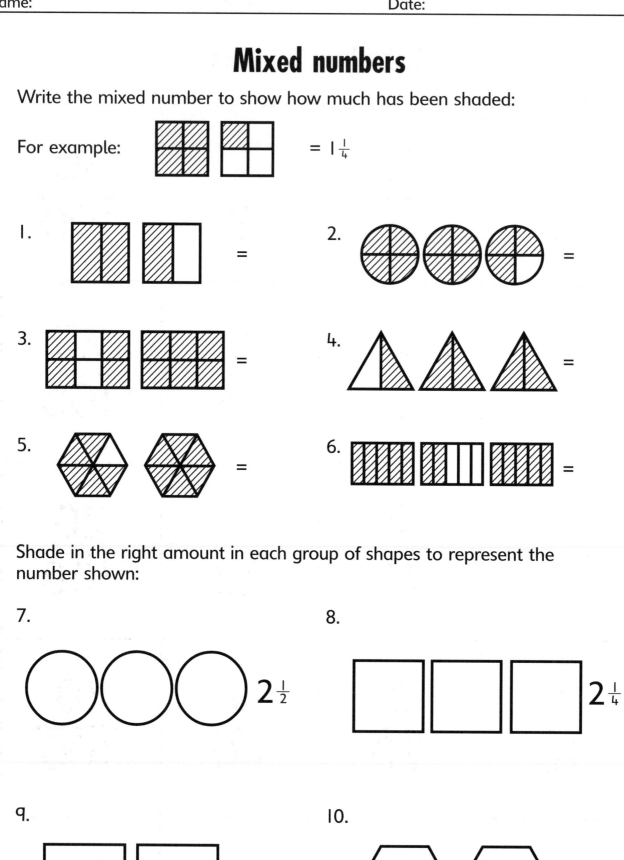

For example: $= 1\frac{1}{4}$

1. $=$

2. $=$

3. $=$

4. $=$

5. $=$

6. $=$

Shade in the right amount in each group of shapes to represent the number shown:

7. $2\frac{1}{2}$

8. $2\frac{1}{4}$

9. $1\frac{3}{5}$

10. $1\frac{1}{3}$

Name: Date:

Equivalent fractions

$\dfrac{1}{2}$	$\dfrac{2}{4}$	$\dfrac{4}{8}$	$\dfrac{50}{100}$
$\dfrac{1}{4}$	$\dfrac{2}{8}$	$\dfrac{4}{16}$	$\dfrac{25}{100}$
$\dfrac{1}{5}$	$\dfrac{2}{10}$	$\dfrac{4}{20}$	$\dfrac{20}{100}$
$\dfrac{1}{10}$	$\dfrac{2}{20}$	$\dfrac{4}{40}$	$\dfrac{10}{100}$
$\dfrac{3}{4}$	$\dfrac{6}{8}$	$\dfrac{12}{16}$	$\dfrac{75}{100}$

Ratio 1

Complete the statement to show the ratio of white squares to black squares.

1.

___ white for every ___ black

2.

___ white for every ___ black

3.

___ white for every ___ black

4.

___ white for every ___ black

5.

___ white for every ___ black

6.

___ white for every ___ black

Shade in the correct number of squares to match the ratio shown.

7.

1 white for every 5 black.

8.

1 white for every 3 black.

9.

1 white for every 1 black.

10.

2 white for every 3 black.

Ratio 2

Work out these problems to fill each set of glasses or jug.

1. 1 part orange for every 3 parts water.

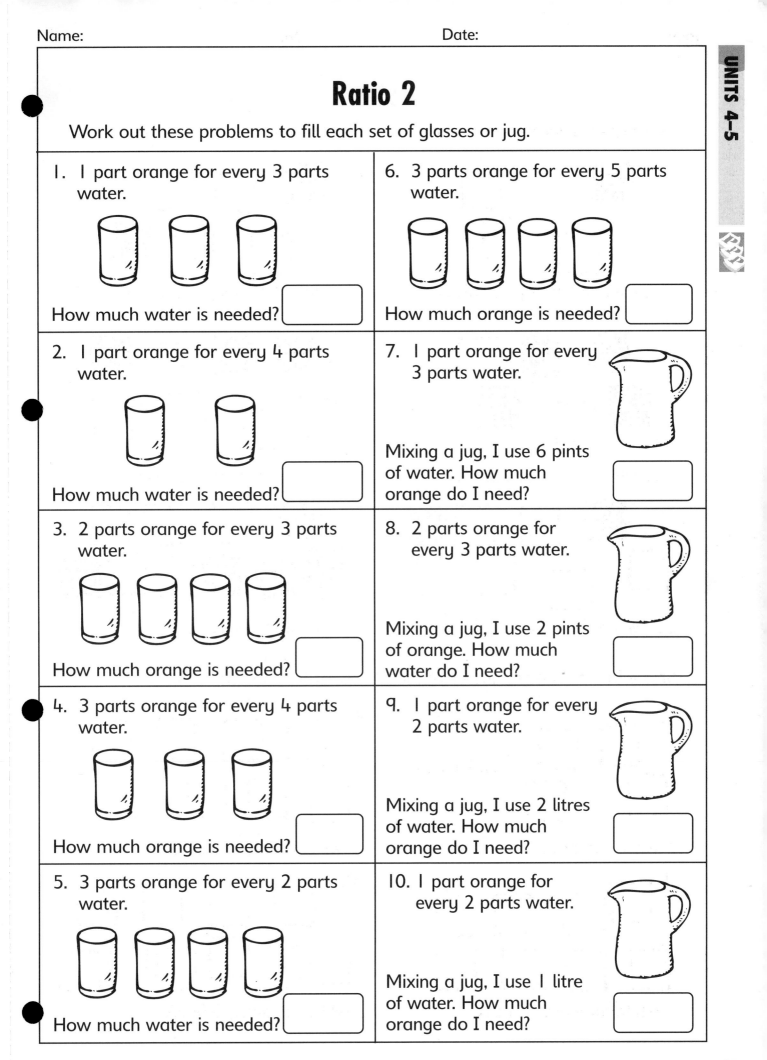

   How much water is needed? ☐

2. 1 part orange for every 4 parts water.

   How much water is needed? ☐

3. 2 parts orange for every 3 parts water.

   How much orange is needed? ☐

4. 3 parts orange for every 4 parts water.

   How much orange is needed? ☐

5. 3 parts orange for every 2 parts water.

   How much water is needed? ☐

6. 3 parts orange for every 5 parts water.

   How much orange is needed? ☐

7. 1 part orange for every 3 parts water.

   Mixing a jug, I use 6 pints of water. How much orange do I need? ☐

8. 2 parts orange for every 3 parts water.

   Mixing a jug, I use 2 pints of orange. How much water do I need? ☐

9. 1 part orange for every 2 parts water.

   Mixing a jug, I use 2 litres of water. How much orange do I need? ☐

10. 1 part orange for every 2 parts water.

    Mixing a jug, I use 1 litre of water. How much orange do I need? ☐

UNIT 6

ORGANISATION (8 LESSONS)

	LEARNING OUTCOMES	ORAL AND MENTAL STARTER	MAIN TEACHING ACTIVITY	PLENARY
LESSON 1 +2	● Solve a problem by representing and interpreting data in tables, charts and diagrams.	HOW MANY DOUBLES?: Double 2-digit numbers against time.	DATA COLLECTION: Collect and display data using tally marks and bar charts. Ask questions about a bar chart.	Discuss what the bar charts show. Discuss whether survey was fair.
LESSON 3	● Solve a problem by representing and interpreting data in tables, charts and diagrams, for example bar line charts where intermediate points have no meaning.	NUMERAL CARDS: Ask questions on multiplication and division facts; pupils hold up numeral cards.	DICE GRAPH: Pose a question; pupils carry out a test and plot a bar line graph.	Compare the different graphs drawn.
LESSON 4	● Solve a problem by representing and interpreting data in tables, charts and diagrams, for example bar line charts, vertical axis labelled in 2s, 5s, 10s, 20s or 100s where intermediate points have no meaning.	MULTIPLE MANIA: Ask quick-fire questions relating to 5×, 10× and 20× tables.	CHANGE THE AXIS: Change labels on vertical axis of a graph. How does it alter the data?	Look at a graph with no labels and discuss what it shows.
LESSON 5	● Solve a problem by representing and interpreting data in tables, charts and diagrams, for example bar line charts, vertical axis labelled in 2s, 5s, 10s, 20s or 100s where intermediate points have no meaning.	THINK OF A NUMBER: Solve number problems related to tables facts.	DATA SOLUTION: Children decide on a question, then collect and display data to answer it.	Discuss what the children found out.
LESSON 6 +7	● Solve a problem by representing and interpreting data in tables, charts and diagrams, for example bar line charts, vertical axis labelled in 2s, 5s, 10s, 20s or 100s where intermediate points may have meaning. ● Develop calculator skills and use a calculator effectively.	MEET THE TARGET: Use a calculator to combine 5 given numbers (with any operations) to make a target number. THINK OF A NUMBER BINGO: Cross out numbers which answer two-step calculation questions.	A TEMPERATURE GRAPH: Look at a graph that shows temperatures over time. Conduct a survey and plot a graph. PLOT A SECOND LINE: Use a graph with 2 lines on it to make comparisons. Pupils ask questions about the data.	Use the graph to ask questions relating to intermediate points. Go through the children's questions.
LESSON 8	● Solve a problem by representing and interpreting data in tables, charts and diagrams, including those generated by a computer. ● Develop calculator skills and use a calculator effectively.	HOW DID I GET THAT?: Pupils use a calculator to solve problems. Discuss possibilities.	DATABASE: Use a computer database to answer questions.	Review how the database was used to find information.

ORAL AND MENTAL SKILLS: Derive quickly: doubles of all whole numbers 1 to 100; division facts corresponding to tables up to 10 × 10. Recognise and extend number sequences formed by counting from any number in steps of constant size. **Know by heart all multiplication facts up to 10 × 10.** Recognise multiples of 2, 3, 4, 5 and 10 up to the 10th multiple. Choose and use appropriate number operations to solve problems. Understand the effect of and the relationship between the four operations.

Lessons 1, 3 and 6 are shown in detail. Lessons 2, 4, 5, 7 and 8 follow on from what has already been taught.

LESSON 1 +2

RESOURCES

2-digit number cards; a stop-watch (or clock with a second hand); pencils; paper.

PREPARATION

Put a pile of 2-digit number cards on each table (multiples of 5 for the less able, numbers to 50 for the core and numbers over 50 for the more able).

LEARNING OUTCOMES

ORAL AND MENTAL STARTER
● Derive quickly doubles of all whole numbers 1 to 100.
MAIN TEACHING ACTIVITY
● Solve a problem by representing data in tables, charts and diagrams.

VOCABULARY

Data, table, chart, graph, tally, axes, label, title.

ORAL AND MENTAL STARTER

HOW MANY DOUBLES?: Tell the children they are going to see how many 2-digit numbers they can double in one minute. They turn cards over and write down each number and its double, while a partner keeps count on a tally chart. After a minute, they swap roles. Then they check each other's work.

MAIN TEACHING ACTIVITY

DATA COLLECTION: Tell the children, *I think most people can do seven or more 2-digit doubles in a minute.* Now tell them they are going to collect information to find out whether you are right. Discuss ways that information could be collected, eg using a tally chart with rows for 1 double, 2 doubles etc.

Collect information together as a class, using the work done in the Oral and mental starter. Ask children to come up and complete the parts of the tally chart, eg 4 children got 6 doubles in a minute. *Could we display this information in a different way?* Stress the importance of labelling charts and graphs accurately. Go through how a bar chart for this information might be labelled. Let the children construct bar charts to display the data.

DIFFERENTIATION

More able: Double numbers over 50 in the Oral and mental starter.
Less able: Double multiples of 5 in the Oral and mental starter.

PLENARY

Look at bar charts drawn by different children. What do they show? Can most of the children do seven or more 2-digit doubles in a minute?

LESSON 2

Repeat the **Oral and mental starter** from Lesson 1. For the **Main teaching activity,** DATA COLLECTION, work with the class to draw a bar chart on the board showing the data from Lesson 1. Ask questions (eg *How many people got seven or more doubles?*) to encourage children to extract information from the chart. As a class, write appropriate questions for the children to answer on paper; then they can write their own questions using their own bar charts. More able children can compare the data from both Oral and mental sessions. In the **Plenary**, discuss if the survey was a fair test and if not, how it could be made fair.

LESSON 3

RESOURCES

Numeral cards (one set per child); 0–6 dice.

PREPARATION

Ask the children to lay out the numeral cards in order on the table in front of them.

VOCABULARY

Data, table, chart, graph, tally, axes, label, title.

LEARNING OUTCOMES
ORAL AND MENTAL STARTER
● **Know by heart all multiplication facts up to 10 × 10**.
● Derive quickly division facts corresponding to tables up to 10 × 10.
MAIN TEACHING ACTIVITY
● Solve a problem by representing and interpreting data in tables, charts and diagrams, for example bar line charts where intermediate points have no meaning.

ORAL AND MENTAL STARTER

NUMERAL CARDS: Ask quick-fire questions recapping multiplication and division facts. The children hold up numeral cards to show the answers.

MAIN TEACHING ACTIVITY

DICE GRAPH: Tell the children they are going to draw a bar line graph to show information. *We want the graph to tell us whether, when a dice is thrown, the number 3 will come up most often.* Discuss possible approaches. Send a dice round the class to be rolled once by each child; record the results on the board as a tally chart. Plot a bar line graph for the information collected. Discuss what information it shows.

Tell the children they are going to do the same, working in pairs to roll a dice 50 times and showing the results in a bar line graph. *What do you think the graph will show?* The children do this.

DIFFERENTIATION

More able: Use graph paper to plot bar line graphs as accurately as possible, with a vertical axis going up in steps of 2.
Less able: Use a graph with the axes already drawn and labelled.

PLENARY

Look at the different graphs that have been drawn. *Are all the results the same? Why not? What do the graphs show?*

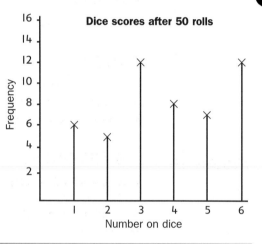

Dice scores after 50 rolls

LEARNING OUTCOMES	**ORAL AND MENTAL STARTER** ● Recognise and extend number sequences formed by counting from any number in steps of a constant size. ● **Know by heart all multiplication facts up to 10 × 10**. **MAIN TEACHING ACTIVITY** ● Solve a problem by representing and interpreting data in tables, charts and diagrams, for example bar line charts, vertical axis labelled in 2s, 5s, 10s, 20s or 100s where intermediate points have no meaning.
RESOURCES	Bar line graphs drawn in previous lesson.
ORAL AND MENTAL STARTER	MULTIPLE MANIA: Count up and back in steps of 5, 10 and 20. Ask questions relating to 5×, 10× and 20× tables; class to respond as a whole or in groups.
MAIN TEACHING ACTIVITY	CHANGE THE AXIS: Look at graphs drawn in the previous lesson; choose one to discuss. Draw it on the board. *What would happen if the vertical axis went up in steps of 2 instead of 1? How would the information change?* Repeat, changing the vertical axis so it goes up in steps of 5, 10 or 20. The children change their own graph and write about how it has changed.
DIFFERENTIATION	More able: Look at vertical axes going up in steps of 3 and 4 as well. Less able: Look at vertical axes going up in steps of 2 and 10.
PLENARY	Draw a bar line graph with no labels. *What does it show us? What could it show us?* (Nothing; we need labels to be able to interpret the graph.) Work with the class to add labels and numbers to the vertical axis. Discuss what information it now shows.

LESSON 5

LEARNING OUTCOMES	ORAL AND MENTAL STARTER ● Recognise multiples of 2, 3, 4, 5, and 10 up to the 10th multiple. MAIN TEACHING ACTIVITY ● Solve a problem by representing and interpreting data in tables, charts and diagrams, for example bar line charts, vertical axis labelled in 2s, 5s, 10s, 20s or 100s where intermediate points have no meaning.
RESOURCES	Multi-sided dice for children to use, if they wish to, for data collection.
ORAL AND MENTAL STARTER	THINK OF A NUMBER: Ask questions based on known facts eg *I'm thinking of a number, it's between 20 and 30, it's an even number and a multiple of 3 and 4.* Children put hands up when they think they know the answer. Take a range of answers and explanations. Repeat several times.
MAIN TEACHING ACTIVITY	DATA SOLUTION: Talk about previous work with graphs. Discuss what information could be collected and displayed on a bar-line graph, eg shoe sizes, number of siblings. Children work in pairs to decide on a question, then collect and display information.
DIFFERENTIATION	More able: Go on to write a description of what their graph shows. Less able: Work with them to prepare a data collection sheet.
PLENARY	During paired work, find out what children are doing. Use this information during the plenary to discuss interesting findings.

LESSON 6 +7

RESOURCES

Number cards; calculators; a graph showing temperature readings (see 'Preparation'); OHP.

PREPARATION

With the children, collect temperatures over the period of a school day (or at the same time each day over the period of a week). Draw a graph axis on a large sheet of paper or acetate with time on the x-axis (9am–9pm) and temperature on the y-axis (0°C–25°C).

LEARNING OUTCOMES

ORAL AND MENTAL STARTER
● Choose and use appropriate number operations to solve problems.
● **Know by heart all multiplication facts up to 10 × 10.**
● Derive quickly division facts corresponding to tables up to 10 × 10.
● Understand the effect of and the relationship between the four operations.
MAIN TEACHING ACTIVITY
● Solve a problem by representing and interpreting data in tables, charts and diagrams, for example bar line charts, vertical axis labelled in 2s, 5s, 10s, 20s or 100s where intermediate points may have meaning.
● Develop calculator skills and use a calculator effectively.

ORAL AND MENTAL STARTER

MEET THE TARGET: Ask a child to pick five digit cards and stick them on the board. Use a calculator to work out a number sentence that uses all 5 numbers once each with any operations, then write the answer on the board. Children use their calculators to try and get as close to this answer as possible. Discuss different solutions. Repeat.

MAIN TEACHING ACTIVITY

A TEMPERATURE GRAPH: Explain to the children that they are going to plot a graph to show temperatures through the day (or from day to day). Write the collected data as a table (see figure right) on the board. Display the graph axes: say that the time is on the horizontal axis and the temperature on the vertical axis. Ask a child to come up and plot the point for the first temperature reading in

9am	12 °C
10am	14 °C
11am	17 °C
12 noon	21 °C
1pm	22 °C
2pm	21 °C
3pm	19 °C
4pm	18 °C
5pm	15 °C
6pm	13 °C
7pm	12 °C
8pm	10 °C
9pm	9 °C

the data that has been collected. Repeat until all the points have been plotted. Explain that these points can be joined up because the data is continuous and the intermediate points have meaning: intermediate values on the y-axis are not known, but can be estimated from the line once the graph is plotted.

Look at the graph. Ask questions relating to plotted points, eg *What is the temperature at 4pm?* Ask children to come up and show how they read the information from the graph.

The children use the same data to plot their own time/temperature graph.

DIFFERENTIATION

More able: Collect temperatures to the nearest 0.5°C. Plot a graph using these values.
Less able: Use given axes. Work as a group with the teacher to plot the first few points.

PLENARY

Look at the graph. Ask questions about it, including questions about intermediate points, eg *What is the approximate temperature at 1.30pm? At what time or times is the temperature 17.5°C?* Ask children to come and point to the appropriate parts of the graph.

LESSON 7

For the **Oral and mental starter**, play THINK OF A NUMBER BINGO: Each child writes down five numbers and crosses off each when it is the answer to a problem, eg *I'm thinking of a number. I multiply it by 3 and add 5, and the answer is 17.* For the **Main teaching activity**, PLOT A SECOND LINE, display the graph from Lesson 6. Display a further set of temperature data and ask children as before to plot a second line on the same axis. Discuss what the 2-line graph tells us. The children then work in pairs to write questions about the new graph. More able children can summarise what is shown; less able children can answer given questions. For the **Plenary**, discuss the results and answer some of the children's questions.

LEARNING OUTCOMES	**ORAL AND MENTAL STARTER** ● Choose and use appropriate number operations to solve problems. **MAIN TEACHING ACTIVITY** ● Solve a problem by representing and interpreting data in tables, charts and diagrams, including those generated by a computer. ● Develop calculator skills and use a calculator effectively.
RESOURCES	Computers; software with database program eg *Find It!*
ORAL AND MENTAL STARTER	HOW DID I GET THAT? The children put a given number into their calculator. Tell them that you performed one or two operations and got that as the answer. Give them time to try things out: what could you have done? Specify the operations performed. Repeat.
MAIN TEACHING ACTIVITY	DATABASE: Look at a computer database with the class (using multiple computers). Discuss how facts could be found. Give the children some questions to answer using the database.
DIFFERENTIATION	More able: Answer questions that involve comparison of data or calculations with more than one step. Less able: Answer questions that require only one step.
PLENARY	Discuss how information was found using the database.

If a room of computers is not available, this activity might be done by groups during Lessons 6–8 and then discussed by the class in Lesson 8.

UNIT 7: Assess & Review

Choose from these activities. During the group activities, some of the children can work with you on practical tasks, while others complete assessment worksheets 1a and 1b which assess their skills in mental and written methods of multiplication, and in the effective use of a calculator. The specific assessment criteria for the assessment sheets are to be found at the bottom of each sheet.

RESOURCES

Numeral cards (one set per child), fraction cards, counters in different colours, 3-digit and 4-digit number cards.

ORAL AND MENTAL STARTER

ASSESSMENT

Can the children:
- **use rapid recall of multiplication facts up to 10 × 10**
- derive rapidly division facts corresponding to tables up to 10 × 10?

RAPID RECALL OF MULTIPLICATION AND DIVISION FACTS: Use the oral and mental activity MULTIPLICATION FACTS (Lesson 2, Unit 2), but extend to include questions that rehearse division as well as multiplication facts. Children hold up numeral cards to show answers when you say *Go!* Note who will need further practice with particular multiplication tables.

GROUP ACTIVITIES

ASSESSMENT

Can the children:
- **multiply or divide any positive integer up to 10 000 by 10 and understand the effect**
- **relate fractions to division**
- solve simple problems using ideas of ratio and proportion?

FRACTION DIVISION: Give each child 24 counters. Ask the children to pick a fraction card with $1/2$, $1/3$, $1/4$, $1/6$ or $1/8$ written on it. They must find that fraction of the counters and explain how they did it. Check that they make the connection with division and use appropriate vocabulary.

MULTIPLICATION/DIVISION BY 10: Give each child a 3-digit number card. Ask the children to multiply their number by 10 and write down the answer. They take turns to read out their answers. Can the next child say what the original number was (by dividing the number read out by 10)? Repeat several times. Now give each child a 3-digit or 4-digit multiple of 10. Ask the children to divide their number by 10 and write down the answer. The children read out their answers as above. Can the next child work out the original number by multiplying the answer by 10? Check that the children are clear about the relationship between multiplication and division.

SIMPLE RATIO: Use the Main teaching activity INTRODUCTION TO RATIO (Lesson 8, Unit 5), but give each child between 3 and 7 counters in 2 different colours. Ask the child to say how many counters there are in each colour, using the vocabulary of ratio; eg 'There are 2 blue counters for every 3 red.' Give each child some extra counters in one of the colours. They must add a number of counters in the other colour to keep the ratio the same as it was originally. Make sure the children use the correct vocabulary: 'for every...'.

Assessment 1a

Complete each of these calculations.

1. $37 \times 4 = (30 \times 4) + ($ ___ $\times$ ___ $) =$

2. $46 \times 6 =$

	40	6
6			$=$

3.
$$35 \times 16 =$$
$$= 70 \times 8$$
$$= 140 \times \text{___}$$
$$= \text{___} \times \text{___}$$
$$= \text{___} \times \text{___}$$

4.
$$\begin{array}{r} 57 \\ \times\ 8 \\ \hline 56 \\ \hline \\ \hline \end{array}$$

Calculate the answer to each of these multiplications. Show your working if you want to.

5. $38 \times 7 =$

6. $24 \times 12 =$

7. $67 \times 8 =$

8. $73 \times 6 =$

9. $39 \times 6 =$

10. $84 \times 5 =$

- Use doubling and halving, starting from known facts.
- Use informal pencil and paper methods for multiplication.
- Begin to use a more formal written method for multiplication.
- Choose and use appropriate ways of calculating.

UNIT 7

Assessment 1b

UNIT 7

You will need a calculator.

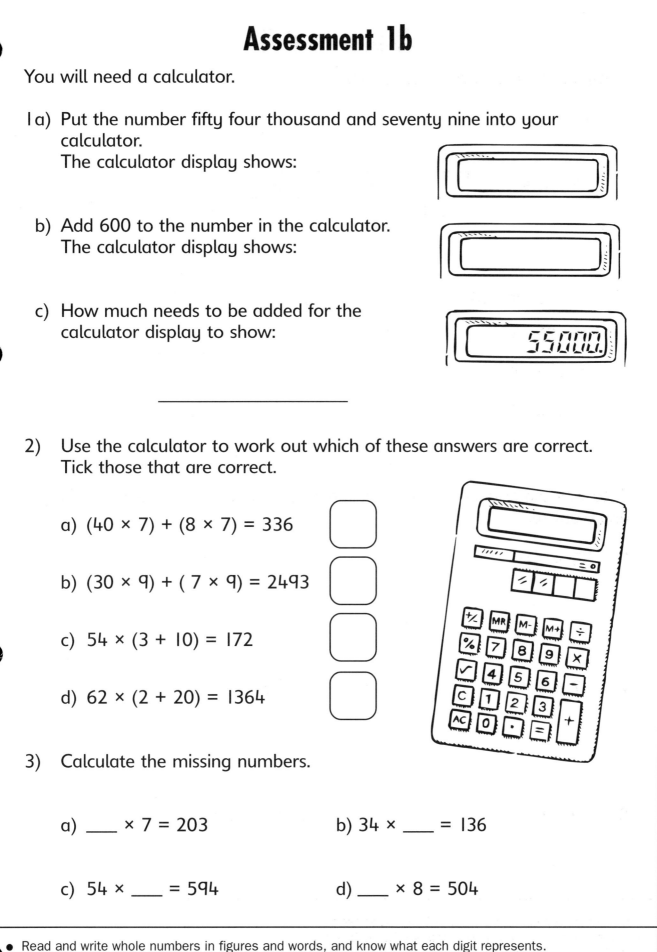

1a) Put the number fifty four thousand and seventy nine into your calculator.
The calculator display shows:

b) Add 600 to the number in the calculator.
The calculator display shows:

c) How much needs to be added for the calculator display to show: **55000.**

_____

2) Use the calculator to work out which of these answers are correct.
Tick those that are correct.

a) $(40 \times 7) + (8 \times 7) = 336$

b) $(30 \times 9) + (7 \times 9) = 2493$

c) $54 \times (3 + 10) = 172$

d) $62 \times (2 + 20) = 1364$

3) Calculate the missing numbers.

a) ___ $\times 7 = 203$ b) $34 \times$ ___ $= 136$

c) $54 \times$ ___ $= 594$ d) ___ $\times 8 = 504$

- Read and write whole numbers in figures and words, and know what each digit represents.
- Develop calculator skills and use a calculator effectively.

UNITS 8-10

ORGANISATION (15 LESSONS)

	LEARNING OUTCOMES	ORAL AND MENTAL STARTER	MAIN TEACHING ACTIVITY	PLENARY
LESSON 1	• **Recognise properties of rectangles**. • Solve mathematical problems or puzzles, recognise and explain patterns and relationships, generalise and predict.	COUNTING STICK: Use a counting stick for multiples and tables questions.	PROPERTIES OF RECTANGLES: Introduce properties of rectangles, revise right angles.	Draw shapes, including some quadrilaterals, that are not rectangles.
LESSON 2	• Identify, estimate and order acute and obtuse angles.	SHAPE DESCRIPTIONS: Guess shapes from information given. Solve number problems involving shapes.	ACUTE AND OBTUSE ANGLES: Classify angles as acute or obtuse.	Look at angles in different shapes.
LESSON 3 + 4	• Classify triangles (isosceles, equilateral, scalene) using criteria such as equal sides, equal angles, lines of symmetry. • Solve mathematical problems or puzzles, recognise and explain patterns and relationships, generalise and predict. • Make shapes with increasing accuracy.	WHAT IS THE QUESTION? eg __ ÷ __ = 3 NUMERAL CARDS: Use numeral cards to respond to questions about multiplication and division facts.	DIFFERENT TYPES OF TRIANGLE: Look at different triangles and discuss their properties. Make triangles on 3 × 3 or 5 × 5 pinboards. How many different ones can you make?	Classify different triangles. Discuss which triangles are similar and which are different.
LESSON 5	• Identify different nets for an open cube. • Make shapes with increasing accuracy. • Solve mathematical problems or puzzles, recognise and explain patterns and relationships, generalise and predict.	FOLLOW ME CARDS: Multiplication and division facts game.	CUBE PUZZLE: Investigate arrangements of squares that form a net for a cube.	Look at net arrangements – make a generalisation about them.
LESSON 6	• Visualise 3-D shapes from 2-D drawings.	FOLLOW ME CARDS: Repeat from Lesson 5, against the clock.	MAKE A SHAPE: Make 3-D shapes corresponding to 2-D pictures.	Discuss how many cubes are showing in a 3-D shape. How many might be missing?
LESSON 7	• Visualise 3-D shapes from 2-D drawings.	FOLLOW ME: Repeat from Lesson 5, against the clock.	HOW MANY MORE CUBES?: Work out how many cubes are needed to complete different 3-D shapes.	Discuss the shapes made by the children.
LESSON 8	• Use, read and write standard metric units (km, m, cm, mm), including their abbreviations, and relationships between them. • Record estimates and readings from scales to a suitable degree of accuracy.	GROUP DOUBLING: Double from group to group, holding up numeral cards to show answers.	NEAREST HALF CENTIMETRE: Estimate length, then measure to nearest half cm.	Discuss suitable units of measurement.
LESSON 9	• Use, read and write standard metric units (km, m, cm, mm), including their abbreviations, and relationships between them. • Record estimates and readings from scales to a suitable degree of accuracy.	GROUP DOUBLING: Repeat from Lesson 8.	CONVERTING LENGTHS: Convert measured lengths from cm to m.	Convert lengths from m to cm.

	LEARNING OUTCOMES	ORAL AND MENTAL STARTER	MAIN TEACHING ACTIVITY	PLENARY
LESSON 10	● Use, read and write standard metric units (km, m, cm, mm), including their abbreviations, and relationships between them. ● Record estimates and readings from scales to a suitable degree of accuracy. ● Measure and draw lines to the nearest millimetre.	CLASS CONVERSION: Convert m to cm by multiplying by 100. Respond as a class.	NEAREST MILLIMETRE: Draw lines the length of things measured. Write the length in cm and mm.	Compare units of length measure, and whether they are appropriate.
LESSON 11	● Use standard metric units (km, m, cm, mm), including their abbreviations, and relationships between them. Know imperial units (mile).	FOLLOW ME CARDS: Repeat from Lesson 5, against the clock.	KILOMETRES TO MILES: Convert measures of long distance.	Check answers on a calculator.
LESSON 12	● **Use all four operations to solve simple word problems involving numbers and quantities** based on 'real life' and measures **(including time).**	FOLLOW ME CARDS: Repeat from Lesson 5, against the clock.	LENGTH PROBLEMS: Solve word problems involving length.	Go through more difficult problems: what was the key information?
LESSON 13	● Use units of time; read the time on a 24-hour digital clock and use 24-hour clock notation, such as 19:53.	CLOCK CARDS: Hold up card clocks to show answers to questions about units of time.	ACTIVITY TIME: Write times as am or pm, or using the 24-hour clock.	What would the children be doing at various given times?
LESSON 14	● Use units of time; read the time on a 24-hour digital clock and use 24-hour clock notation, such as 19:53. Use timetables.	CLOCK FACES: Convert 24-hour time to display on analogue clock.	PLAN A JOURNEY: Use local bus/train timetables to plan a journey.	Look at journeys involving both a bus and a train.
LESSON 15	● **Use all four operations to solve simple word problems involving numbers and quantities** based on 'real life' and measures **(including time).**	GROUP BINGO: Multiplication and division questions with answers on cards.	TIME PROBLEMS: Solve word problems involving time.	Convert times to 12-hour or 24-hour clock.

ORAL AND MENTAL SKILLS: Know by heart all multiplication facts up to 10 × 10. Use known facts and place value to multiply mentally. Derive quickly or continue to derive quickly: division facts corresponding to tables up to 10 × 10; doubles of all whole numbers 1 to 100 (eg 78 × 2). Describe and visualise 2-D shapes (Year 4 revision). Use standard metric units (km, m, cm, mm) including their abbreviations and relationships between them. Use units of time; read the time on a 24-hour digital clock and use 24-hour clock notation, such as 19:53.

Lessons 1–3, 6, 8 and 12–14 are shown in detail. Lessons 4, 5, 7, 9–11 and 15 follow on from what has already been taught.

RESOURCES

A counting stick; square dotty paper; pin boards or geoboards; elastic bands; rulers; pencils.

PREPARATION

Draw a rectangle accurately on the board. Cut sheets of dotty paper to show 5 × 5 dots.

VOCABULARY

Multiple, quadrilateral, rectangle, square, right angle, bisect, parallel, equal, congruent.

LEARNING OUTCOMES

ORAL AND MENTAL STARTER
● **Know by heart all multiplication facts up to 10 × 10**.
● Use known facts and place value to multiply mentally.

MAIN TEACHING ACTIVITY
● **Recognise properties of rectangles**.
● Solve mathematical problems or puzzles, recognise and explain patterns and relationships, generalise and predict.

ORAL AND MENTAL STARTER

COUNTING STICK: Hold up a counting stick. Tell the children that they are going to count in 4s. *Imagine each mark on the stick is worth 4.* Show them where zero and 40 would be. Count up in 4s together, pointing to the appropriate divisions. Count back down again. Repeat with the children counting unaided. Point to various divisions: *What number would be here? How do you know? If you know 4 × 7, what else could you work out?* (8 × 7, 4 × 14, 4 × 70 and so on – write these on the board to encourage other ideas).

MAIN TEACHING ACTIVITY

PROPERTIES OF RECTANGLES: Tell the children that they are going to look at the properties of rectangles. Ask children to discuss in pairs how they might describe a rectangle, then ask the class to describe the properties of a rectangle. Look for descriptions such as 'four sides, four right angles, two pairs of parallel equal sides, symmetrical'. Revise the concept of right angles. Now ask children to suggest shapes with one of these properties that are not rectangles, eg any quadrilateral has 4 sides. Remember that a square is a special kind of rectangle. Point to the rectangle drawn on the board. Ask children to come and point to parts of it to help describe the properties being discussed. Show how the two diagonals bisect one another (see figure, right).

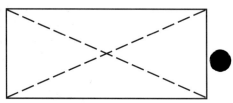

Give children several pieces of the dotty paper cut to size. They should work in pairs: one child draws a rectangle and describes it for the other to copy; they compare, then swap roles.

DIFFERENTIATION

More able: Draw rectangles on squared paper to nearest half centimetre.
Less able: Working in a group and following teacher instructions, use an elastic band with a pin board or geoboard to make a rectangle.

PLENARY

Draw different quadrilaterals on the board: *Which ones are rectangles?* Point to ones that are not: *How do you know this isn't a rectangle?* Draw 5 × 5 dots on the board; ask a child to come up and draw a rectangle. Draw another rectangle that has the same dimensions but a different orientation. Explain that the two rectangles are congruent. Repeat with squares, reinforcing the idea that a square is a special type of rectangle; include a square that is not congruent with the others.

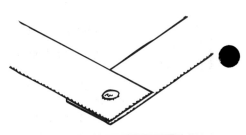

RESOURCES

Some card shapes, 2 strips of card (30cm × 2.5cm approx.), a split-pin paper fastener, squared paper.

PREPARATION

Cut out the strips of card and join them at one end with a paper fastener (see above).

VOCABULARY

Angle, turn, estimate, acute, obtuse, right angle, rectangle, square, triangle, pentagon, hexagon, heptagon, octagon.

LEARNING OUTCOMES

ORAL AND MENTAL STARTER
● Describe and visualise 2-D shapes.
● **Know by heart all multiplication facts up to 10 × 10.**
MAIN TEACHING ACTIVITY
● Identify, estimate and order acute and obtuse angles.

ORAL AND MENTAL STARTER

SHAPE DESCRIPTIONS: Hide a card shape behind your back and give clues to help the children guess what it is, eg *It has 4 sides, 4 right angles...* Change shapes; the children can ask you questions in order to guess what it is, but you can only answer *Yes* or *No.*

Repeat. Now ask groups questions which relate multiplication facts to shapes, eg *If I draw 6 squares, how many sides will I draw? If I draw 5 pentagons, how many vertices is that?*

MAIN TEACHING ACTIVITY

ACUTE AND OBTUSE ANGLES: Tell the children they are going to look at different types of angle. Ask them to discuss quickly, in pairs, what an angle is. Take some different answers. Hold up the joined card strips and turn one strip to form a right angle. Emphasise that an angle is a measure of turn. Put the strips back together; ask a child to use them to show an angle that is smaller than a right angle. Repeat with another child. Explain that an angle smaller than a right angle is called an acute angle. Repeat with an angle larger than a right angle; explain that this is called an obtuse angle. Ask children to draw examples of acute and obtuse angles on the board.

Give each child two small pieces of squared paper. Ask the children to draw one acute and one obtuse angle. In groups of four or more, they should order all the angles drawn from the smallest to the largest; then swap angles with another group and repeat.

DIFFERENTIATION

More able: Use angle measurers or protractors to measure each angle drawn. As an extension, use a pencil and ruler to draw a picture using only straight lines (eg a building or yacht); mark all acute angles red, obtuse angles green and right angles blue.
Less able: Work with the teacher.

PLENARY

Take some of the angles drawn and discuss the order they should go in. Discuss the angles in some different regular shapes, including triangles (to lead into the next lesson).

RESOURCES

Rulers; pencils; card; Blu-Tack; pin boards or geoboards; elastic bands; square dotty paper.

PREPARATION

Cut 4 playing-card sized cards per child. Draw a right-angled, an equilateral, an isosceles and a scalene triangle on the board. Blu-Tack a piece of paper over each.

VOCABULARY

Triangle, equilateral, isosceles, scalene, right-angled, angles, symmetrical, sides.

LEARNING OUTCOMES

ORAL AND MENTAL STARTER
● Derive quickly division facts corresponding to tables up to 10 × 10.
● **Know by heart all multiplication facts up to 10 × 10.**
MAIN TEACHING ACTIVITY
● Classify triangles (isosceles, equilateral, scalene) using criteria such as equal sides, equal angles, lines of symmetry.
● Solve mathematical problems or puzzles, recognise and explain patterns and relationships, generalise and predict.
● Make shapes with increasing accuracy.

ORAL AND MENTAL STARTER

WHAT IS THE QUESTION?: Write a 'blank' division question on the board: ___ ÷ ___ = 3. Ask the children, working in groups, to come up with as many different questions that give this answer as they can. Write a question from each group on the board. Repeat for a different answer. Discuss ways to check solutions.

MAIN TEACHING ACTIVITY

DIFFERENT TYPES OF TRIANGLE: tell the children they are going to look at the properties of different types of triangle. Uncover two triangles on the board. Ask what is the same about them, and what is different. Draw out the properties of each type. Tell the children the names of these types of triangle and write them on the board. Uncover one of the other triangles; discuss similarities and differences, then say and write down what type of triangle it is. Repeat with the last triangle. Ask different children to come and draw more examples of each type of triangle on the board. Ask questions such as: *Can a scalene triangle also be equilateral? Why not? Can it be right-angled? Why?*

Ask the children to work in groups of four or six. Each child draws one of each type of triangle on a separate piece of card; then the group plays a matching game. If a triangle has a right angle in it, it must be matched to another right-angled triangle.

DIFFERENTIATION

Less able: Before playing the game, sort a set of cards with triangles already drawn on into sets (with teacher guidance).
More able: Play in larger groups.

PLENARY

Draw a table on the board with rows big enough to fit the cards in, and headings as shown in the figure below. Ask why the right-angled/equilateral box has been shaded. (Because you can't have a right-angled equilateral triangle.) Take a set of cards made by one of the groups, and discuss with each group where each card should go in the table. Ask children to place the cards in the appropriate boxes.

	Right-angled	Not right-angled
Equilateral		
Scalene		
Isosceles		

LESSON 4

For the **Oral and mental starter**, children hold up NUMERAL CARDS to respond to questions about multiplication and division facts. In the **Main teaching activity**, go over Lesson 3. Pairs of children use a 3 × 3 or 5 × 5 array of pins to make as many different triangles as they can, then draw them on dotty paper and label them according to type. Less able children can work only on a 3 × 3 array. More able children can go straight on to dotty paper. In the **Plenary**, compare some triangles drawn on arrays of dots on the board; discuss what is 'the same' and what is 'different'.

LESSON 5

LEARNING OUTCOMES	**ORAL AND MENTAL STARTER** ● **Know by heart all multiplication facts up to 10 × 10.** ● Derive quickly or continue to derive quickly division facts corresponding to tables up to 10 × 10. **MAIN TEACHING ACTIVITY** ● Identify different nets for an open cube. ● Make shapes with increasing accuracy. ● Solve mathematical problems or puzzles, recognise and explain patterns and relationships, generalise and predict.
RESOURCES	Clixi or Polydron, squared paper, scissors, cards photocopied from page 67.
ORAL AND MENTAL STARTER	FOLLOW ME CARDS: Play a multiplication and division 'Follow me' game with cards from photocopiable page 67. Choose a child to hold up a card; the child who has the answer to the calculation on his or her card says it and the next calculation that has to be done; and so on until game loops back to first player.
MAIN TEACHING ACTIVITY	CUBE PUZZLE: Look at different ways of arranging five squares to make a net for an open cube. Demonstrate two ways using Clixi or Polydron. Ask the children to suggest two more ways. Three examples are shown opposite.
DIFFERENTIATION	Less able: Work in pairs with Clixi or Polydron to find as many nets as they can. More able: Draw the nets on squared paper, then cut them out to check.
PLENARY	Discuss nets which did/didn't work. Try to make a generalisations about the position of the faces in relation to each other.

RESOURCES

Interlocking cubes; photocopiable page 68; 'follow me' cards from Lesson 5; a stopwatch (or watch with a second hand).

PREPARATION

Draw four 3-D shapes, each made up of 5 to 10 cubes, on the board. Draw some so that the children may not be able to see all the cubes. Put some interlocking cubes on each table.

VOCABULARY

2-D, 3-D, depth, cube, cuboid.

LEARNING OUTCOMES

ORAL AND MENTAL STARTER
● **Know by heart all multiplication facts up to 10 × 10.**
● Derive quickly or continue to derive quickly: division facts corresponding to tables up to 10 × 10.

MAIN TEACHING ACTIVITY
● Visualise 3-D shapes from 2-D drawings.

ORAL AND MENTAL STARTER

FOLLOW ME CARDS: Repeat 'Follow me' game from Lesson 5. Play against the clock.

MAIN TEACHING ACTIVITY

MAKE A SHAPE: Tell the children that they are going to see some 2-D drawings of 3-D shapes. Discuss what 2-D and 3-D stand for, and what they mean. Show them the first picture you have drawn. Ask them to work in pairs, using the cubes on the table to make the shapes. Discuss whether the shapes they have made are accurate, and if the drawing could represent more than one shape; for example, with or without cubes on the part we can't see. Repeat with other shapes.

Give the children a copy of photocopiable page 68. Ask them to make each of the shapes shown with cubes.

DIFFERENTIATION

More able: Work with triangular dotty paper to make up their own shapes and draw them accurately.
Less able: Work with pictures of shapes made from 4, 5 or 6 cubes.

PLENARY

Look at drawn shapes where some cubes might be missing. Discuss how many might be missing. *What is the least number of cubes there could be in this shape? What is the greatest number?* Ask a child who has done the extension activity to draw one of his or her shapes and explain how he or she did it.

LESSON 7

LEARNING OUTCOMES	ORAL AND MENTAL STARTER ● **Know by heart all multiplication facts up to 10 × 10**. ● Derive quickly or continue to derive quickly division facts corresponding to tables up to 10 × 10. **MAIN TEACHING ACTIVITY** ● Visualise 3-D shapes from 2-D drawings.
RESOURCES	Interlocking cubes; shape drawings; 'Follow me' cards from Lesson 5.
ORAL AND MENTAL STARTER	FOLLOW ME CARDS: Repeat from Lesson 5. Can the class beat their previous best time?
MAIN TEACHING ACTIVITY	HOW MANY MORE CUBES?: The children work out how many extra cubes are needed to complete a shape. Show a cube 2 × 2 × 2. With one cube missing, ask how many more cubes are needed to complete the cube. Repeat with other cubes and cuboids. Give the children drawings of partly complete cube/cuboid shapes made with cubes. They work in pairs to make the part shown using one colour of cube, then complete the shape using another colour.
DIFFERENTIATION	More able: Make part of a cube/cuboid, draw it on triangular dotty paper, then work out how many cubes are needed to complete it. Less able: Given parts of cubes/cuboids already made, work together to complete the shapes using as few cubes as possible.
PLENARY	Go through the shapes that have been completed by the core of the class.

LESSON 8

RESOURCES

Numeral cards; rulers; pencils; metre stick.

PREPARATION

Write on the board a list of things that could be measured in centimetres, eg pencil, thumb, foot, exercise book, numeral card.

VOCABULARY

Double, millimetre, centimetre, metre, kilometre, estimate, unit of measurement.

LEARNING OUTCOMES

ORAL AND MENTAL STARTER

● Derive quickly or continue to derive quickly: doubles of all whole numbers 1 to 100 (eg 78 × 2).

MAIN TEACHING ACTIVITY

● Use, read and write standard metric units (km, m, cm, mm), including their abbreviations, and relationships between them.

● Record estimates and readings from scales to a suitable degree of accuracy.

ORAL AND MENTAL STARTER

GROUP DOUBLING: Give a group a starting number. They must all hold up numeral cards to show the double; the next group must show numeral cards to double that double and so on. Continue until a group has to hold up more than 2 numeral cards – that group starts the next round.

MAIN TEACHING ACTIVITY

NEAREST HALF CENTIMETRE: Tell the children they are going to estimate and measure lengths to the nearest half centimetre. *A centimetre is a unit of measurement for measuring length. Can you think of any others?* (Metre, kilometre, millimetre, mile, foot etc.) Write these on the board, but separate metric from imperial units. Tell the class that you are going to concentrate on the metric units of measurement. Ask children to show a centimetre, using their thumb and forefinger. Look at a centimetre on a ruler. Draw some lines on the board and ask children to estimate (*What does estimate mean?*) their length; then ask children to come up and measure them. Remind them to measure from 0 on the ruler, not from 1. Encourage them to measure to the nearest half centimetre. *Is it nearer to the halfway mark or to the next whole centimetre?*

Ask the children to draw a table with things to measure (in centimetres) down the left-hand side, estimates in the middle column and actual measurements in the third column. They can copy things to measure from your list, adding at least two things of their own.

DIFFERENTIATION

More able: Measure to nearest millimetre.
Less able: measure to the nearest whole centimetre.

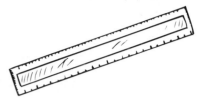

PLENARY

Go over the lengths found for different items. Discuss any differences, eg in thumb length. *Why might that be?* Discuss which things in the classroom it might not be appropriate to measure in centimetres, eg width of floor, height of ceiling.

LESSON 9

LEARNING OUTCOMES	**ORAL AND MENTAL STARTER** ● Derive quickly or continue to derive quickly doubles of all whole numbers 1 to 100 (eg 78 × 2). **MAIN TEACHING ACTIVITY** ● Use, read and write standard metric units (km, m, cm, mm), including their abbreviations, and relationships between them. ● Record estimates and readings from scales to a suitable degree of accuracy.
RESOURCES	Metre sticks; rulers; tape measures.
ORAL AND MENTAL STARTER	GROUP DOUBLING: Repeat from Lesson 8.
MAIN TEACHING ACTIVITY	CONVERTING LENGTHS: Hold up a metre stick. *How many centimetres? How could we write 200cm in metres? Or 350cm?* Estimate, then measure things in the classroom together. Write measurements in cm then in m; discuss the relationship. Children choose items to measure and convert cm to m.
DIFFERENTIATION	More able: Write in cm, m and m with cm; eg 350cm = 3.5m = 3m 50cm Less able: Work with teacher, measuring items from a given list.
PLENARY	*If we know a length in metres (eg 1.40m), what is it in centimetres?* Work through some examples.

LESSON 10

LEARNING OUTCOMES	**ORAL AND MENTAL STARTER** ● Use, read and write standard metric units (km, m, cm, mm), including their abbreviations, and relationships between them. **MAIN TEACHING ACTIVITY** ● Use, read and write standard metric units (km, m, cm, mm), including their abbreviations, and relationships between them. ● Record estimates and readings from scales to a suitable degree of accuracy. ● Measure and draw lines to the nearest millimetre. ● Suggest suitable units and measuring equipment to estimate or measure length.
RESOURCES	Rulers; pencils; paper.
ORAL AND MENTAL STARTER	CLASS CONVERSION: Give the children a measurement in metres (eg 2m). Ask them how many centimetres that is. Repeat with 1.75m and other examples; ask individuals how they worked them out.
MAIN TEACHING ACTIVITY	NEAREST MILLIMETRE: Measure three items as a class. Write each measurement in centimetres, then in millimetres; then draw a line that is that length. Call on individuals to do each part of the activity. The children work in pairs to find 5 items that they estimate to be less than 10cm long, estimate the length of each to the nearest mm, then measure it and draw a line the same length.
DIFFERENTIATION	More able: Draw picture of item using real dimensions. Less able: Work with teacher to develop accuracy to nearest half centimetre.
PLENARY	Look at some measurement values, eg a book 160m wide. *Is that correct? What unit of measurement should it be? What might you measure it with?* Try more examples. Emphasise the importance of using the correct unit.

LESSON 11

LEARNING OUTCOMES	**ORAL AND MENTAL STARTER** ● **Know by heart all multiplication facts up to 10 × 10**. ● Derive quickly or continue to derive quickly division facts corresponding to tables up to 10 × 10. **MAIN TEACHING ACTIVITY** ● Use, read and write standard metric units (km, m, cm, mm), including their abbreviations, and relationships between them. ● Know imperial units (mile).
RESOURCES	'Follow me' cards from Lesson 5; stopwatch; metre stick; road map; OHP calculator.
ORAL AND MENTAL STARTER	FOLLOW ME CARDS: Repeat from Lesson 5. Can the class beat their previous best time?
MAIN TEACHING ACTIVITY	KILOMETRES TO MILES: Discuss what unit you would use to measure longer distances, eg London to Liverpool. Explain that mile is an imperial measure and kilometre is a metric measure. Show a metre stick and say that 1000 metres make 1km, and 1 mile is approximately 1.5km. Do some conversions of miles to km as a class. Using a road map, ask children to find the distance between given places in miles and convert them to km.
DIFFERENTIATION	More able: Go on to convert back from km to miles. Less able: Convert only multiples of 10 miles.
PLENARY	Check some of the conversions using an OHP calculator.

LESSON 12

RESOURCES

Photocopiable page 69; 'Follow me' cards from Lesson 5.

PREPARATION

Write two problems on the board (see main teaching activity).

<table>
<tr><td>VOCABULARY</td></tr>
<tr><td>Centimetres, metres, kilometres, miles, imperial, metric.</td></tr>
</table>

LEARNING OUTCOMES

ORAL AND MENTAL STARTER

● **Know by heart all multiplication facts up to 10 × 10**.

● Derive quickly or continue to derive quickly division facts corresponding to tables up to 10 × 10.

MAIN TEACHING ACTIVITY

● **Use all four operations to solve simple word problems involving numbers and quantities** based on 'real life' and measures **(including time)**.

ORAL AND MENTAL STARTER

FOLLOW ME CARDS: Repeat from Lesson 5. Can the class beat their previous best time?

MAIN TEACHING ACTIVITY

LENGTH PROBLEMS: Tell the children that today's lesson is about solving problems that involve measures. Read a problem from the board together: *Sally is putting up two shelves. Each needs to measure 85cm. She buys a piece of wood that measures 2m. Once she has cut the lengths for the two shelves, what length of wood will be left over?* Ask the children

what this problem is asking. *What information have we got? What do we need to do first?* Work through the problem.

Ask the children to convert the answer into metres. Repeat with different values, eg three shelves, each 75cm long, a piece of wood 2.5 metres long.

Work through a two-step problem: *James has to travel 100 miles to Bromsgrove. If he travels at a speed of 75 kilometres an hour, how long will it take him to get there?*

Give each child a copy of photocopiable page 69. Let the children work through the problems.

DIFFERENTIATION

More able: Start with the two-step problems in Section B of the sheet.
Less able: Talk through the problems in Section A of the sheet with the teacher. Which operation does each question need?

PLENARY

Ask each group to say which problem they found most difficult. Discuss with the class what was the key information in the problem, and work through it together.

LESSON 13

RESOURCES

Clock cards with moveable hands; a large clock face with moveable hands.

PREPARATION

Make sure every child has a clock card.
Draw a grid on the board (see figure right).

Activity	Time am/pm	24 hour
Get up		
Go to school		
Playtime		
Home time		

LEARNING OUTCOMES

ORAL AND MENTAL STARTER
● Use vocabulary related to time.
● Read time from an analogue clock to the nearest minute. (Both Year 4 revision.)

MAIN TEACHING ACTIVITY
● Use units of time; read the time on a 24-hour digital clock and use 24-hour clock notation, such as 19:53.

ORAL AND MENTAL STARTER

CLOCK CARDS: Start with quick questions to revise units of time, eg *How many minutes in an hour? How many hours in a day?* Then ask the children to show times on their clock cards, eg *ten-thirty, eleven forty-five.* Show a time on a large clock face and ask the children to show you what time it will be a given number of minutes or hours later.

MAIN TEACHING ACTIVITY

ACTIVITY TIME: Tell the children that this lesson is about using the 24-hour clock. Write 16:30 on the board as it would appear on a digital clock. Ask the children where they might see the time written like that (eg alarm clock, video, cooker clock). Explain that it is given as a 24-hour time because there are 24 hours in a day. Look at the clock face. Count on from 12 to 16 to show that 16:00 is the same as 4pm.

Look at the grid on the board. Ask a child to say what time he or she gets up. Write this in the grid, eg first 7:30am and then 07:30. Repeat for other activities, encouraging the children to say whether the time is am or pm and then to convert it into 24-hour time. Ask them to fill in other activities they might do during the day. Expand the grid as necessary.

DIFFERENTIATION

More able: Work through the activity, then answer questions such as *If the time showed 23:00, what would that be on the ordinary clock?* Work with the teacher to convert from 24-hour time.
Less able: Read the times needed from a sheet with the conversions written on (eg 1am = 01:00).

PLENARY

Ask the children what they might be doing at given times. Give times as am or pm, or use the 24-hour clock. Take a range of answers and discuss which ones are sensible.

LESSON 14

RESOURCES
Local bus and train timetables; clock cards.

PREPARATION
Obtain local bus and train timetables. Copy part of a timetable onto acetate or the board.

LEARNING OUTCOMES

VOCABULARY

Day, hour, minute, second, 24-hour clock, digital, analogue, half past, quarter to.

ORAL AND MENTAL STARTER
● Use units of time; read the time on a 24-hour digital clock and use 24-hour clock notation, such as 19:53.
MAIN TEACHING ACTIVITY
● Use units of time; read the time on a 24-hour digital clock and use 24-hour clock notation, such as 19:53. Use timetables.

ORAL AND MENTAL STARTER
CLOCK FACES: Give 24-hour clock times; the children show the corresponding 12-hour times on their clock card faces.

MAIN TEACHING ACTIVITY
PLAN A JOURNEY: Tell the children they are going to use timetables to plan a journey. Look at the part of a timetable on an OHP or the board. Ask questions about it, eg *If the bus leaves the church at 08:00, when does it arrive at the High Street? How long does a journey from The Fox Inn to the city centre take?* Ask children to come out and point to the appropriate parts of the timetable to explain how they did it. Now ask each group to come up with a question about the timetable. The groups then pose their questions to the class.

Pass around all the timetables you have. The children work in pairs to write five questions relating to a timetable, then swap questions with another pair to find answers.

DIFFERENTIATION
Middle and more able: Work in mixed-ability pairs.
Less able: Answer questions from the teacher about the enlarged timetable extract.

PLENARY
Discuss questions that pairs found particularly difficult. Look at a timetable for a bus and a train; ask questions which relate to both timetables, eg *If I want to catch the 17:50 train, what is the latest bus I can get from the mosque?*

LESSON 15

LEARNING OUTCOMES	**ORAL AND MENTAL STARTER** ● **Know by heart all multiplication facts up to 10 × 10.** ● Derive quickly or continue to derive quickly: division facts corresponding to tables up to 10 × 10. **MAIN TEACHING ACTIVITY** ● **Use all four operations to solve simple word problems involving numbers and quantities** based on 'real life' and measures **(including time).**
RESOURCES	Photocopiable page 70, number cards 1–20 (one set per group of 3 or 4).
ORAL AND MENTAL STARTER	GROUP BINGO: Each group picks 6 number cards and places them face up on their table. Ask questions about multiplication and division facts; if a group has the answer, they can turn over the card. The first group to turn over all their cards wins. Discuss answers and methods after each question.
MAIN TEACHING ACTIVITY	TIME PROBLEMS: Work through photocopiable page 70 as a class.
DIFFERENTIATION	More able: Go straight to section B of the sheet. Less able: Select correct answers to section A from a list on the board.
PLENARY	Go through some of the questions. Convert the answers to the 12-hour or 24-hour clock as appropriate.

Follow me cards – Multiplication and division

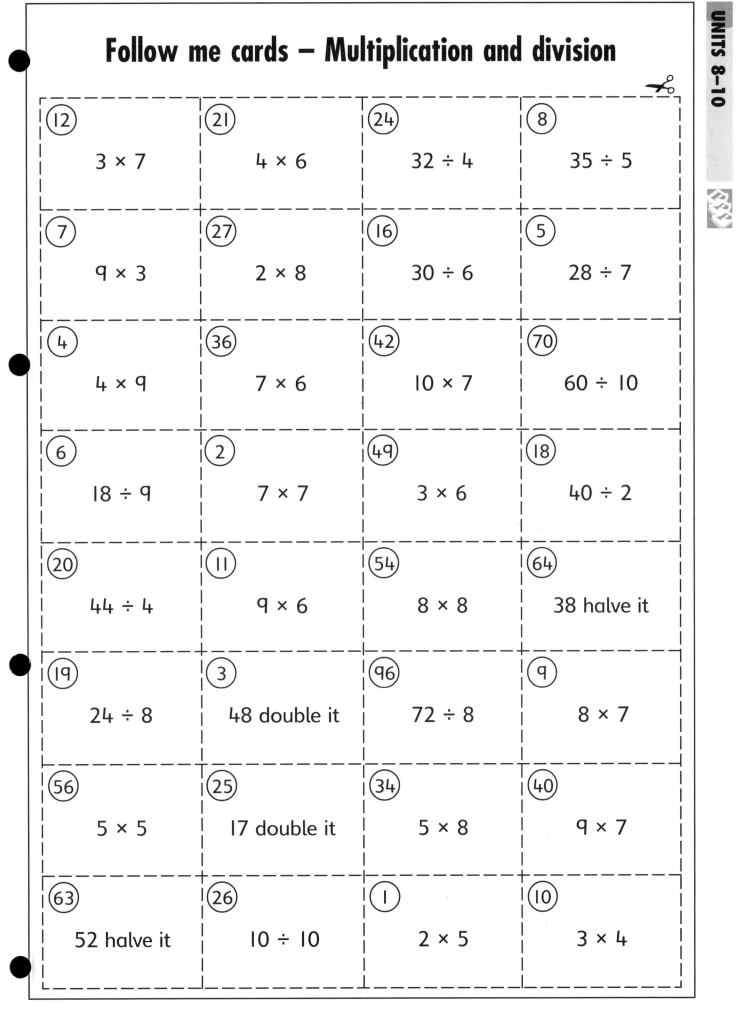

(12) 3 × 7	(21) 4 × 6	(24) 32 ÷ 4	(8) 35 ÷ 5
(7) 9 × 3	(27) 2 × 8	(16) 30 ÷ 6	(5) 28 ÷ 7
(4) 4 × 9	(36) 7 × 6	(42) 10 × 7	(70) 60 ÷ 10
(6) 18 ÷ 9	(2) 7 × 7	(49) 3 × 6	(18) 40 ÷ 2
(20) 44 ÷ 4	(11) 9 × 6	(54) 8 × 8	(64) 38 halve it
(19) 24 ÷ 8	(3) 48 double it	(96) 72 ÷ 8	(9) 8 × 7
(56) 5 × 5	(25) 17 double it	(34) 5 × 8	(40) 9 × 7
(63) 52 halve it	(26) 10 ÷ 10	(1) 2 × 5	(10) 3 × 4

Cube shapes

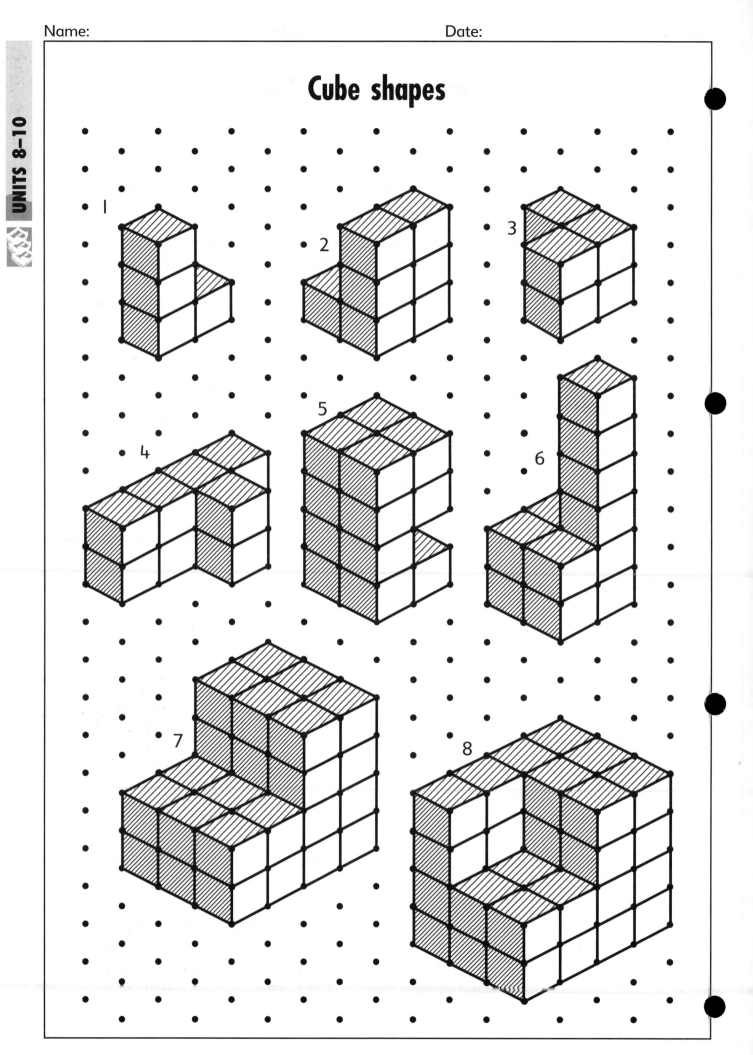

Name: Date:

Measurement problems

SECTION A

1. John is 162cm tall. His brother Harry is 127cm tall. How much taller is John than Harry?

2. Sarah walks 250m to get from home to the shop. Her school is a further 375m down the road. How far does she live from school?

3. Stephen has $4\frac{1}{2}$ metres of ribbon to wrap 3 identical presents. What is the maximum amount of ribbon he can use for each present?

4. A garage is 3m 40cm long. A car measures 1m 80cm in length. What is the difference in length between the garage and the car?

5. A gardener plants bulbs in a row, 15cm apart. If he plants 10 bulbs, what is the distance between the first and last bulb in the row?

6. Sam is 98cm tall. A tree in his garden is three times as tall as he is. What is the height of the tree in metres and centimetres?

- ✂

SECTION B

1. Karen runs 1547m of a 3km race. How far does she still have to run?

2. Tim uses 2 pieces of wrapping paper from a 3m roll. One is 75cm long and the other is 90cm long. How much paper is left on the roll?

3. Peter has a garden 6 metres long. Fence panels are 150cm long. How many panels does he need to stretch the length of the garden?

4. A boy measures 1m 70cm. His sister measures 138cm. What is the difference between their two heights?

5. Pat wants to make 3 shelves: one 120cm long, another 95cm long and the third 115cm long. He has a plank of wood 3m long to cut the shelves from. Does he have enough wood? Explain your answer.

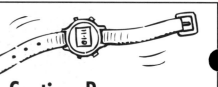

Time problems

Section A

Try to answer each of the questions below:

1. A maths lesson starts at 09:25 and finishes 50 minutes later. At what time does it end?
2. A coach journey takes 90 minutes. If the journey ends at 13:15, at what time did it start?
3. Kate leaves home at 07:45 and arrives at school at 08:20. How long does her journey take?
4. A film starts at 14:35 and ends at 17:05. Will a 3-hour videotape be long enought to record it?
5. School starts at 08:50 and ends at 15:20. How long is the school day?

BUS TIMETABLE				
High St	10.05	10.34	11.17	12.26
Church	10.12	10.41	11.24	12.33
School	10.16	10.45	11.28	12.37
Bus Stn	10.25	10.54	11.37	12.46

Use the timetable above.

6. How long does the journey take from the High Street to the bus station?
7. If the bus leaves the church at 11:24, what time does it reach the bus station?
8. A bus arrives at the school at 12:37. At what time did it leave the High Street?

Section B

Try to answer each of the questions below:

1. Ranjit gets up at 06:45. He spends 30 minutes getting ready and 1 hour and 15 minutes driving to work. At what time does he arrive at work?
2. A train finishes its $3\frac{1}{2}$ hour journey at 2:05pm. At what time did the journey start?
3. A film lasts $2\frac{1}{2}$ hours. It starts at 11:40am. At what time does it finish?
4. The flight from London to New York takes 6 hours and 40 minutes. A flight lands 15 minutes late at 19:20. When did it take off?

TRAIN TIMETABLE				
King's Lynn	07:45	—	09:30	10:46
Cambridge	09:05	10:12	10:45	12:15
Bishop's Stortford	09:25	—	11:05	12:35
Stansted	09:35	—	11:13	—
Harrow	09:50	—	11:28	12:55
Liverpool St	10:08	10:57	11:44	13:12

Use the timetable above.

5. What is the start time of the slowest train from King's Lynn to Liverpool St? How long does that journey take?
6. If I need to be at a meeting in London (Liverpool St Station) for 11:15, which is the latest train I can catch from Cambridge?

Use the timetable above to make up some questions of your own.

ORGANISATION (5 LESSONS)

LEARNING OUTCOMES	ORAL AND MENTAL STARTER	MAIN TEACHING ACTIVITY	PLENARY
LESSON 1 • Add several numbers (eg four or five single-digit numbers, or multiples of 10 such as 40 + 50 + 80). • Use knowledge of sums of odd/even numbers. Check the sum of several numbers by adding in the reverse order.	MAKE 20: Team game to make a total of 20 by adding successive dice rolls.	FIVE DICE: Roll dice to generate numbers, adding up totals by finding pairs that make 10.	Look at adding multiples of 10.
LESSON 2 • Partition into H, T and U, adding the most significant digits first. • Use informal pencil and paper methods to support, record or explain additions. • Estimate by approximating (round to the nearest 10 or 100), then check result.	ROUNDING: Say what a number shown with cards is to the nearest 10 or 100.	3-DIGIT ADDITION: Approximate first, then use partitioning and recombining.	Check answers. Use an informal written method to lead into the standard method.
LESSON 3 • **Extend written methods to: column addition of two** or more **integers less than 10 000**. • Check with an equivalent calculation. • Develop calculator skills and use a calculator effectively.	APPROXIMATE ANSWERS: Give approximate answers to 3-digit additions. Who is closest?	WRITTEN 3-DIGIT ADDITION: Go over standard written method. Reinforce place value.	Check answers using the inverse operation on a calculator.
LESSON 4 • Find differences by counting up through next multiple of 10, 100 or 1000, eg **calculate mentally a difference such as 8006 – 2993**. • Check with the inverse operation when using a calculator.	PAIRS TO 100: Add on units and tens to make a pair of numbers that total 100.	FIND THE DIFFERENCE: Use a blank number line to count up using multiples of 10 and 100. Check with a calculator.	Extend the idea to more difficult subtractions.
LESSON 5 • **Use all four operations to solve simple word problems involving numbers** based on 'real life' or money, using one or more steps. • Choose and use appropriate number operations to solve problems and appropriate ways of calculating: mental, mental with jottings, written methods, calculator. • Develop calculator skills effectively.	INVENT A LOOP: Develop calculation loops between given numbers.	PROBLEM SOLVING: Decide on most appropriate ways to solve word problems.	Discuss the methods used. Which were the most appropriate?

ORAL AND MENTAL SKILLS: Continue to know by heart: addition and subtraction facts for all numbers to 20 (Year 4 revision). Use known number facts and place value to add or subtract mentally, including any pair of two-digit numbers (Year 4 revision). Round any integer up to 1000 to the nearest 10 or 100 (Year 4 revision). Estimate by approximating (round to the nearest 10 or 100), then check result. Derive quickly or continue to derive quickly: all two-digit pairs that total 100 (eg 43 + 57).

Lessons 1, 2 and 4 are shown in detail. Lessons 3 and 5 follow on from what has already been taught.

LESSON 1

RESOURCES
6-sided and 10-sided dice.

PREPARATION
Put a 6- and 10-sided dice on each table. Divide the board into four columns headed A–D.

VOCABULARY

Add, total, sum, odd, even, multiple.

LEARNING OUTCOMES
ORAL AND MENTAL STARTER
● Continue to know by heart: addition and subtraction facts for all numbers to 20.
MAIN TEACHING ACTIVITY
● Add several numbers (eg four or five single-digit numbers, or multiples of 10 such as 40 + 50 + 80).
● Use knowledge of sums of odd/even numbers.
● Check the sum of several numbers by adding in the reverse order.

ORAL AND MENTAL STARTER
MAKE 20: Divide the class into four teams and label them A–D. The aim is to make a score of exactly 20. The teams take it in turns to roll a 6-sided dice; they can either keep the numbers they have rolled or give them to another team. When a team gets close to 20 they can 'stick'; if they go over 20, they are out. The team closest to 20 at the end wins.

MAIN TEACHING ACTIVITY
FIVE DICE: Write five numbers between 1 and 6 on the board, eg 3 + 5 + 6 + 4 + 2. Ask the class: *Without adding the numbers up, do you think this will give an odd or an even total?* Discuss how they know (adding even numbers will give an even answer, and so will adding two odd numbers, so the answer will be even). To help find the total, look for pairs or groups of numbers that will give a total of 10; 6 + 4 and 3 + 5 + 2. Once the answer has been worked out, check by adding the numbers in a different order.

Roll a dice five times to generate more numbers, then go through the stages: *Will it be odd or even?* Look for numbers that total 10. Check by adding in a different order.

Children roll a 10-sided dice to generate their own numbers for adding together.

DIFFERENTIATION
More able: Pick number cards showing multiples of 10. Find pairs with a total of 100 to help add several multiples of 10.
Less able: Roll a 6-sided dice.

PLENARY
Write 3 + 5 + 2 = on the board. Ask the children to find the total. *If we know that 3 + 5 + 2 = 10, what can you tell me about 30 + 50 + 20?* Do other examples, emphasizing how you can use addition of single-digit numbers to help you add 2-digit multiples of 10.

RESOURCES
Arrow cards (a large set for whole-class use); numeral cards (one set per table and another for teacher).

PREPARATION
Draw a blank number line on the board. Put a set of numeral cards on each table.

VOCABULARY

Add, total, partition, most significant, hundreds, tens, units, approximate, round.

LEARNING OUTCOMES
ORAL AND MENTAL STARTER
● Round any integer up to 1000 to the nearest 10 or 100.
MAIN TEACHING ACTIVITY
● Estimate by approximating (round to the nearest 10 or 100), then check result.
● Partition into H, T and U, adding the most significant digits first.
● Use informal pencil and paper methods to support, record or explain additions.

ORAL AND MENTAL STARTER
ROUNDING: Point to the blank number line. Write 20 at one end and 30 at the other. Ask a child to show where 27 would go. Ask the class: *Is it nearer to 20 or 30?* Change the multiples of 10 at either end, then ask a child to put a number in between them. Ask the class: *Which end is it nearer to?* Put multiples of 100 at either end of the line and repeat. Hold up numeral cards to form 2- and 3-digit numbers; ask the class to say which ten or hundred the number shown is closest to.

MAIN TEACHING ACTIVITY
3-DIGIT ADDITION: Write 256 + 138 = on the board. Tell the children that they are going to add these numbers by adding the most significant digit first; but before they add them, they will approximate by rounding each number to the nearest 100. Write an approximate answer on the board: 400. Make the numbers using arrow cards and take them apart to show how they are partitioned. *Which digit is worth the most in 256? The 2. How much is it worth? Two hundred.* Repeat for the second number. *What is 200 add 100?* Point to the appropriate digits. *Three hundred.* Write 300 next to the = sign. *Which is the next most significant digit in 256? The 5. How much is it worth? Fifty* (encourage the children to say 'fifty' rather than 'five tens'). Repeat with the second number. *Fifty and thirty makes...? Eighty.* Write + 80 next to 300 on the board. Repeat for the units, asking which is the least significant digit. Then recombine.

Repeat the process for another pair of 3-digit numbers.

The children generate their own pair of 3-digit numbers by picking numeral cards. Let them choose whether to write down the steps or do it mentally. They will probably need your support throughout this activity and may need you to go through further examples.

DIFFERENTIATION
More able: Should be able to work without teacher guidance.
Less able: Work with 2-digit numbers. For some, restrict the digits to 1–5 so there is no bridging of 10.

PLENARY
Work through some answers. This time, add the least significant digit first. Set this out (see figure right) to lead into the standard written method in Lesson 3.

```
  3 7 4
+ 1 5 7
  ─────
    1 1
  1 2 0
  4 0 0
  ─────
  5 3 1
```

LEARNING OUTCOMES	**ORAL AND MENTAL STARTER** ● Estimate by approximating (round to the nearest 10 or 100), then check result. **MAIN TEACHING ACTIVITY** ● **Extend written methods to: column addition of two** or more **integers less than 10 000**. ● Check with an equivalent calculation. ● Develop calculator skills and use a calculator effectively.
RESOURCES	Calculators, worksheets or published texts with 3 digit addition.
ORAL AND MENTAL STARTER	APPROXIMATE ANSWERS: show a 3-digit addition written on the board for about 5 seconds, then cover it up. Take an approximation from each group and write them on the board. Who is closest? Discuss ways of approximating. Repeat.
MAIN TEACHING ACTIVITY	WRITTEN 3-DIGIT ADDITION: Write two 3-digit numbers (eg 275 and 128) as a vertical addition. Work through the calculation, using the standard written method. When carrying the 10, stress that the total of the units is 13, which is 1 ten and 3 more, so the 1 ten goes in the tens column. When adding tens, stress that they are '70' and '20' not '7' and '2'. Give the children more additions to work through.
DIFFERENTIATION	More able: Make up some additions of their own that they think are difficult and explain why they are difficult. Include some additions of more than two integers. Less able: Use multibase equipment if necessary.
PLENARY	Write some calculations on the board: some correct, some incorrect. *Which ones do you think are correct?* Include some where you need to add two 4-digit numbers. Check using a calculator, subtracting the number added from the total.

RESOURCES

Calculators; blank number lines; pencils; paper.

PREPARATION

Draw a blank number line on the board.

VOCABULARY

Add, next ten, next hundred, multiple, inverse.

LEARNING OUTCOMES

ORAL AND MENTAL STARTER
● Derive quickly or continue to derive quickly: all pairs that total 100 (eg 43 + 57).
MAIN TEACHING ACTIVITY
● Find differences by counting up through next multiple of 10, 100 or 1000, eg **calculate mentally a difference such as 8006 – 2993**.
● Check with the inverse operation when using a calculator.

ORAL AND MENTAL STARTER

PAIRS TO 100: Divide the class into four groups. The first group says a 2-digit number; the second says how many to the next ten and what the next ten is; the third group says how many to 100, and the fourth group says the numbers to make 100. (eg '34'; 'Add 6 makes 40'; 'Add 60 makes 100'; '34 and 66 make 100'.) Repeat with the same number to clarify. Change the starting group and number and repeat.

MAIN TEACHING ACTIVITY

FIND THE DIFFERENCE: Tell the children they are going to find the difference between two numbers by counting up to the next ten, hundred or thousand as appropriate. Write 3000 – 2785 on the board; then write 2785 at one end of the blank number line and 3000 at the other. *We are going to take jumps along this number line. The first jump is to the next ten. How many to the next ten? 5.* Draw a small jump on the number line; write + 5 and then 2790 on the line. *How many to the next hundred?* Carry on to 1000, then add up the jumps. 5 + 10 + 200 = 215. Repeat with other numbers.

The children work in groups of four. The first child picks the calculation: a multiple of 1000 take away a lower number, eg 4000 – 1367. The next child says how many to the next ten, the third how many to the next hundred, and the fourth how many to the next thousand. The second, third and fourth children work out the answer; the first child checks on a calculator by adding the answer to the number subtracted. They should record their calculations.

DIFFERENTIATION

More able: Extend to near-multiples of 1000, eg 3005 – 2178.
Less able: Start with pairs of 2-digit numbers, then go on to 3-digit numbers, using a blank number line and a hundred square to help.

PLENARY

Work through a couple of examples. Check together, using an OHP calculator if available.
Ask: *If we can do 3000 – 2648 using this method, how might it help us do 3015 – 2648?*
Work through the problem.

LESSON 5

LEARNING OUTCOMES	**ORAL AND MENTAL STARTER** ● Use known number facts and place value to add or subtract mentally, including any pair of two-digit numbers. **MAIN TEACHING ACTIVITY** ● **Use all four operations to solve simple word problems involving numbers** based on 'real life' or money, using one or more steps. ● Choose and use appropriate number operations to solve problems, and appropriate ways of calculating: mental, mental with jottings, written methods, calculator. ● Develop calculator skills and use a calculator effectively.
RESOURCES	Photocopiable page 76, enough 2-digit number cards for each child to have a different number.
ORAL AND MENTAL STARTER	INVENT A LOOP: Give out 2-digit number cards. The children must say what calculation they would do to the number on their card to get to the number on the card of the person sitting next to them. Continue round the room; the last child has to get back to the first one's number using only + and –.
MAIN TEACHING ACTIVITY	PROBLEM SOLVING: Work through some word problems together (as in Lesson 9, Unit 3). The children must decide on the correct operation. Encourage them to use the information available and to decide what method to use – mental, mental with jottings, written method or calculator. They must be able to explain why they chose that method. The children go on to complete photocopiable page 76.
DIFFERENTIATION	More able: Write some problems of their own if they finish. Less able: Concentrate on one-step problems first.
PLENARY	Discuss which was the most appropriate method to solve each problem.

Mixed problems

Section A

1. Cans of cola come in crates of 24. How many cans are there in 7 crates?

2. In 8 boxes of pencils, there are a total of 64 pencils. How many pencils are in each box?

3. The children sit in groups of 6. How many groups of 6 are there in a class of 42 children?

4. A tape costs £1.99. How much do 5 such tapes cost?

5. How many books that cost £1.50 each can you buy with £12?

6. 300 children are travelling to the theme park. Each coach takes 50 children. How many coaches are needed?

7. Ella saves £2.50 a week from his pocket money. How much money has he saved in 6 weeks?

8. How long would it take to save £6 at a rate of £1.20 a week?

9. In 7 packs of felt-tipped pens there are 105 pens. How many pens are there in a pack?

10. 8 chocolate bars cost a total of £2.40. How much does one chocolate bar cost?

11. Each egg box takes 6 eggs. How many egg boxes would be needed to hold 45 eggs?

12. At lunch, the children sit at tables of 8. How many tables will be needed to seat 62 children?

Section B

1. Katie has £10. She buys 5 packs of stickers at 60p each. How much money will she have left?

2. Parminder saves £1.25 a week. If he saves for 6 weeks, how much more will he need to reach a total of £10?

3. There are 300 seats in the school hall. 8 rows of 28 are filled. How many seats are left?

4. Ian has 123 stickers. He gives his brother 33 and divides the rest up between 6 friends. How many stickers do they each get?

5. Jo-Jer buys a bag of sweets. She takes seven and shares the rest equally between eight friends, who get six each. How many sweets were in the bag?

6. Martin buys 6 cans of cola at 25p each and 4 chocolate bars at 32p each. How much change does he get from £5?

7. For a party, Danny makes some sandwiches. A loaf of bread that costs 57p makes 40 small sandwiches. About 500 sandwiches are needed for the party. How many loaves of bread are needed, and how much will all the bread cost? Explain your answer.

8. Danny cuts up 12 large cakes for the party. Each cake contains 15 slices. How many more cakes will be needed if there are to be 300 cake slices in total?

UNIT 12

ORGANISATION (5 LESSONS)

	LEARNING OUTCOMES	ORAL AND MENTAL STARTER	MAIN TEACHING ACTIVITY	PLENARY
LESSON 1	● Recognise and extend number sequences formed by counting from any number in steps of constant size, extending beyond zero when counting back, eg count on in steps of 25 to 1000. ● Solve mathematical problems or puzzles, recognise and explain patterns and relationships, generalise and predict.	CHANTING: Chant together in steps of given size from various starting-points.	TARGET NUMBER: Groups count in steps of various sizes from various starting numbers.	Look at patterns in number sequences.
LESSON 2	● Recognise and extend number sequences formed by counting from any number in steps of constant size, eg count on in steps of 25 to 1000. ● Solve mathematical problems or puzzles, recognise and explain patterns and relationships, generalise and predict. ● Make and investigate a general statement about familiar numbers by finding examples that satisfy it. Explain a generalised relationship in words.	TARGET NUMBER: Repeat from main teaching activity in Lesson 1.	CREATING SEQUENCES: Use a constant addition function to generate sequences. Fill in missing numbers in a given sequence.	Discuss how missing numbers can be worked out: what information do you need?
LESSON 3	● Recognise and extend number sequences formed by counting from any number in steps of constant size. ● Make and investigate a general statement about familiar numbers by finding examples that satisfy it. Explain a generalised relationship in words.	MULTIPLE COUNT: Count in multiples of different sizes. Answer questions about a given times table.	PATTERNS IN SEQUENCES: Look for patterns in addition sequences; complete some given sequences.	Discuss the patterns observed.
LESSON 4	● Make general statements about odd or even numbers, including the outcome of sums. ● Solve mathematical problems or puzzles, recognise and explain patterns and relationships, generalise and predict, suggest extensions asking 'What if...?'	MAKE A NUMBER: Mental addition and subtraction game.	ODD OR EVEN: Say whether the answer is odd or even when different integers are added or subtracted.	Discuss which combinations will give an odd/even answer and why.
LESSON 5	● Make general statements about odd or even numbers, including the outcome of differences. ● Solve mathematical problems or puzzles, recognise and explain patterns and relationships, generalise and predict; suggest extensions asking 'What if...?'	I'M THINKING OF A NUMBER: Guess a number from facts about it, holding up numeral cards to answer.	ODD OR EVEN 2: Continue to explore odd and even differences between numbers.	Use this knowledge to say whether answers may be correct.

ORAL AND MENTAL SKILLS: Recognise and extend number sequences formed by counting from any number in steps of constant size, extending beyond zero when counting back, eg count on in steps of 25 to 1000. Recognise multiples of 6, 7, 8, 9 to the 10th multiple. Continue to know addition and subtraction facts for all numbers to 20 (Year 4 revision). Recognise odd and even numbers (Year 4 revision). **Know by heart all multiplication facts up to 10 × 10.**

Lesson 1 follows on from related work in Unit 11. Lesson 2 is shown in detail. Lessons 3–5 follow on from what has already been taught.

LESSON 1

LEARNING OUTCOMES	ORAL AND MENTAL STARTER ● Recognise and extend number sequences formed by counting from any number in steps of constant size, extending beyond zero when counting back. MAIN TEACHING ACTIVITY ● Recognise and extend number sequences formed by counting from any number in steps of constant size, extending beyond zero when counting back, eg count on in steps of 25 to 1000. ● Solve mathematical problems or puzzles, recognise and explain patterns and relationships, generalise and predict.
RESOURCES	6- and 10-sided dice; 2-digit number cards; blank dice with 2, 3, 5 and 10 written on.
ORAL AND MENTAL STARTER	CHANTING: Start a sequence; the class join in when they know what it is. Try sequences starting at a range of numbers (not just zero), with steps of constant size. Let a group start a sequence and other groups take turns to say the next number.
MAIN TEACHING ACTIVITY	TARGET NUMBER: Roll a dice (6- or 10-sided); if a 1 is rolled, roll again. This gives the size of step. Pick a 2-digit number card up to 50; this is the start number. Groups take turns to say the next number in the sequence, eg 27, 32, 37... Continue until a group goes over 50 and scores a point. Then play in individual groups; what do they notice about the patterns?
DIFFERENTIATION	More able: Roll a dice, pick a card as before and go back in steps of constant size to –50. Less able: Pick a card, roll a dice with only the numbers 2, 3, 5 and 10. Go up to 50.
PLENARY	Look at patterns in number sequences, eg for steps of 5 (27, 32, 37...), *What do you notice about every other number? Why is that?*

LESSON 2

RESOURCES

Calculators; an OHP calculator if available.

PREPARATION

Write some sequences that go up or down in steps of constant size on the board. Leave some numbers blank, eg 1, 5, 9, 13, 17, __, __, 29.

VOCABULARY
Sequence, pattern, step, constant, predict, relationship.

LEARNING OUTCOMES

ORAL AND MENTAL STARTER
● Recognise and extend number sequences formed by counting from any number in steps of constant size, extending beyond zero when counting back, eg count on in steps of 25 to 1000.

MAIN TEACHING ACTIVITY
● Recognise and extend number sequences formed by counting from any number in steps of constant size, eg count on in steps of 25 to 1000.
● Solve mathematical problems or puzzles, recognise and explain patterns and relationships, generalise and predict.
● Make and investigate a general statement about familiar numbers by finding examples that satisfy it. Explain a generalised relationship in words.

ORAL AND MENTAL STARTER

TARGET NUMBER: Play the game from the Main teaching activity of Lesson 1. Which group can be the first to score 5 points?

MAIN TEACHING ACTIVITY

CREATING SEQUENCES: Ask for a single-digit number (eg 7) and put it into an OHP calculator (if available). Roll a dice to generate the step (eg 4). Put + 4 into the calculator and press =. The display should read 11. Press = again, so that the display reads 15. Ask what the display will read if you press the = sign again (19). If an OHP calculator is not available, give each pair a calculator and tell them what to put into it. Repeat with steps of different sizes, including some decimal numbers (eg start at 0.1 and go up in steps of 0.2). Do an example where the constant function is used to go backwards.

Give each pair of children a calculator. They each create their own sequence using the constant function, write down the sequence they have created with some numbers missing and swap with their partner who has to work out what the missing numbers are. They can repeat this several times.

DIFFERENTIATION

More able: Work on sequences with decimal and negative numbers.
Less able: Pick a number card for the starting number and work only with positive integers.

PLENARY

Write on the board some of the sequences that have been generated with some numbers missing. Ask the children to work out the missing numbers. Discuss how they did it and what information they needed.

LEARNING OUTCOMES	**ORAL AND MENTAL STARTER** ● Recognise multiples of 6, 7, 8, 9 to the 10th multiple. **MAIN TEACHING ACTIVITY** ● Recognise and extend number sequences formed by counting from any number in steps of constant size. ● Make and investigate a general statement about familiar numbers by finding examples that satisfy it. Explain a generalised relationship in words.
RESOURCES	10-sided dice, photocopiable page 81.
ORAL AND MENTAL STARTER	MULTIPLE COUNT: Chant the multiples of 7 as a class. Ask groups questions related to 7× table, eg *How many 7s in 35? What is 8 lots of 7?* Each group answers together. Repeat with other multiples, eg 8 and 9.
MAIN TEACHING ACTIVITY	PATTERNS IN SEQUENCES: Count in steps of 10 from 27: *27, 37, 47...* Ask the children to join in when they know what you are doing. Discuss the pattern in the numbers: *What do you notice?* (The number in the tens column goes up by 1 each time, the number in the units column stays the same). Count in steps of 20; ask what the children notice. Repeat several times, including patterns with descending numbers. The children complete photocopiable page 81, writing sentences to describe and explain the patterns on the back of the sheet.
DIFFERENTIATION	More able: Investigate number sequences chosen by the children and explain the patterns. Less able: Work in a group with the teacher to draw out information about the patterns.
PLENARY	Discuss what the children have noticed. Explain why these patterns occur.

UNIT 12

LESSON 4

LEARNING OUTCOMES	**ORAL AND MENTAL STARTER** ● Continue to know addition and subtraction facts for all numbers to 20. **MAIN TEACHING ACTIVITY** ● Make general statements about odd or even numbers, including the outcomes of sums. ● Solve mathematical problems or puzzles, recognise and explain patterns and relationships, generalise and predict, suggest extensions asking 'What if...?'
RESOURCES	Sets of number cards 0–20; interlocking cubes.
ORAL AND MENTAL STARTER	MAKE A NUMBER: Give each pair of children three number cards. Say a target number; the pair have to hold up two cards that have a total or a difference of the target number. Each correct answer wins a cube. Which is the first pair to collect three cubes?
MAIN TEACHING ACTIVITY	ODD OR EVEN: Pick out three single-digit numbers (from a set of cards) and put them on the board. Ask the children whether the total will be odd or even, and discuss how they know. Repeat with different combinations of odd and even numbers. Ask the children to work in pairs to investigate whether the answer will be odd or even when three or four numbers are added.
DIFFERENTIATION	More able: Write a conclusion as to why 'Even + Even + Even = Even' etc. Less able: Work with teacher to structure an investigation.
PLENARY	Write 'Odd + Odd + Even = Even' on the board. Ask the children whether it is correct. *Will the answer always be even? Why?* Look at other combinations and totals.

LESSON 5

LEARNING OUTCOMES	**ORAL AND MENTAL STARTER** ● Recognise odd and even numbers. ● **Know by heart all multiplication facts up to 10 × 10.** **MAIN TEACHING ACTIVITY** ● Make a general statement about odd or even numbers, including the outcome of differences. ● Solve mathematical problems or puzzles, recognise and explain patterns and relationships, generalise and predict; suggest extensions asking 'What if...?'
RESOURCES	Numeral cards (one set per pupil); a set of 2-digit number cards.
ORAL AND MENTAL STARTER	I'M THINKING OF A NUMBER: Think of a number and describe it to the children, eg for 35: *It is an odd number between 30 and 40; it is in the 7 times table.* Children hold up numeral cards to answer.
MAIN TEACHING ACTIVITY	ODD AND EVEN 2: Write two 2-digit numbers on the board as a subtraction, eg 45 – 27. *Will the answer be odd or even? How do you know? If we write two odd numbers on the board to make a subtraction, will the answer be odd or even?* Ask various children to pick 2-digit numbers from the pack until eight have been generated. Write them on the board. *Pick two numbers that will give an even-number answer. Pick two numbers that will give an odd-number answer.* The children pick their own cards, each with two 2-digit numbers. How many subtractions can they write using the cards chosen that will give an even answer?
DIFFERENTIATION	More able: Subtract two 2-digit numbers from a 3-digit number. *When is the answer odd? When is it even?* Less able: Use three cards to form a 2-digit subtract a single digit calculation, with an even number answer.
PLENARY	Discuss what the children found out. Write some 2-digit subtractions on the board, with answers – some right, some wrong. Ask the children to say which answers cannot be right, using their knowledge of odd and even numbers.

Sequences

Fill in the missing numbers in each sequence.
Write a sentence to describe each sequence and explain what is happening.

1. _____, 23, _____, 43, 53, 63, _____, _____, _____, 103

_____

2. _____, 147, 247, _____, _____, 547, 647, 747, _____

_____

3. 2, 7, 12, 17, _____, 27, _____, _____, 42, _____, _____

_____

4. 16, 66, 116, 166, _____, _____, 316, _____, _____

_____

5. _____, 47, 72, 97, _____, _____, 172, 197, _____

_____

6. 19, 34, _____, 64, 79, _____, _____, 124, _____, 154, _____

_____

7. _____, _____, _____, 40, _____, _____, 70, _____, _____, _____, _____, 120

_____

8. 326, _____, _____, _____, _____, 826, _____, _____, 1126

_____

9. _____, 77, _____, 177, _____, _____, 327, _____, _____, 477

_____

10. _____, _____, _____, 112, _____, 162, _____, _____, 237

_____

UNIT 13: Assess & Review

Choose from these activities. During the group activities, some of the children can work with you on practical tasks, while others complete assessment worksheets 2a and 2b which assess their skills in mental and written methods of addition and subtraction and in solving word problems involving numbers and quantities. The specific assessment criteria for the assessment sheets are to be found at the bottom of each sheet.

RESOURCES

2-D card polygons, bus timetables, pencils, paper.

ORAL AND MENTAL STARTER

ASSESSMENT
Can the children:
● **use rapid recall of multiplication and division facts to 10 × 10**
● derive quickly: doubles of all whole numbers 1 to 100?

RAPID RECALL AND DERIVATION OF MULTIPLICATION, DIVISION AND DOUBLES FACTS: Give the children a quick mental test where they write the answers. Set 12 questions: four multiplication, four division and four doubles. Use a range of vocabulary, eg *multiply, times, product, divide, share, double, multiply by 2*. Read each question twice, and give the children 5 seconds to write each answer.

GROUP ACTIVITIES

ASSESSMENT
Can the children:
● **recognise properties of rectangles**
● **use all four operations to solve simple word problems involving numbers and quantities (including time), explaining methods and reasoning**
● **calculate mentally a difference such as 8006 – 2993**?

SHAPES: Put some card polygons on the table, eg rectangle, square, triangles (various types), trapezium, parallelogram, kite. The children take turns to describe one of the shapes, using properties such as length of sides and size of corners. Other children have to try and guess which shape is being described. Listen for correct and accurate use of vocabulary. (You may need to model the activity initially.)

WORD PROBLEMS: Give each child in the group a local bus timetable. Ask the children questions about it in turn, eg *How long does it take to get from ___ to ___? If I left ___ at ___, when would I get to ___? Where would I be at ____?* The children can be given questions in pairs and asked to explain to the rest of the group how they worked them out.

FIND THE DIFFERENCE: Give each child a subtraction which involves finding a small difference between two 4-digit numbers. Write each one down for the children to see, eg 3009 – 1988 etc. Ask each child to work out the answer, and write it down in some way (eg informal jotting or using a number line) and to explain their method to the rest of the group.

Assessment 2a

Complete the calculations below:

1. 2 + 8 + 5 + ___ + = 24

2. 7 + 8 + ___ + 4 + 6 = 29

3. 30 + 50 + 70 =_____

4. 90 + 60 + 50 + 60 = _____

5. 20 + ___ + 70 + 30 = 200

6. 70 + 40 + ___ + 80 = 250

Tick the additions below that are correct:

7.
```
  2 5 7
+ 1 4 6
-------
  3 9 3  □
```

8.
```
  5 3 8
+ 2 9 1
-------
  8 2 9  □
```

9.
```
  7 2 5
+ 3 6 8
-------
1 0 9 3  □
```

10.
```
  6 5 3
+ 7 6 8
-------
1 3 2 1  □
```

11.
```
  4 8 6
+ 6 1 9
-------
1 1 0 5  □
```

12.
```
  8 2 7
+ 9 4 5
-------
1 7 7 3  □
```

Complete the additions below.

13.
```
  2 1 9
+ 4 3 6
-------
```

14.
```
  3 7 2
+ 5 3 9
-------
```

15.
```
  4 5 7
+ 7 1 6
-------
```

16.
```
  1 3 4 2
+ 1 5 3 9
---------
```

17.
```
  2 7 3 1
+ 1 4 6 2
---------
```

18.
```
  4 1 1 6
+ 3 4 9 7
---------
```

- Add several numbers (eg four or five single digits, or multiples of 10 such as 40 + 50 + 80).
- **Extend written methods to column addition of two or more integers less than 10 000.**

Assessment 2b

Find the difference between the numbers at either end of the number line (you can use the number line to help you).

1996   3004

2985   5007

3899   7002

2970   4016

2888   5018

Look at each of the problems below. Decide which calculation will give the correct answer and underline it.

1. Simon is 197cm tall. The door to his room is 2m high. How much taller is the door than Simon?

a) 197 + 2   b) 197 – 2   c) 200 – 197   d) 200 + 197

Explain your answer. _____

_____

2. Shana has a £5 note. She gives it to the shopkeeper and receives £2.31 change. How much did she spend?

a) 500 + 231   b) 500 – 231   c) 5 – 231   d) 231 + 5

Explain your answer. _____

_____

- Calculate mentally a difference such as 8006 – 2993.
- Use all four operations to solve simple word problems involving numbers and quantities.

TERM 2

This term's work reinforces the work of the previous term. Children continue to develop written methods and mental strategies with all four rules, and to solve problems. Work with decimal numbers (with up to two decimal places) includes ordering decimals and recognising their fraction equivalents. Children are introduced to simple percentages. Looking at square numbers and tests of divisibility extends their understanding of the properties of numbers. In 'Shape and space', the emphasis is on symmetry, reflection, parallel and perpendicular lines and reading and plotting co-ordinates. In 'Measures', the focus on length continues with the introduction of work on perimeter and area, while work on capacity involves estimating and measuring and is extended to converting litres to millilitres. Work in 'Handling data' continues to look at solving problems through the interpretation of data and introduces the concept of the mode.

ENLARGE THIS SHEET TO A3 AND USE IT AS YOUR MEDIUM-TERM PLANNING GRID.

Oral and mental: Read and write whole numbers in figures and words, and know what each digit represents. Multiply or divide any positive integer up to 1000 by 10 and understand the effect. **Know by heart all multiplication facts up to 10 × 10.** Derive quickly: all two-digit pairs that total 100; division facts corresponding to tables up to 10 × 10; doubles of all whole numbers 1 to 100, and the corresponding halves; doubles of multiples of 10. Choose and use appropriate number operations to solve problems. **Relate fractions to division**, and use division to find simple fractions. Recognise and extend number sequences formed by counting from any number in steps of constant size, extending beyond zero when counting back, eg count in steps of 0.1. Know what each digit represents in a number with up to 2 decimal places. Describe and visualize 2-D shapes.

UNIT	TOPIC	OBJECTIVES: CHILDREN WILL BE TAUGHT TO
1	Place value, ordering and rounding Using a calculator	● Use the vocabulary of comparing and ordering numbers, including symbols such as <, >, =; give one or more numbers lying between two given numbers; order a set of integers less than 1 million. ● Use the vocabulary of estimation and approximation. Make and justify estimates of large numbers, and estimate simple proportions. ● **Multiply or divide any positive integer up to 10 000 by 10 or 100** (eg 9900 ÷ 10, 2060 ÷ 100). ● Round any integer up to 10 000 to the nearest 10, 100 or 1000. ● Develop calculator skills and use a calculator effectively.
2–3	Understanding × and ÷ Mental calculation strategies (× and ÷) Pencil and paper procedures (× and ÷) Money and 'real life' problems Making decisions and checking results, including using a calculator	● Understand the effect of and relationships between the four operations, and the principles (not the names) of the arithmetic laws as they apply to multiplication. Begin to use brackets. ● Begin to express a quotient as a fraction, or as a decimal when dividing a whole number by 2, 4, 5 or 10. ● Round up or down after division, depending on the context. ● Use factors (eg 8 × 12 = 8 × 4 × 3). ● Use closely related facts (eg multiply by 19 or 21 by multiplying by 20 and adjusting). ● Partition, eg 47 × 6 = (40 × 6) + (7 × 6). ● Use the relationship between multiplication and division. ● Approximate first. Use informal pencil and paper methods to support, record or explain multiplications. ● Extend written methods to: short multiplication of HTU by U. ● **Use all four operations to solve simple word problems involving numbers and quantities** based on 'real life' and money, using one or more steps. ● Estimate by approximating (round to the nearest 10 or 100), then check result. ● Check with the inverse operation when using a calculator. ● Check with an equivalent calculation. ● Develop calculator skills and use a calculator effectively.
4	Fractions, decimals and percentages Using a calculator	● **Relate fractions to division**, and use division to find simple fractions, including tenths and hundredths, of numbers and quantities. ● **Use decimal notation for tenths and hundredths.** ● Know what each digit represents in a number with up to two decimal places. ● Derive quickly decimals that total 1. ● Order a set of numbers or measurements with the same number of decimal places. ● Begin to understand percentage as the number of parts in every 100. ● Express one half, one quarter, three quarters, and tenths and hundredths as percentages. ● **Relate fractions to their decimal representations**: that is, recognise the equivalence between decimal and fraction forms of one half, one quarter, three quarters... and tenths and hundredths (eg $7/_{10}$ = 0.7). ● Find simple percentages of small whole-number quantities. ● Develop calculator skills and use a calculator effectively.
5	Shape and space Reasoning about shapes	● Recognise reflective symmetry in regular polygons: for example, know that a square has four axes of symmetry and an equilateral triangle has three. ● Recognise where a shape will be after reflection in a mirror line parallel to one side (sides not all parallel or perpendicular to the mirror line). ● **Recognise perpendicular and parallel lines.** ● Complete symmetrical patterns with two lines of symmetry at right angles (using squared paper or a pegboard). ● Read and plot co-ordinates in the first quadrant. ● Make and investigate a general statement about shapes by finding examples that satisfy it. ● Explain methods and reasoning, orally and in writing.
6	Assess and review	See the key objectives on the relevant pages.

Oral and mental: Derive quickly: all two-digit pairs that total 100; decimals that total 1; pairs of multiples of 50 that total 1000; division facts corresponding to tables up to 10 × 10. **Know by heart all multiplication facts up to 10 × 10.** Know by heart addition and subtraction facts for all numbers to 20. Use known number facts and place value for mental addition and subtraction. Estimate by approximating (round to nearest 10 or 100), then check result. Choose and use appropriate number operations to solve problems. Know and apply tests of divisibility by 2, 4, 5, 10 or 100. Recognise and extend number sequences formed by counting from any number in steps of constant size. Recognise multiples of 6, 7, 8, 9 up to the 10th multiple.

UNIT	TOPIC	OBJECTIVES: CHILDREN WILL BE TAUGHT TO
7–8	Measures, including problems Handling data	● Use, read and write standard metric units (l, ml), including their abbreviations, and relationships between them. Convert larger to smaller units (l to ml). ● Know imperial units (pint, gallon). ● Suggest suitable units and measuring equipment to estimate or measure capacity. ● Record estimates and readings from scales to a suitable degree of accuracy. ● Understand, measure and calculate perimeters of regular polygons. ● **Understand area measured in square centimetres (cm²). Understand and use the formula in words 'length × breadth' for the area of a rectangle.** ● **Use all four operations to solve simple word problems involving numbers and quantities** based on real life and measures, using one or more steps. ● Solve a problem by representing and interpreting data in tables, charts, graphs and diagrams, for example: bar line charts, vertical axis labelled in 2s, 5s, 10s, 20s or 100s. ● Find the mode of a set of data.
9–10	Mental calculation strategies (+ and −) Pencil and paper procedures (+ and −) Money and 'real life' problems Making decisions and checking results, including using a calculator	● Add several numbers (eg multiples of 10, such as 40 + 50 + 80). ● Add or subtract the nearest multiple of 10, then adjust. ● Partition into H, T and U, adding the most significant digits first. ● Use informal pencil and paper methods to support, record or explain additions and subtractions. **Extend written methods to: column addition/subtraction of two integers less than 10 000; addition of more than two integers less than 10 000; addition or subtraction of a pair of decimal fractions, both with one or both with two decimal places.** ● **Use all four operations to solve simple word problems involving numbers and quantities** based on 'real life' and money, using one or more steps. **Explain methods and reasoning.** ● Choose and use appropriate number operations to solve problems, and appropriate ways of calculating: mental, mental with jottings, written methods, calculator. ● Check the sum of several numbers by adding in the reverse order. ● Check with an equivalent calculation. ● Check with the inverse operation when using a calculator.
11	Properties of numbers Reasoning about numbers	● Know squares of numbers to at least 10 × 10. ● Know and apply tests of divisibility by 2, 4, 5, 10 or 100. ● Recognise multiples of 6, 7, 8, 9 up to the 10th multiple. ● Solve mathematical problems or puzzles, recognise and explain patterns and relationships, generalize and predict. ● Explain methods and reasoning, orally and in writing. ● Make and investigate a general statement about familiar numbers by finding examples that satisfy it; explain a generalized relationship in words.
12	Assess and review	See the key objectives on the relevant pages.

UNIT 1

ORGANISATION (3 LESSONS)

	LEARNING OUTCOMES	ORAL AND MENTAL STARTER	MAIN TEACHING ACTIVITY	PLENARY
LESSON 1	● Use the vocabulary of comparing and ordering numbers, including symbols such as <, >, =; give one or more numbers lying between two given numbers; order a set of integers less than 1 million. ● Use the vocabulary of estimation and approximation; make and justify estimates of large numbers, and estimate simple proportions.	BUILDING NUMBERS: Count in tens, hundreds, thousands and ten thousands, then build up numbers.	NUMBERS ON THE LINE: Position given numbers on a number line.	Discuss fractions along the number line.
LESSON 2	● **Multiply or divide any positive integer up to 10 000 by 10 or 100** (eg 9900 ÷ 10, 2060 ÷ 100) **and understand the effect**. ● Develop calculator skills and use a calculator effectively.	MULTIPLY AND DIVIDE BY 10: Hold up answers using numeral cards.	MISSING PICTURE: Solve a puzzle by multiplying and dividing by 10.	Use a calculator to make a target number by multiplying or dividing by 10 or 100.
LESSON 3	● Round any integer up to 10 000 to the nearest 10, 100 or 1000.	PAIRS TO 100: Repeat from Lesson 4, Unit 11 of Term 1.	WHAT IS IT NEARLY?: Use a number line to round numbers.	Give estimates of answers to sums.

ORAL AND MENTAL SKILLS: Read and write whole numbers in figures and words, and know what each digit represents. Multiply or divide any integer up to 1000 by 10 and understand the effect (Year 4 revision). Derive quickly or continue to derive quickly all two-digit pairs that total 100.

Lessons 1 and 3 are shown in detail. Lesson 2 follows on from what has already been taught.

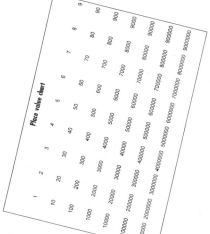

LESSON 1

RESOURCES
Place value chart (photocopiable page 24), enlarged to A3 size.

PREPARATION
Draw a blank number line on the board. Put the A3 place value chart where all the class can see it.

LEARNING OUTCOMES

ORAL AND MENTAL STARTER
● Read and write whole numbers in figures and words, and know what each digit represents.

MAIN TEACHING ACTIVITY
● Understand the vocabulary of comparing and ordering numbers, including symbols such as <, >, =; give one or more numbers lying between two given numbers; order a set of integers less than 1 million.
● Use the vocabulary of estimation and approximation; make and justify estimates of large numbers, and estimate simple proportions.

VOCABULARY

Units, ones, tens, hundreds, thousands, ten thousand, hundred thousand, million, digit, one-digit number, two-digit number..., numeral, place value.

ORAL AND MENTAL STARTER

BUILDING NUMBERS: Count up in multiples of 10 as a class; repeat for multiples of 100, 1000, 10 000. Point to the tens numbers on the place value chart (as in Lesson 1, Unit 1 of Term 1), and build up larger numbers. Repeat, asking children to come and write numbers on the board.

MAIN TEACHING ACTIVITY

NUMBERS ON THE LINE: Look at the blank number line on the board. Write 10 000 at one end and 11 000 at the other. Ask children to read both numbers. *Which number comes halfway between these two numbers? 10 500.* Ask a child to write it on the number line. Write 10 278; ask a child to come and write it on the number line. *Why have you put it there? Should it be nearer to 10 000 or 10 500? How do you know?* Repeat with other numbers within the range. Decide which thousand or hundred each number would be rounded to.

Ask a child for a 5-digit number. *Which two thousands does it lie between?* Write the two thousands at either end of the number line on the board, then ask a child to place the number on the line.

Children draw their own number lines and work in pairs. The first child says a 5-digit number; the partner writes it on the number line, then says another 5-digit number in the range. The first child writes it on the number line. Continue until each child has written 3 numbers on the line.

DIFFERENTIATION

More able: Use 6-digit numbers.
Less able: Use 4-digit numbers.

PLENARY

Discuss the positions of different numbers along the line. Write 10 000 at one end and 20 000 at the other. Ask: *Which number comes halfway along? A quarter of the way along? Three quarters of the way along? One fifth of the way along? How far along the line would 14 000 be?*

LEARNING OUTCOMES	**ORAL AND MENTAL STARTER** ● Multiply or divide any integer up to 1000 by 10 and understand the effect. **MAIN TEACHING ACTIVITY** ● **Multiply or divide any positive integer up to 10 000 by 10 or 100 and understand the effect** (eg 9900 ÷ 10, 2060 ÷ 100). ● Develop calculator skills and use a calculator effectively.
RESOURCES	Numeral cards 0–9 (give each child 1 set, plus 2 extra zeros and 1 decimal point); calculators; photocopiable page 90; OHP calculator (if available).
ORAL AND MENTAL STARTER	MULTIPLY AND DIVIDE BY 10: Ask children to hold up a number (eg 34), multiply it by 10 and hold up the answer. Repeat multiply by 10 and discuss what they notice each time. Do some repeat dividing by 10 (start with multiples of 10), then discuss.
MAIN TEACHING ACTIVITY	MISSING PICTURE: Recap what happens when a number is multiplied or divided by 10 or 100. Complete page 90, finding the missing picture by shading answers to the questions.
DIFFERENTIATION	More able: Go on to make their own missing picture puzzle using multiplication and division by 10 and 100. Less able: Support this group, guiding them through the first few questions.
PLENARY	If OHP calculator is available, put in a 3- or 4-digit multiple of 10 or 100 (eg 670). *If I want the calculator to show 6.7, what will I have to divide by?* Children can try in pairs with their own calculators, then someone can come up and put ÷ 100 = into the OHP calculator. (If no OHP calculator is available, just take the answer.)

LESSON 3

RESOURCES
2-digit number cards.

PREPARATION
Draw a blank number line on the board.

VOCABULARY
Round, nearest, roughly, nearly, approximately.

LEARNING OUTCOMES

ORAL AND MENTAL STARTER
● Derive quickly or continue to derive quickly all two-digit pairs that total 100.

MAIN TEACHING ACTIVITY
● Round any integer up to 10 000 to the nearest 10, 100 or 1000.

ORAL AND MENTAL STARTER

PAIRS TO 100: Repeat from Lesson 4, Unit 11 of Term 1.

MAIN TEACHING ACTIVITY

WHAT IS IT NEARLY?: Write a 3-digit number on the board, eg 457. Ask the children which two hundreds it lies between (400 and 500). Write them at either end of the number line, then ask a child to write where 457 would go. *Is it nearer to 400 or 500? 500. We say that 457 is 500 to the nearest hundred.* Write 450 and 460 in the appropriate places on the line. *The number lies between these two multiples of 10. Which one is it closer to? 460. We say that 457 is 460 to the nearest 10.* Repeat the process with a 4-digit number, starting by rounding to the nearest 1000.

The children draw a table in their books (see figure below). They make 4-digit numbers by picking numeral cards in pairs, then fill in the table for at least 10 numbers.

Number	Rounded to the nearest 1000	Rounded to the nearest 100	Rounded to the nearest 10

DIFFERENTIATION

More able: Round 5-digit numbers to the nearest 10 000, 1000, 100 and 10.
Less able: Start with 3-digit numbers.

PLENARY

Write an addition on the board, eg 489 + 327 =. Ask the children to give you an approximate answer to the nearest 100. Ask the children for six to eight 4-digit numbers and write them on the board. Ask the children to select two numbers that will give a total of about 6000. Ask them how they did it.

Missing picture

Shade in the triangles that contain the answers to the questions below to reveal the picture.

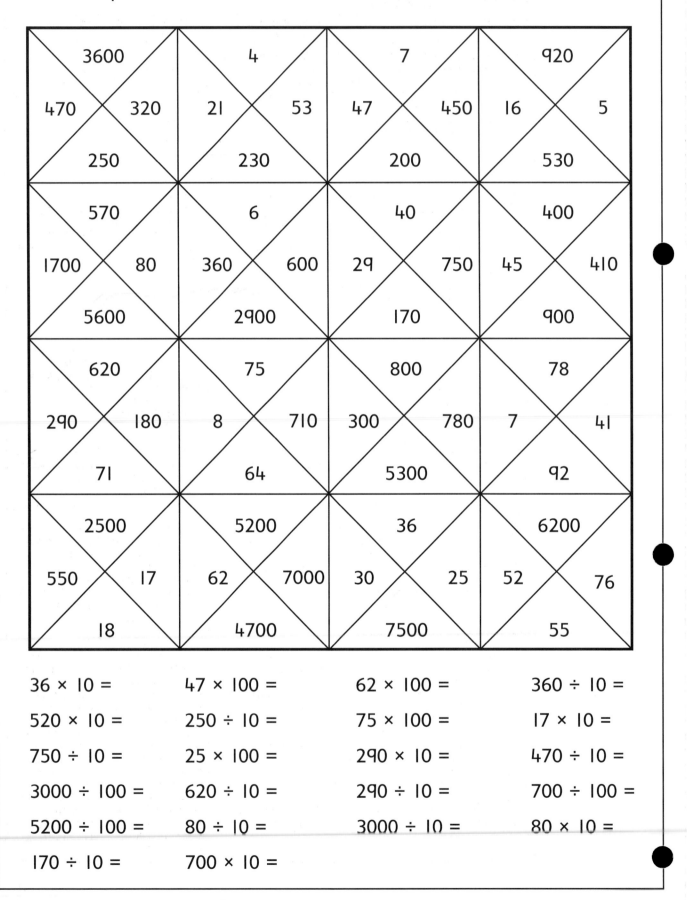

36 × 10 =	47 × 100 =	62 × 100 =	360 ÷ 10 =
520 × 10 =	250 ÷ 10 =	75 × 100 =	17 × 10 =
750 ÷ 10 =	25 × 100 =	290 × 10 =	470 ÷ 10 =
3000 ÷ 100 =	620 ÷ 10 =	290 ÷ 10 =	700 ÷ 100 =
5200 ÷ 100 =	80 ÷ 10 =	3000 ÷ 10 =	80 × 10 =
170 ÷ 10 =	700 × 10 =		

ORGANISATION (10 WEEKS)

LEARNING OUTCOMES	ORAL AND MENTAL STARTER	MAIN TEACHING ACTIVITY	PLENARY
LESSON 1 ● Understand the effect of and relationships between the four operations, and the principles (not the names) of the arithmetic laws as they apply to multiplication. Begin to use brackets. ● Use factors (eg $8 \times 12 = 8 \times 4 \times 3$). ● Check with an equivalent calculation. ● Develop calculator skills and use a calculator effectively.	FACTOR PAIRS: Hold up numeral cards to show factors of a given number.	FACTOR MULTIPLICATION: Use a calculator to check the effect of multiplying using factors.	Use a calculator to check whether calculations are equivalent.
LESSON 2 + 3 ● Understand the effect of and relationships between the four operations, and the principles (not the names) of the arithmetic laws as they apply to multiplication. Begin to use brackets. ● Use closely related facts (eg multiply by 19 or 21 by multiplying by 20 and adjusting).	FACTOR PAIRS: Repeat from Lesson 1. DOUBLES ROUND THE ROOM: Repeat from Lesson 5, Unit 2 of Term 1.	MULTIPLY BY 20: Use factors of 20 to do this mentally. Use adjustment strategies to multiply by 19 or 21.	Extend to multiplying by 19. Extend to multiplying by eg 29 or 41.
LESSON 4 + 5 ● Partition, eg $47 \times 6 = (40 \times 6) + (7 \times 6)$. ● Approximate first. Use informal pencil and paper methods to support, record or explain multiplications. ● Estimate by approximating (round to the nearest 10 or 100), then check result. ● Check with the inverse operation when using a calculator. ● **Extend written methods to short multiplication of HTU by U.**	CHANTING MULTIPLES: Multiply by multiples of 10. MORE MULTIPLES: Multiply by multiples of 10 and of 100.	TU × U: Give approximate answers to 2-digit × 1-digit multiplication, then calculate using partition. Give approximate answers to 3-digit × 1-digit multiplication, then calculate using partition.	Extend to multiplying HTU by U. Use approximation to judge whether multiplications may be correct.
LESSON 6 ● Understand the effect of and relationships between the four operations. ● Use the relationship between multiplication and division. ● Check with the inverse operation when using a calculator. ● Develop calculator skills and use a calculator effectively.	COUNTING STICK: Use a counting stick to count multiples of 6 and 7.	MULTIPLICATION OR DIVISION?: Use a calculator to multiply. Say what answers to corresponding divisions will be.	Solve 'missing number' problems by relating multiplication to division.
LESSON 7 + 8 ● Begin to express a quotient as a fraction, or as a decimal when dividing a whole number by 2, 4, 5 or 10. ● Check with the inverse operation when using a calculator. ● Develop calculator skills and use a calculator effectively.	HALVING ROUND THE ROOM: Repeat from Lesson 2, Unit 4 of Term 1. DIVISION BINGO: Repeat from Lesson 4, Unit 2 of Term 1.	REMAINDERS AS FRACTIONS: Carry out divisions and write remainders as fractions. Write answers to divisions as decimals. Check by multiplying.	Write fractions (halves and quarters) as decimals. Write answers to divisions as decimals, then as fractions.
LESSON 9 ● Round up or down after division, depending on the context.	DIVISION BINGO: Repeat from Lesson 4, Unit 2 of Term 1.	UP OR DOWN: Solve division word problems, rounding up or down as context requires.	Go through the questions; discuss any difficulties.

LEARNING OUTCOMES	ORAL AND MENTAL STARTER	MAIN TEACHING ACTIVITY	PLENARY
● **Use all four operations to solve simple word problems involving numbers and quantities based on 'real life' and money, using one or more steps.** ● Check with the inverse operation when using a calculator. ● Develop calculator skills and use a calculator effectively.	WHAT IS THE QUESTION?: Combine given numbers in any way to make a target number.	WHICH OPERATION?: Solve word problems, deciding whether to use multiplication or division.	Check with the inverse operation using a calculator.

LESSON 10

ORAL AND MENTAL SKILLS: Know by heart all multiplication facts to 10 × 10. Derive quickly: division facts corresponding to tables up to 10 × 10; doubles of all whole numbers 1 to 100, and the corresponding halves. Choose and use appropriate number operations to solve problems.

Lessons 1, 2, 6, 7 and 10 are shown in detail. Lessons 3–5, 8 and 9 follow on from what has already been taught.

LESSON 1

RESOURCES
Numeral cards 0–9 (1 set per child); a set of 2-digit number cards (10–50 excluding prime numbers) per pair; calculators.

PREPARATION
Each child should have a set of 0–9 numeral cards spread out in front of him or her.

LEARNING OUTCOMES

ORAL AND MENTAL STARTER
● **Know by heart all multiplication facts to 10 × 10.**
● Derive quickly division facts for corresponding tables up to 10 × 10.

MAIN TEACHING ACTIVITY
● Understand the effect of and relationships between the four operations, and the principles (not the names) of the arithmetic laws as they apply to multiplication. Begin to use brackets.
● Use factors (eg 8 × 12 = 8 × 4 × 3).
● Check with an equivalent calculation.
● Develop calculator skills and use a calculator effectively.

ORAL AND MENTAL STARTER

FACTOR PAIRS: Tell the children they are going to hear a number and they should hold up two numbers that, when multiplied together, will make the number they heard. (So for 12, they may hold up 3 and 4 or 2 and 6.) For each number, discuss the possibilities after the children have shown their answers. Which numbers do not have factors between 0 and 9?

MAIN TEACHING ACTIVITY

FACTOR MULTIPLICATION: Tell the children they are going to do some multiplication using factors. Write 6 × 24 = on the board, then 2 × 3 × 24 =. Ask the children to work them both out on the calculator, and discuss what they notice. Explain why they both have the same answer by putting brackets round 2 × 3 and saying: *2 × 3 is the same as 6, so we can use factors to make the calculation easier.* Write another multiplication on the board, eg 12 × 16 =. Ask how we could make it easier, eg 3 × 4 × 16 or 12 × 4 × 4. Check with a calculator. Now ask the children to turn their calculators off. Write another calculation on the board, eg 8 × 26 =. Write it in another form, asking children for their ideas. Work through it to calculate the answer.

Children work in pairs, using a number card from the set 4, 6, 8, 9, 12 and a 2-digit number card between 10 and 30 to generate questions. They should write down each calculation and an equivalent, then calculate the answer.

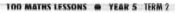

DIFFERENTIATION

More able: Use a number card from the set 8, 12, 16, 18 and a 2-digit number card 30–50.
Less able: Use a number card from the set 4, 6, 8, 9 and a 2-digit number card 10–20.

PLENARY

Write some pairs of calculations on the board, eg 12 × 24 = 3 × 4 × 12 × 2. Make some equivalent and some not. Children work in pairs to decide which are equivalent. Discuss as a class, and check together using a calculator.

LESSON 2 + 3

RESOURCES

6-sided and 10-sided dice; numeral cards 0–9 (one set per child).

PREPARATION

See Lesson 1.

VOCABULARY
Multiply, multiple, product, factor, double.

LEARNING OUTCOMES

ORAL AND MENTAL STARTER
● **Know by heart all multiplication facts to 10 × 10.**
● Derive quickly: division facts for corresponding tables up to 10 × 10; doubles of all whole numbers 1 to 100.
MAIN TEACHING ACTIVITY
● Understand the effect of and relationships between the four operations, and the principles (not the names) of the arithmetic laws as they apply to multiplication. Begin to use brackets.
● Use closely related facts (eg multiply by 19 or 21 by multiplying by 20 and adjusting).

ORAL AND MENTAL STARTER

FACTOR PAIRS: Repeat from Lesson 1.

MAIN TEACHING ACTIVITY

MULTIPLY BY 20: Tell the children they are going to multiply numbers by 20 in their heads. Refer to Lesson 1 – *We can use factors to make multiplication easier. What factors of 20 might we use?* Brainstorm possible factors. Discuss why it might be best to use 10 and 2: it's easy to multiply by 10 and double. Write 14 × 20 on the board. *What is 14 multiplied by 10?* Write 140. *So what is 14 multiplied by 20? 280.* Repeat with other examples. Write the stages on the board. Discuss whether brackets are needed, ie *Does the order of the calculation matter?*

Generate some other numbers by rolling a dice. Write questions on the board, eg 38 × 20. Encourage children to do the whole process in their heads.

The children generate their own 2-digit numbers using a 10-sided dice, then write down calculations and solutions. They might also need to jot down the middle stage (eg multiplying by 10).

DIFFERENTIATION

More able: Generate 3-digit numbers using a 10-sided dice.
Less able: Generate 2-digit numbers using a 6-sided dice. They might need to be encouraged to write down the middle stage initially.

PLENARY

Write 20 × 14 =. *If we know that 20 lots of 14 is 280, how could we use that to calculate 19 lots of 14?* Discuss the children's ideas and do a couple of examples to lead into Lesson 3.

LESSON 4 +5

LESSON 3

For the **Oral and mental starter**, repeat DOUBLES ROUND THE ROOM from Lesson 5, Unit 2 of Term 1. For the **Main teaching activity**, extend Lesson 2: go over MULTIPLYING BY 20, then use adjustment to multiply by 19 or 21. Go through some examples. Children generate numbers as in Lesson 2 and multiply each one by 20, 19 and 21; they choose their own way to record. More able children can be extended as in Lesson 2; less able children can consolidate multiplying by 20. For the **Plenary**, try multiplying by other near-multiples, eg 29 or 41.

LEARNING OUTCOMES	**ORAL AND MENTAL STARTER** ● **Know by heart all multiplication facts to 10 × 10.** **MAIN TEACHING ACTIVITY** ● Partition, eg 47 × 6 = (40 × 6) + (7 × 6). ● Approximate first. Use informal pencil and paper methods to support, record or explain multiplication. ● Estimate by approximating (round to the nearest 10 or 100), then check the result. ● Check with the inverse operation when using a calculator. ● **Extend written methods to short multiplication of HTU by U.**
RESOURCES	Numeral cards; 2-digit number cards: 6-sided and 10-sided dice.
ORAL AND MENTAL STARTER	CHANTING MULTIPLES: Divide class in two. Give first group a multiplication, eg 3 × 6. They respond as a whole (you may have to repeat the question and ask them to respond again). Give second group a connected calculation using a multiple of 10, eg 3 × 60; they respond as a whole. Repeat several times, alternating which group has the starting calculation. For Lesson 5 (MORE MULTIPLES), repeat with class in 3 groups. First group do a 1-digit by 1-digit multiplication (eg 4 × 6), second group extend to multiple of 10 (40 × 6), third group to multiple of 100 (400 × 6).
MAIN TEACHING ACTIVITY	TU × U: Tell the children they are going to multiply a 2-digit number by a 1-digit number, but they are going to approximate the answer first (eg 38 × 3 is approximately 40 × 3). Write the approximation on the board. Carry out calculation usng the method as in Lesson 4, Unit 2 of Term 1 (partitioning and using grid). Children generate questions by picking a 3–9 numeral card and a 30–100 number card. They should use approximation for each calculation. For Lesson 5, extend the grid method to HTU × U. Children generate calculations using numeral cards for the 3-digit number and a 6-sided dice for the multiplier.
DIFFERENTIATION	More able: Go on to 3-digit numbers. In LESSON 5, go on to use a 10-sided dice for the multiplier. Less able: Use numeral cards 2–5 and number cards 20–40. In LESSON 5, consolidate TU × U.
PLENARY	Discuss how the grid method might be used for multiplication of HTU by U. In Lesson 5, write some multiplications and answers on the board; the children use approximation to decide which answers may be correct.

RESOURCES

Counting stick; calculators (one per pair); photocopiable page 98.

PREPARATION

Distribute the resources needed.

LEARNING OUTCOMES

ORAL AND MENTAL STARTER
● **Know by heart all multiplication facts to 10 × 10.**
MAIN TEACHING ACTIVITY
● Understand the effect of and relationships between the four operations.
● Use the relationship between multiplication and division.
● Check with the inverse operation when using a calculator.
● Develop calculator skills and use a calculator effectively.

ORAL AND MENTAL STARTER

COUNTING STICK: Tell the children they are going to use the counting stick to count in sixes. Point to divisions on the stick as the children chant the numbers. Then ask multiplication and division questions related to the 6 times table; encourage them to use the counting stick. Repeat for multiples of 7.

MAIN TEACHING ACTIVITY

MULTIPLICATION OR DIVISION?: Tell the children they are going to use the relationship between multiplication and division to calculate the answers to some questions. Write 28 × 7 on the board; ask the children to calculate the answer on a calculator. Write the answer on the board. Then write 196 ÷ 7. Ask the children to work out the answer to this without using the calculator. Discuss how they know it will be 28. Do some other examples, each time asking half the class to calculate the answer to a multiplication without using the calculator. Work out the corresponding divisions. Do some examples where division leads to multiplication, eg *If 256 ÷ 8 = 32, what is 32 × 8?*

The children work through photocopiable page 98.

DIFFERENTIATION

More able: After completing the sheet, choose two 2-digit number cards to make up a multiplication and write the corresponding division.
Less able: Work on examples within the first ten tables, eg: 7 × 8 = 56, 56 ÷ 8 = 7.

PLENARY

Look at 'missing number' problems, eg 216 ÷ __ = 36. *Will you use multiplication or division to find the answer? How can we check the answer is correct?*

RESOURCES

6-sided and 10-sided dice, sets of 2-digit number cards, interlocking cubes, calculators.

PREPARATION

Take out the even 2-digit number cards to use in the Oral and mental starter (Lesson 7).

LEARNING OUTCOMES

ORAL AND MENTAL STARTER
● Derive quickly: corresponding halves of all doubles of whole numbers 1 to 100; division facts corresponding to tables up to 10 × 10.
MAIN TEACHING ACTIVITY
● Begin to express a quotient as a fraction, or as a decimal when dividing a whole number by 2, 4, 5 or 10.
● Check with the inverse operation when using a calculator.
● Develop calculator skills and use a calculator effectively.

ORAL AND MENTAL STARTER

HALVES ROUND THE ROOM: Repeat from Lesson 2, Unit 4 of Term 1.

MAIN TEACHING ACTIVITY

REMAINDERS AS FRACTIONS: Tell the children they are going to carry out some divisions and write the remainders as fractions. Write 15 ÷ 4 = on the board. Hold up a tower of 15 cubes. Read out the calculation to the class. *How many lots of 4 in 15?* Break off 3 lots of 4 cubes, so 3 are left over. Write 3 next to the = sign and say: *There are 3 complete towers of 4.* Hold up the 3 left over and say: *There are 3 left. What fraction of 4 is this?* Hold up a tower of 4 to compare. *It is three quarters of 4 or 3 out of 4.* Write ³/₄ next to the 3. Repeat the process several times with different divisors, 19 ÷ 6, 23 ÷ 5, 27 ÷ 8.

LESSON 7 + 8

The children generate questions of their own by picking a number card 15–30 and rolling a 6-sided dice (if 1 is rolled, roll again).

DIFFERENTIATION

More able: Use number cards 30–50 and 10-sided dice.
Less able: Work in pairs, using cubes to support the process.

PLENARY

Look at a range of answers when the divisor is 2. *What do you notice about the answers? Either a whole number or a half in the answer. How could we write that as a decimal?* Use a calculator to show $1 \div 2 = 0.5$. Repeat for questions where the divisor is 4. *How can we write these as decimals?*

LESSON 8

For the **Oral and mental starter**, repeat DIVISION BINGO from Lesson 4, Unit 2 of Term 1. For the **Main teaching activity**, extend Lesson 7 to writing remainders as decimals. Go over the Plenary of Lesson 7. Use a calculator to divide by 5 or 10. Go through some divisions together without calculators. Check by multiplying answer and divisor. Children generate questions as in Lesson 7, picking a number card 2, 4, 5 or 10 for the divisor. More able children can divide by 3 and 9, using a calculator to begin with. Less able children can divide by 2 or 10 only. In the **Plenary**, go through some questions: write answers as decimals, then as fractions.

LEARNING OUTCOMES	**ORAL AND MENTAL STARTER** ● Derive quickly or continue to derive quickly: division facts corresponding to tables up to 10×10. **MAIN TEACHING ACTIVITY** ● Round up or down after division, depending on the context.
RESOURCES	Photocopiable page 99.
ORAL AND MENTAL STARTER	DIVISION BINGO: Repeat from Lesson 4, Unit 2 of Term 1.
MAIN TEACHING ACTIVITY	UP OR DOWN: Tell the children they are going to look at some problems using division, and will need to decide whether the answer should be rounded up or down. Use the first three questions from the sheet (but change the numbers) to illustrate using pictures, objects and/or children. The children then work through photocopiable page 99.
DIFFERENTIATION	More able: Write some problems where the answers will need to be rounded up. Less able: Work through the first few problems together, supported by the teacher.
PLENARY	Go through the questions. Ask the class which ones they found most difficult, and illustrate these questions.

RESOURCES

Photocopiable page 100; large sheets of paper.

PREPARATION

Write suitable numbers in section B of photocopiable page 100 to differentiate the problems for core and more able pupils (see 'Differentiation'). Write the 'Vocabulary' words (in the same order) and a 2-column table with the headings $\times$ and $\div$ on the board.

VOCABULARY

Multiplication,
division,
multiply,
divide,
lots of,
group, share,
times,
product.

LEARNING OUTCOMES

ORAL AND MENTAL STARTER

● Choose and use appropriate number operations to solve problems.

MAIN TEACHING ACTIVITY

● **Use all four operations to solve simple word problems involving numbers and quantities** based on 'real life' and money, using one or more steps.

● Check with the inverse operation when using a calculator.

● Develop calculator skills and use a calculator effectively.

ORAL AND MENTAL STARTER

WHAT IS THE QUESTION?: Write four single-digit numbers and a 2-digit multiple of 10 on the board. Ask a child for a 3-digit number. The class work in pairs to try and get as close to the 3-digit number as possible, using each number once only and with any operations. Discuss different answers. *Who was the closest?*

MAIN TEACHING ACTIVITY

WHICH OPERATION?: Tell the children they are going to solve some multiplication and division word problems. Discuss which words on the board should go under the × sign and which under the ÷ sign. Write a multiplication problem and a division problem from Section A of photocopiable page 100 on the board. Tell the class that one is a multiplication problem and one is a division problem. Ask them to discuss in pairs which is which. After about a minute, discuss as a class which is which and how they know. *What information in the problem tells us which is multiplication and which is division?* Work through some of the questions in Section A.

Ask the pairs to write a division or multiplication problem on a large sheet of paper (give them 3 minutes). Choose one multiplication and one division to do as a class. Then the children complete the whole of the photocopiable sheet.

DIFFERENTIATION

More able: Try some of the 3-digit by 1-digit multiplication and division problems in Section B of the sheet.

Less able: Aim to complete Section A of the sheet.

PLENARY

Go through some of the problems. Divide the class in two: one half give an answer, the other half check on a calculator using the inverse operation. Swap roles and repeat.

Multiplication and division

Complete all the calculations below. Use the first calculation in each pair to help you complete the second calculation.

1. $16 \times 4 =$ _____   _____ $\div 4 = 16$

2. $27 \times 3 =$ _____ $81 \div 3 =$ _____

3. $28 \times 5 =$ _____ $140 \div$ _____ $= 5$

4. $24 \times 9 =$ _____   _____ $\div 9 = 24$

5. $33 \times 8 =$ _____ $264 \div 8 =$ _____

6. $26 \times 8 =$ _____   _____ $\div 8 = 26$

7. $42 \times 3 =$ _____ $126 \div$ _____ $= 42$

8. $36 \times 5 =$ _____   _____ $\div 5 = 36$

Complete each multiplication below, then rearrange the numbers to make a correct division.

9. $5 \times 19 =$ _____   _____ $\div$ _____ $=$ _____

10. $37 \times 4 =$ _____   _____ $\div$ _____ $=$ _____

11. $46 \times 10 =$ _____   _____ $\div$ _____ $=$ _____

12. $18 \times 7 =$ _____   _____ $\div$ _____ $=$ _____

Division problems

1. A tent holds 6 people. There are 44 scouts in a scout camp. How many tents do they need?

2. 37 children will sit in rows. There are 4 chairs in each row. How many rows of chairs will be needed?

3. A pack of pencils holds 4 pencils. For a class of 30 children, how many packets are needed?

4. There are 42 children in a class. They sit in groups of 5. How many complete groups are there?

5. 35 children sit in groups of 3. How many groups will there be altogether?

6. A bag of crisps cost 10p. Sam gets £1.15 pocket money. How many bags of crisps can he buy?

7. There are 10 felt-tipped pens in a packet. If there are 124 pens in a tray, how many packets would they fill?

8. Jenny's Dad has cooked 23 roast potatoes for Sunday lunch. If there are 6 people in the family, what is the least number of potatoes each will get if the potatoes are split evenly?

9. Simon has 50p. How many 4p chews can he buy?

10. Sarah has 27 sweets to divide between herself and 3 friends. If the sweets are shared as evenly as possible, what is the biggest number of sweets anyone will get?

UNITS 2–3

Which operation, × or ÷?

Section A

1. A packet contains 12 sweets. How many sweets are there in 8 packets?

2. A ruler costs 30p. Each child in a group of 6 needs a new ruler. How much will this cost altogether?

3. Children are asked to get into groups of 8 in the school hall. There are 72 children in the hall. How many groups will they make?

4. A rail ticket costs £15. How much would 6 tickets cost?

5. In the hall, there are 9 rows of 14 chairs. How many chairs are there?

6. A tin holds 32 biscuits. A group of children empty the tin by taking 4 biscuits each. How many children are in the group?

7. There are 56 cakes in packets on the table. There are 7 packets on the table. How many cakes are there in each packet?

8. Cans of cola come in packs of 12. How many packs would contain 60 cans?

Section B

1. There are ____ passengers on an aeroplane. They sit in rows of 6. How many rows are there?

2a. Pencils cost 8p each. A school has ____ pupils. If a pencil is bought for each pupil, how much will that cost the school altogether?

  b. The ____ pencils arrive in boxes of 8. How many boxes are used to hold all the pencils?

3. A farmer puts the ____ eggs that his hens have laid into boxes. There are 6 eggs in each box. How many boxes are needed?

4. An aeroplane ticket costs £____. If 6 friends travel, how much will it cost them altogether?

5. Exercise books come in packets with ____ in each packet. A school buys 7 packets. How many exercise books is that?

6a. On his daily trips to work and back, Pedro drives ____ miles. Over the working week (5 days), how many miles does he travel?

  b. His car does about 50 miles to the gallon. Approximately how many gallons of petrol will he have to buy during the working week?

UNIT 4

ORGANISATION (5 LESSONS)

LEARNING OUTCOMES	ORAL AND MENTAL STARTER	MAIN TEACHING ACTIVITY	PLENARY
LESSON 1 • **Relate fractions to division**, and use division to find simple fractions, including tenths and hundredths, of numbers and quantities.	SHOW ME: Find unitary fractions of given numbers.	FRACTIONS OF NUMBERS: Find non-unitary fractions of given numbers.	Compare equivalent fractions.
LESSON 2 • **Use decimal notation for tenths and hundredths**. • Know what each digit represents in a number with up to two decimal places.	COUNTING: Count on in steps of 0.1 and 0.5.	BUILDING DECIMALS: Use arrow cards to build decimal numbers.	Pick arrow cards and ask children to combine them, making a decimal number.
LESSON 3 • Order a set of numbers or measurements with the same number of decimal places. • Derive quickly decimals that total 1.	MYSTERY NUMBER: Find a decimal number by asking questions.	ORDERING DECIMALS: Work in groups to order a set of decimal numbers.	How much to make 10?
LESSON 4 • Begin to understand percentage as the number of parts in every 100. • Express one half, one quarter, three quarters, and tenths and hundredths as percentages. • **Relate fractions to their decimal representations**: that is, recognise the equivalence between decimal and fraction forms of one half, one quarter, three quarters... and tenths and hundredths (eg $^7/_{10}$ = 0.7). • Develop calculator skills and use a calculator effectively.	PAIRS TO 100: Hold up numeral cards to make a given number up to 100.	MATCHING ON A NUMBER LINE: Match fractions to equivalent decimals and percentages.	Quick-fire questions about what fractions are equivalent to given percentages.
LESSON 5 • Find simple percentages of small whole-number quantities. • Develop calculator skills and use a calculator effectively.	HALVING ROUND THE ROOM: Repeat from Lesson 2, Unit 4 of Term 1.	PERCENTAGE GRID: Find simple percentages mentally; check using calculator.	Calculate and compare discounted prices.

ORAL AND MENTAL SKILLS: Relate fractions to division, and use division to find simple fractions. Recognise and extend number sequences formed by counting from any number in steps of constant size, extending beyond zero when counting back, eg count on in steps of 0.1. Know what each digit represents in a number with up to two decimal places. Derive quickly or continue to derive quickly: all two-digit pairs that total 100, the corresponding halves of doubles of all whole numbers 1 to 100.

Lessons 2, 4 and 5 are shown in detail. Lesson 1 follows on from related work in Term 1. Lesson 3 follows on from what has already been taught in this unit.

LESSON 1

LEARNING OUTCOMES	**ORAL AND MENTAL STARTER** ● **Relate fractions to division**, and use division to find simple fractions. **MAIN TEACHING ACTIVITY** ● **Relate fractions to division**, and use division to find simple fractions, including tenths and hundredths, of numbers and quantities.
RESOURCES	Numeral cards (one set per child); photocopiable page 106.
ORAL AND MENTAL STARTER	SHOW ME: Ask children to find unitary fractions of given numbers, eg *What is half of 16? Quarter of 20? $1/6$ of 12?* Children hold up numeral cards to show answers. Discuss different methods.
MAIN TEACHING ACTIVITY	FRACTIONS OF NUMBERS: Tell the children they are going to find fractions of given numbers or quantities. Refer back to the Oral and mental session, then ask: *What extra step you would need to find $2/3$ or $3/4$ of something?* Encourage the children to try dividing by the denominator and then multiplying by the numerator. Do several examples. Children complete photocopiable page 106.
DIFFERENTIATION	More able: Write some similar questions of their own, using integers that are divisible by the denominator of the fraction. Less able: Try only the (a) parts of questions 1–10 on the sheet.Less able:
PLENARY	Look at equivalent fractions, eg write What is $2/4$ of 18? What is $3/6$ of 18? on the board. Ask children to tell you what they notice about the two questions.

LESSON 2

RESOURCES

Decimal arrow cards; numeral cards.

PREPARATION

Make a set of decimal arrow cards large enough for the whole class to see, going to hundredths.

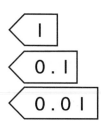

LEARNING OUTCOMES

ORAL AND MENTAL STARTER
● Recognise and extend number sequences formed by counting from any number in steps of constant size, extending beyond zero when counting back, eg count on in steps of 0.1.
MAIN TEACHING ACTIVITY
● **Use decimal notation for tenths and hundredths.**
● Know what each digit represents in a number with up to two decimal places.

ORAL AND MENTAL STARTER

COUNTING: Count together in steps of 0.1, first from 0 and then from another starting point. Say three steps in a sequence, then ask a group to say the next one (eg 0.7, 0.8, 0.9, __). Repeat with steps of 0.5.

MAIN TEACHING ACTIVITY

BUILDING DECIMALS: Write the number 1.7 on the board and read it as a class. Say *This is one and seven tenths*, pointing to each part of the number. Ask a child to come and find the arrow card that has the number that the 1 is worth, and another child to find the arrow card that has the number that the 7 is worth. Put the arrow cards together to show that they make 1.7. Write = 1 + 0.7 on the board next to 1.7. Repeat with another number, asking what the different parts are worth.

Go on to 2-place decimal numbers: choose three numeral cards to make a decimal number, eg 2.74. Write the number on the board and ask children to write the different parts it is made of, ie 2 + 0.7 + 0.04.

The children generate their own decimal numbers and break them into parts.

DIFFERENTIATION

More able: Go into 3-place decimals.
Less able: Start with 1-place decimal numbers.

PLENARY

Pick a whole number, a tenths card and a hundredths card from the arrow cards. Place them randomly on the board and ask children what number they will show when they are put together. Ask a child to write it on the board. Repeat.

LEARNING OUTCOMES	ORAL AND MENTAL STARTER
	● Know what each digit represents in a number with up to 2 decimal places. **MAIN TEACHING ACTIVITY** ● Order a set of numbers or measurements with the same number of decimal places. ● Derive quickly decimals that total 1.
RESOURCES	6 pieces of A5 card with a different 1-place decimal number written on each; pieces of card (approximately playing card size).
ORAL AND MENTAL STARTER	MYSTERY NUMBER: Tell the children you are thinking of a 1-place decimal number between 1 and 20. They must ask questions to find out what the number is; the answers can only be yes or no. Write some of the information on the board.
MAIN TEACHING ACTIVITY	ORDERING DECIMALS: Tell the children they are going to order decimal numbers. Ask a child to come out and hold a large card with a decimal number written on for the class to see. Ask another child to hold another number. Consult the class: *Is it more or less than the first number?* Repeat until all 6 numbers are in order. Ask questions, eg *How much needs to be added to 0.3 to make a whole 1?* Count on in steps of 0.1 together to check. In groups of 4, children each write a different 1-place decimal number between 1 and 5 on a card, then order the 4 numbers.
DIFFERENTIATION	More able: Use 2-place decimal numbers. Less able: Work in mixed-ability groups.
PLENARY	Pick 2 numeral cards to form a 1-place decimal number (eg 2.7). Ask: *How much must be added to reach the next whole number? How much to make 10?* Encourage children to work mentally: *0.3 and then 7, so answer is 7.3.*

RESOURCES

String; pegs; pieces of A5 card; photocopiable page 107; calculators (or OHP version if available).

PREPARATION

Write fractions $^1/_{10}$, $^2/_{10}$... $^9/_{10}$, and $^1/_4$, $^1/_2$, $^3/_4$; decimals 0.1, 0.2... 0.9, and 0.25 and 0.75; percentages 10%, 20%... 100%, and 25%, 75%; 0 and 1 each on a separate piece of A5 card. Make sets of small cards from photocopiable page 107. Hang the string at the front of the class to make a number line at the children's height.

VOCABULARY

Fraction, percentage, decimal, equivalent, tenths, hundredths, out of 100.

LEARNING OUTCOMES

ORAL AND MENTAL STARTER
● Derive quickly or continue to derive quickly: all two-digit pairs that total 100.
MAIN TEACHING ACTIVITY
● Begin to understand percentage as the number of parts in every 100.
● **Relate fractions to their decimal representations**: that is, recognise the equivalence between decimal and fraction forms of one half, one quarter, three quarters and tenths and hundredths (eg $^7/_{10} = 0.7$).
● Express one half, one quarter, three quarters, and tenths and hundredths as percentages.
● Develop calculator skills and use a calculator effectively.

ORAL AND MENTAL STARTER

PAIRS TO 100: Give the children a 2-digit number; they hold up numeral cards to show the number needed to make it up to 100.

MAIN TEACHING ACTIVITY

MATCHING ON A NUMBER LINE: Tell the children they are going to look at the equivalence between fractions, decimals and percentages. Peg 0 and 1 at either end of the number line. Hold up 0.5 and ask a child to come and peg it on the line. Discuss positioning. Repeat with other decimal numbers, ending with 0.25 and 0.75. Repeat with the fractions: ask children to peg fractions onto their equivalent decimals. Ask various children to check the equivalence on a calculator (or OHP calculator if possible) by dividing the numerator by the denominator. Repeat with percentages; start with 50%, and ask what it means.

The children then play a matching game (Pelmanism) with their cards from photocopiable page 107. It may be helpful to model this game by playing yourself against the class initially.

DIFFERENTIATION

More able: Use the full set of cards for the game.
Middles: Leave out those fractions not in their simplest form, and the matching percentages and decimals.
Less able: Leave out those cards that are not multiples of one tenth (eg 0.25, 25%, $1/4$).

PLENARY

Ask quick-fire questions, eg *What percentage is equivalent to $3/4$? How would you find 50% of something? What about 10%?* Do some examples.

RESOURCES

Percentage cards used for matching game in Lesson 4, calculators.

PREPARATION

Sort sets of percentage cards for different groups (see 'Differentiation'). Copy a blank version of the grid (see figure below) onto a worksheet, writing in different numbers for different groups. Draw the blank grid on the board.

LESSON 5

	10%	50%	25%
20			
60			

VOCABULARY

Percentage, out of 100.

LEARNING OUTCOMES

ORAL AND MENTAL STARTER
● Derive quickly the corresponding halves of all doubles of whole numbers 1 to 100.
MAIN TEACHING ACTIVITY
● Find simple percentages of small whole-number quantities.
● Develop calculator skills and use a calculator effectively.

ORAL AND MENTAL STARTER

HALVING ROUND THE ROOM: Repeat from Lesson 2, Unit 4 of Term 1.

MAIN TEACHING ACTIVITY

PERCENTAGE GRID: Tell the children they are going to find percentages of different numbers. *How do you find 50%? Halve it. Why? Because 50% is equal to half.* Give the class several numbers to find 50% of. Ask them how to find 10% of a number, then how they could use this to help them find 20% (ie find 10% and double it). Repeat with other percentages, eg 30%. Encourage children to think of how they could use what they already know to work out given percentages. Write appropriate numbers and percentages to head the rows and columns in the grid on the board. With the children's help, complete the grid. Remind them of equivalence with decimals to help them with calculation. They should check the answers using calculators.

The children complete their own grid on the worksheet, selecting percentages from cards 10%, 20%, 25%, 50%, 75% and working out percentages of the numbers already written in the grid.

DIFFERENTIATION

More able: Select percentages from the full range of cards (excluding 10%, 50%, 25%).
Less able: Use grid with percentages already written in.

PLENARY

Write '25% off £20' and '20% off £25' on the board. Discuss with the class which would be the better deal. Encourage them to justify their answers. A case can be made for either choice!

Fractions of numbers

1 a) $\frac{1}{3}$ of 9 =   b) $\frac{2}{3}$ of 9 =

2 a) $\frac{1}{4}$ of 16 =   b) $\frac{3}{4}$ of 16 =

3 a) $\frac{1}{5}$ of 20 =   b) $\frac{3}{5}$ of 20 =

4 a) $\frac{1}{4}$ of 40 =   b) $\frac{3}{4}$ of 40 =

5 a) $\frac{1}{5}$ of 30 =   b) $\frac{2}{5}$ of 30 =

6 a) $\frac{1}{6}$ of 30 =   b) $\frac{2}{6}$ of 30 =

7 a) $\frac{1}{3}$ of 21 =   b) $\frac{2}{3}$ of 21 =

8 a) $\frac{1}{8}$ of 40 =   b) $\frac{3}{8}$ of 40 =

9 a) $\frac{1}{5}$ of 40 =   b) $\frac{4}{5}$ of 40 =

10 a) $\frac{1}{8}$ of 48 =   b) $\frac{5}{8}$ of 48 =

Fill in the missing part of each fraction.

11 a) $\frac{\square}{3}$ of 6 = 2   b) $\frac{\square}{3}$ of 6 = 4

12 a) $\frac{\square}{5}$ of 10 = 4   b) $\frac{\square}{5}$ of 10 = 8

13 a) $\frac{\square}{7}$ of 21 = 6   b) $\frac{\square}{7}$ of 21 = 15

14 a) $\frac{\square}{10}$ of 50 = 15   b) $\frac{\square}{10}$ of 50 = 35

15 a) $\frac{\square}{8}$ of 32 = 12   b) $\frac{\square}{8}$ of 32 = 28

16 a) $\frac{\square}{9}$ of 54 = 6   b) $\frac{\square}{9}$ of 54 = 24

Fraction, decimal and percentage cards

$\dfrac{3}{4}$	50%	$\dfrac{3}{10}$	$\dfrac{1}{10}$
0.75	$\dfrac{3}{6}$	0.3	10%
$\dfrac{8}{10}$	$\dfrac{6}{10}$	$\dfrac{4}{10}$	$\dfrac{2}{10}$
$\dfrac{4}{5}$	$\dfrac{3}{5}$	0.4	20%
80%	60%	$\dfrac{2}{5}$	$\dfrac{2}{10}$
0.8	0.6	40%	$\dfrac{1}{5}$
$\dfrac{9}{10}$	$\dfrac{7}{10}$	$\dfrac{1}{2}$	25%
90%	0.7	0.5	0.25

UNIT 5

ORGANISATION (8 LESSONS)

	LEARNING OUTCOMES	ORAL AND MENTAL STARTER	MAIN TEACHING ACTIVITY	PLENARY
LESSON 1 +2	• Recognise reflective symmetry in regular polygons: for example, know that a square has four axes of symmetry and an equilateral triangle has three. • Make and investigate a general statement about shapes by finding examples that satisfy it. • Explain methods and reasoning, orally and in writing.	GUESS THE SHAPE: Answer questions to help teacher guess a shape. MULTIPLICATION BINGO: Crossing off answers to questions on a sheet.	LINES OF SYMMETRY: Describe polygons in terms of lines of symmetry. SHAPE DESCRIPTIONS: Guess shapes from descriptions. Describe shapes.	Look at regular polygons in terms of lines of symmetry. Children try to guess shapes from each other's descriptions.
LESSON 3 +4	• **Recognise perpendicular and parallel lines.** • Recognise where a shape will be after reflection in a mirror line parallel to one side (sides not all parallel or perpendicular to the mirror line).	GUESS THE SHAPE: Repeat from Lesson 1. PAIRS TO 100: Repeat from Lesson 4, Unit 4.	REFLECT A SHAPE: Draw reflection of shape drawn by partner. Extend from Lesson 3 by using more complex shapes.	Identify errors in a relection drawing. Look at shapes reflected in two mirrors.
LESSON 5	• Complete symmetrical patterns with two lines of symmetry at right angles (using squared paper or pegboard).	DOUBLING ROUND THE ROOM: Repeat from Lesson 5, Unit 2 of Term 1, but use multiples of 5.	SYMMETRY PATTERNS: Complete patterns by drawing reflections.	Change incorrect symmetrical patterns.
LESSON 6 +7	• Read and plot co-ordinates in the first quadrant.	GUESS THE SHAPE: Repeat from Lesson 1, but use the term 'parallel'. NUMERAL CARDS: Answer quick-fire multiplication and division questions.	INTRODUCTION TO CO-ORDINATES: Plot given co-ordinates. Plot given co-ordinates to make a 'mystery picture'.	Plot co-ordinates to hit a 'hidden' target. State co-ordinates of points needed to complete a shape.
LESSON 8	• Recognise where a shape will be after a translation.	HALVING ROUND THE ROOM: Repeat from Lesson 2, Unit 4, Term 1.	TRANSLATING SHAPES: draw or describe a translation.	Describe a translation shown.

ORAL AND MENTAL SKILLS: Describe and visualise 2-D shapes (Year 4 revision). **Know by heart all multiplication facts to 10 × 10**. Derive quickly or continue to derive quickly: division facts corresponding to tables up to 10 × 10; all two-digit pairs that total 100; doubles of multiples of 10 to 1000; the corresponding halves of all doubles of whole numbers 1 to 100.

Lessons 1, 3, 5 and 6 are shown in detail. Lessons 2, 4, 7 and 8 follow on from what has already been taught.

RESOURCES

Shape templates (eg squares, triangles, rectangles, pentagons, hexagons, heptagons, octagons); Blu-Tack; mirrors; paper; pencils.

PREPARATION

Cut out some large regular shapes (see above) from coloured paper.

VOCABULARY

Triangle,
equilateral,
isosceles,
rectangle,
square,
pentagon,
hexagon,
heptagon,
octagon, side,
right angle,
acute, obtuse,
straight,
curved, equal,
mirror line,
line of
symmetry,
axis of
symmetry,
symmetrical.

LEARNING OUTCOMES

ORAL AND MENTAL STARTER
● Describe and visualise 2-D shapes.
● **Know by heart all multiplication facts to 10 × 10.**

MAIN TEACHING ACTIVITY
● Recognise reflective symmetry in regular polygons: for example, know that a square has four axes of symmetry and an equilateral triangle has three.
● Make and investigate a general statement about shapes by finding examples that satisfy it.
● Explain methods and reasoning, orally and in writing.

ORAL AND MENTAL STARTER

GUESS THE SHAPE: Ask a child to pick a shape and stick it on the board so the class can see it but you can't (ie your back is to the board). Ask the class questions to help you guess what the shape is, eg *Does it have more than 4 sides? Are all the sides the same length?* The answers can only be yes or no. Continue until you guess the shape. Information can be jotted on the board. You and the class then swap roles.

MAIN TEACHING ACTIVITY

LINES OF SYMMETRY: Hold up a square, fold it in half and open it out. Tell the class that this shape is symmetrical. *What does that mean?* Point to the fold line and explain that it is a line of symmetry: *The shape can be folded in half along this line so that each half is the mirror image of the other half.* Demonstrate using a mirror. Ask a child to come up and fold the shape in half another way so that it shows a line of symmetry. Repeat until all the lines of symmetry are shown. Write 'Square: 4 lines of symmetry' on the board. Repeat with a non-square rectangle (an oblong), emphasising that the diagonal is not a line of symmetry. Fold the shape to show that the two halves don't match.

The children cut out and fold shapes, using shape templates to draw round and mirrors to check. *How many lines of symmetry does a shape with equal sides and angles have?*

DIFFERENTIATION

Differentiate by outcome.

PLENARY

Ask the children to show you shapes that have equal sides and angles (ie regular polygons). Count the number of lines of symmetry on each shape, and discuss what the children notice. Look at some other shapes (eg isosceles triangle) to show that these do not have the same number of lines of symmetry as they do sides.

LESSON 2

For the **Oral and mental starter**, play MULTIPLICATION BINGO: write multiples of 6 (up to 72) on the board; children write down 5 of the numbers, then cross them out if they are the answers to multiplication fact questions such as *What is 3 lots of 8?* For the **Main teaching activity**, extend the Oral and mental starter from Lesson 1: describe a regular shape, giving facts about number of lines, number and type of angles, length of sides, lines of symmetry. Children try to guess what it is. *Could it be any other shape? Why not?* Children work in pairs to draw regular shapes (with templates) and write desciptions of each other's shapes. More able children could work with non-regular shapes. In the **Plenary**, some children read out their descriptions: can the others guess the shapes?

LESSON 3 + 4

RESOURCES

Squared paper; Blu-tack; coloured card.

PREPARATION

Cut 10 squares (each approximately 10cm square) from coloured card (all the same colour).

LEARNING OUTCOMES

ORAL AND MENTAL STARTER

- Describe and visualise 2-D shapes.
- Derive quickly: all two-digit pairs that total 100.

MAIN TEACHING ACTIVITY

- **Recognise perpendicular and parallel lines**.
- Recognise where a shape will be after reflection in a mirror line parallel to one side (sides not all parallel or perpendicular to the mirror line).

ORAL AND MENTAL STARTER

GUESS THE SHAPE: Repeat from Lesson 1.

MAIN TEACHING ACTIVITY

REFLECT A SHAPE: Tell the children they are going to reflect shapes in a mirror line. Draw a mirror line on the board. Use Blu-Tack to stick five of the squares onto one side of the mirror line (see figure, left). Say that all the sides of this shape are either perpendicular or parallel to the mirror line, and explain these terms. Invite a child to use the other five squares to show where the reflected image of the shape would be in the mirror line. Once the image has been made on the board, say that the original shape and its image should be exactly the same distance away from the mirror. Repeat with another arrangement of the five squares.

The children use squared paper to draw their own arrangement of five squares, making sure that all the sides are parallel or perpendicular to the mirror line, then swap with a partner and draw the reflected image.

DIFFERENTIATION

Differentiate by outcome.

PLENARY

Arrange the 10 squares on the board so that the reflection is incorrect. *What is wrong with this reflection?* Repeat.

LESSON 4

For the **Oral and mental starter**, repeat PAIRS TO 100 from Lesson 4, Unit 4. For the **Main teaching activity**, extend Lesson 3 by looking at reflecting shapes where only one side is parallel to the mirror line. Use five squares, but cut some diagonally in half to make triangles. More able children can look at shapes where no sides are parallel to the mirror line. Less able children can consolidate Lesson 3. In the **Plenary**, look at what happens when a shape is reflected in two mirrors (ie reflected in both the x- and the y-axis).

RESOURCES

Large square sheets of squared paper; large counters in various colours; Blu-Tack; photocopiable page 113.

PREPARATION

Fold a large square sheet of squared paper twice into quarters, so that it has a cross across the middle (two lines of symmetry at right angles). Attach it to the board. Stick counters in two different colours on the sheet to make a symmetrical pattern. Remove two or three counters so that the pattern is incomplete (see figure right).

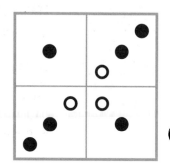

VOCABULARY

Double, multiple, equal, mirror line, line of symmetry, axis of symmetry, symmetrical, reflect, reflection.

LEARNING OUTCOMES

ORAL AND MENTAL STARTER
● Derive quickly or continue to derive quickly: doubles of multiples of 10.

MAIN TEACHING ACTIVITY
● Complete symmetrical patterns with two lines of symmetry at right angles (using squared paper or pegboard).

ORAL AND MENTAL STARTER

DOUBLING ROUND THE ROOM: Repeat from Lesson 5, Unit 2 of Term 1, except that the first group chooses a 2-digit multiple of 5 from a list on the board to start with. Continue until over 1000.

MAIN TEACHING ACTIVITY

SYMMETRY PATTERNS: Tell the children they are going to complete symmetrical patterns. Look at the pattern made with the counters on the squared paper. Explain that this pattern has two lines of symmetry (point to the folds on the paper), but that it is not complete. Ask what needs to be added to the pattern to make it complete. Invite children to come up and stick additional counters onto the squared paper. When it is complete, add an additional counter. *How many more counters will I need to add to complete this pattern? Three.* Repeat, this time removing some counters from a section. *Which counters will need to be removed?* Take all the counters off the sheet, then put some back in one quadrant. *If this was reflected in this mirror line* (point to the vertical line), *what would the image look like?* Once it has been reflected in the vertical mirror line, repeat in the horizontal.

The children work in threes. Each has a piece of squared paper folded into four. They colour a given number of squares in one quarter and pass it to the next child, who colours the reflection in the vertical mirror line; then it is passed to the third child, who reflects the whole image in the horizontal mirror line. The children go on to complete photocopiable page 113 individually.

DIFFERENTIATION

More able: Use isometric paper to generate patterns with more than two lines of symmetry.
Less able: Working in pairs, each folds a piece of paper in two (one line of symmetry) and make a pattern using a given number of squares on one half of the paper, then swap with a partner for reflection.

PLENARY

Look at some incomplete symmetrical patterns on squared paper. *How do these need to be changed so that they are correct?*

RESOURCES

Squared paper; numeral cards (one set per child); photocopiable page 114.

PREPARATION

Draw a grid and pair of axes on the board. Plot points at (4,1), (4,5), (1,1) and (1,5).

VOCABULARY

Grid, row, column, origin, co-ordinates, x-axis, y-axis, quadrant.

LEARNING OUTCOMES

ORAL AND MENTAL STARTER
● Describe and visualise 2-D shapes.
● **Know by heart all multiplication facts to 10 × 10**.
● Derive quickly or continue to derive quickly division facts corresponding to tables up to 10 × 10.

MAIN TEACHING ACTIVITY
● Read and plot co-ordinates in the first quadrant.

ORAL AND MENTAL STARTER

GUESS THE SHAPE: Repeat from Lesson 1, Unit 5; also include questions about pairs of parallel sides.

MAIN TEACHING ACTIVITY

INTRODUCTION TO CO-ORDINATES: Tell the children they are going to read and plot co-ordinates in the first quadrant. Explain these terms. Look at the grid on the board. Point to the point (4,1) and say: *The co-ordinate of this point is (4,1), 4 along the x-axis and 1 up the y-axis.* Invite a child to come and label one of the other points, and to justify the label. Repeat with the other points. Invite a child to come and plot a given point. Do the rest of the class agree? Repeat.

The children draw their own axis on a 10 × 10 grid on squared paper, then draw a picture (eg a house, boat or face) by plotting points and joining them together. They should label all the points plotted.

DIFFERENTIATION

Differentiate by outcome.

PLENARY

Tell the children that you have a target for them to hit, across several points on a grid. They suggest co-ordinates and come and plot them on a large grid on the board; you say whether each is a hit or a miss – and whether a miss is close. Mark hits with a large cross. How many goes are needed to 'take out' the whole target?

LESSON 7

For the **Oral and mental starter**, ask questions about multiplication and division facts up to 10 × 10; the children hold up numeral cards to answer. For the **Main teaching activity**, draw and number a pair of axes on the board; the children work in pairs to copy this on paper. Now give them points to plot which make a simple picture. They label each point with a letter: A (6,4), B (5,3), C (3,2), D (1,3), E (3,4), F (6,2). Finally, they join the points in alphabetical order. *What have you drawn?* Plot the points as a class. The children complete photocopiable page 114. More able children can make up their own co-ordinates for a picture, giving them letters or numbers for joining up. In the **Plenary**, plot three corners of a square on the board grid. Ask what the co-ordinates of the fourth corner are. Discuss how the children worked it out. Repeat with other shapes (eg hexagon, parallelogram).

LEARNING OUTCOMES	**ORAL AND MENTAL STARTER** ● Derive quickly the corresponding halves of all doubles of whole numbers 1 to 100. **MAIN TEACHING ACTIVITY** ● Recognise where a shape will be after a translation.
RESOURCES	Squared paper.
ORAL AND MENTAL STARTER	HALVING ROUND THE ROOM: Repeat from Lesson 2, Unit 4 of Term 1.
MAIN TEACHING ACTIVITY	Tell the children they are going to translate shapes. Explain that translation is sliding a shape along a straight line, without rotation or reflection. Show an example. Draw a rectangle 4 squares by 3 squares on a co-ordinate grid on the board. Ask where the shape would be if it moved two squares to the left. Ask a child to come up and draw the position of the shape. Repeat with other translations. Children work in pairs to draw a shape on a grid (using squared paper); one child draws the shape after translation without the other seeing, then describes the translation to the partner, who tries to draw the new position. They swap roles and repeat.
DIFFERENTIATION	More able: Use more complex shapes. Less able: Use cut-out shapes to perform translation.
PLENARY	Draw a shape on the board and its position after a translation. Ask the children to describe the translation. Repeat.

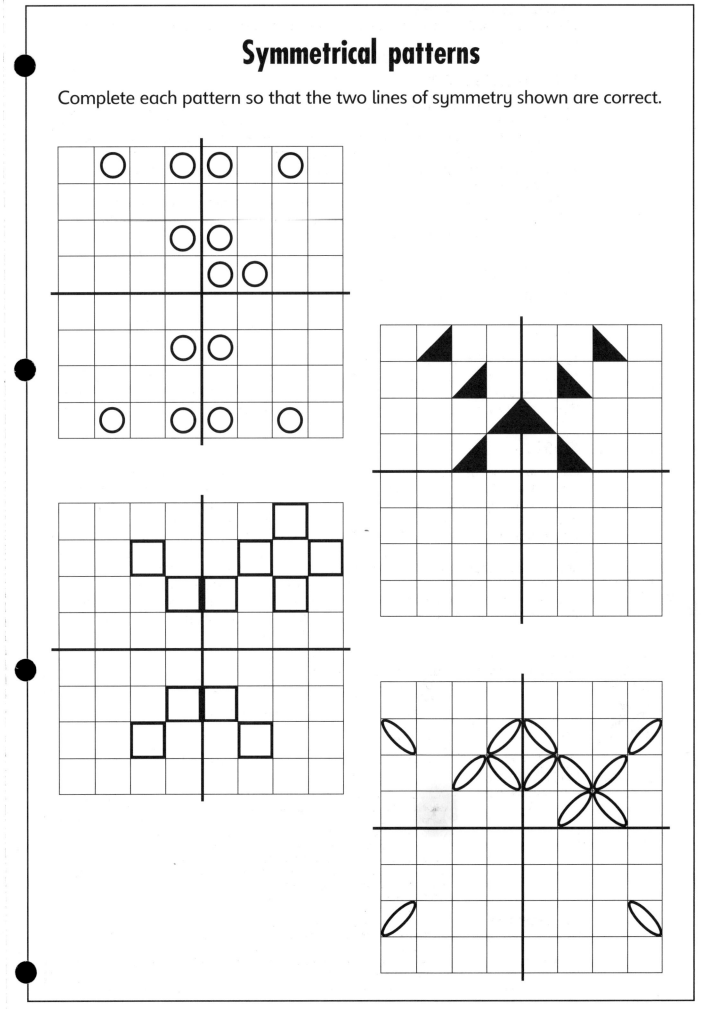

Name: Date:

Symmetrical patterns

Complete each pattern so that the two lines of symmetry shown are correct.

Name: Date:

Co-ordinates picture

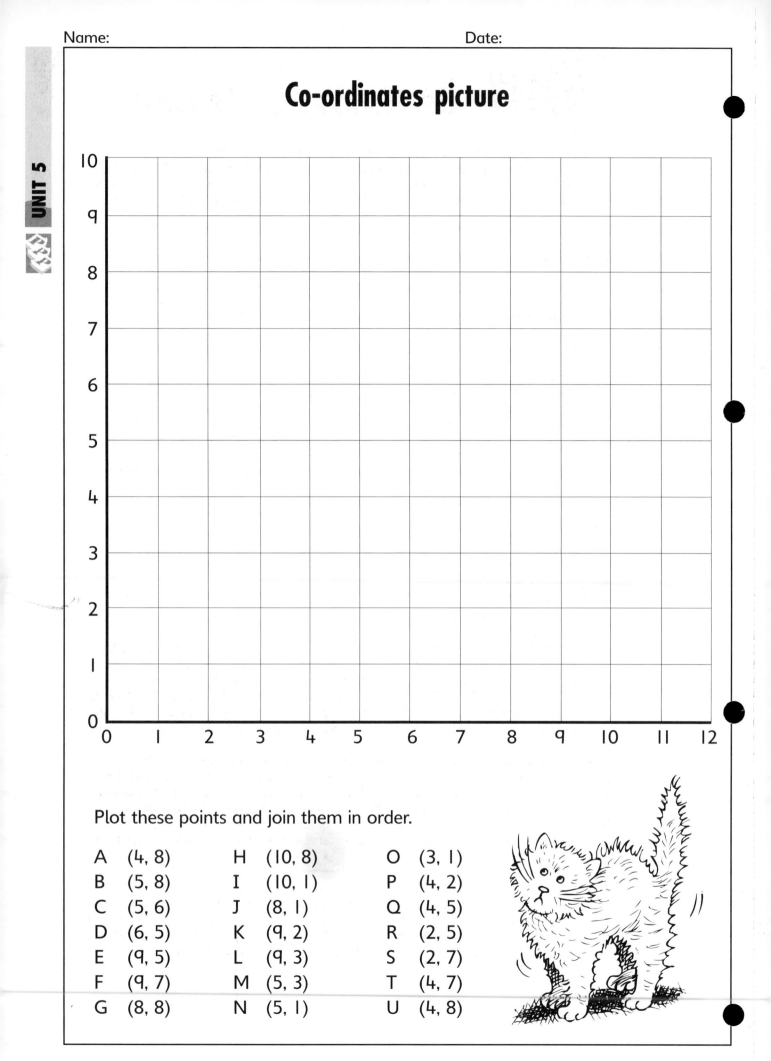

Plot these points and join them in order.

A	(4, 8)	H	(10, 8)	O	(3, 1)
B	(5, 8)	I	(10, 1)	P	(4, 2)
C	(5, 6)	J	(8, 1)	Q	(4, 5)
D	(6, 5)	K	(9, 2)	R	(2, 5)
E	(9, 5)	L	(9, 3)	S	(2, 7)
F	(9, 7)	M	(5, 3)	T	(4, 7)
G	(8, 8)	N	(5, 1)	U	(4, 8)

UNIT 6: Assess & Review

Choose from these activities. During the group activities, some of the children can work with you on practical tasks, while others complete assessment worksheets 3a and 3b which assess their skills in working with place value, decimals and fractions. The specific assessment criteria for the assessment sheets are to be found at the bottom of each sheet.

RESOURCES

Numeral cards (one set per child); 2-D shapes.

ORAL AND MENTAL STARTER

ASSESSMENT
Can the children derive quickly:
● all two-digit pairs that total 100
● the corresponding halves of doubles of all whole numbers 1 to 100?

SHOW ME: Give the children a 2-digit number. Ask them to hold up pairs of numeral cards to make the number which will add to your number to total 100. They shouldn't hold up their cards until you say *Go!* Repeat several times. Then give numbers to halve (any even number to 200); the children show their answers when you say *Go!* Note who takes longer, and who will need further practice.

GROUP ACTIVITIES

ASSESSMENT
Can the children:
● multiply mentally by using closely related facts
● **recognise parallel and perpendicular lines**
● round any integer up to 10 000 to the nearest 10, 100 or 1000?

USE THIS ANSWER TO HELP YOU: Write a calculation on a flip chart, eg 24 × 10 = 240. Ask children to use that to calculate 24 × 20 and write down the answer. Ask one child to explain how he or she did it. Repeat for a different calculation, using a different connection, eg *37 × 10 = 370, so what is 37 × 9?* Or *28 × 20 = 560, so what is 28 × 21?* Continue until each child has had the opportunity to explain how he or she calculated an answer. Check that the children are using the previous calculation to help them.

PARALLEL AND PERPENDICULAR: Give each child a range of 2-D shapes. Give them problems relating to the terms parallel and perpendicular, eg *Find me a shape that has at least one pair of parallel lines.* Ask each child to hold up the shape he or she has chosen and show where there is a pair of parallel lines, and whether there are any other pairs. Repeat with other instructions, eg two pairs of parallel lines, a side that is perpendicular to another side on the shape. Check the children can select shapes appropriately and explain their choices.

MAKE ME A NUMBER: Give each child four numeral cards: 2, 3, 5, 7. Ask them to make various numbers, eg one that can be rounded to 3000, one that can be rounded to 7500. The children arrange their cards to form a number (without the others seeing), then reveal it, read it out and explain why it can be rounded to the number given. Check the children can determine the range of numbers that can be rounded to a given number.

Assessment 3a

Complete the calculations below.

1.   37 × _____ = 370

2.   _____ × 10 = 560

3.   _____ × 100 = 2700

4.   430 × _____ = 4300

5.   2100 ÷ _____ = 21

6.   7800 ÷ 100 = _____

7.   _____ ÷ 10 = 39

8.   _____ ÷ 100 = 64

9.   350 ___ 10 = 3500

10. 8100 ___ 100 = 81

11. 350 ___ 10 = 35

12. 92 ___ 100 = 9200

Decide which operations you would use to calculate the fractions below.
Write them in the order you would use them.
The first one has been done for you.

$\frac{3}{4}$ of 12   12   (÷3   ÷4   ×3   ×4)   ÷4 ×3 _____

$\frac{2}{5}$ of 20   20   (÷2   ÷5   ×2   ×5)   _____

$\frac{2}{3}$ of 12   12   (×3   ×2   ÷2   ÷3)   _____

$\frac{5}{6}$ of 18   18   (×5   ×6   ÷5   ÷6)   _____

$\frac{3}{5}$ of 15   15   (×5   ÷5   ×3   ÷3)   _____

$\frac{3}{4}$ of 16   16   (÷4   ×4   ×3   ÷3)   _____

- **Multiply and divide any positive integer up to 10 000 by 10 or 100 and understand the effect.**
- **Relate fractions to division.**

Assessment 3b

Write what the 4 digit is worth in each of the numbers below. Choose from:

| 4 tens | 4 units | 4 tenths | 4 hundredths |

1. 4.37   4 _____

2. 24.05   4 _____

3. 3.04   4 _____

4. 21.4   4 _____

5. 6.49   4 _____

6. 7.54   4 _____

7. 54.79   4 _____

8. 9.41   4 _____

Join each fraction to an equivalent decimal.

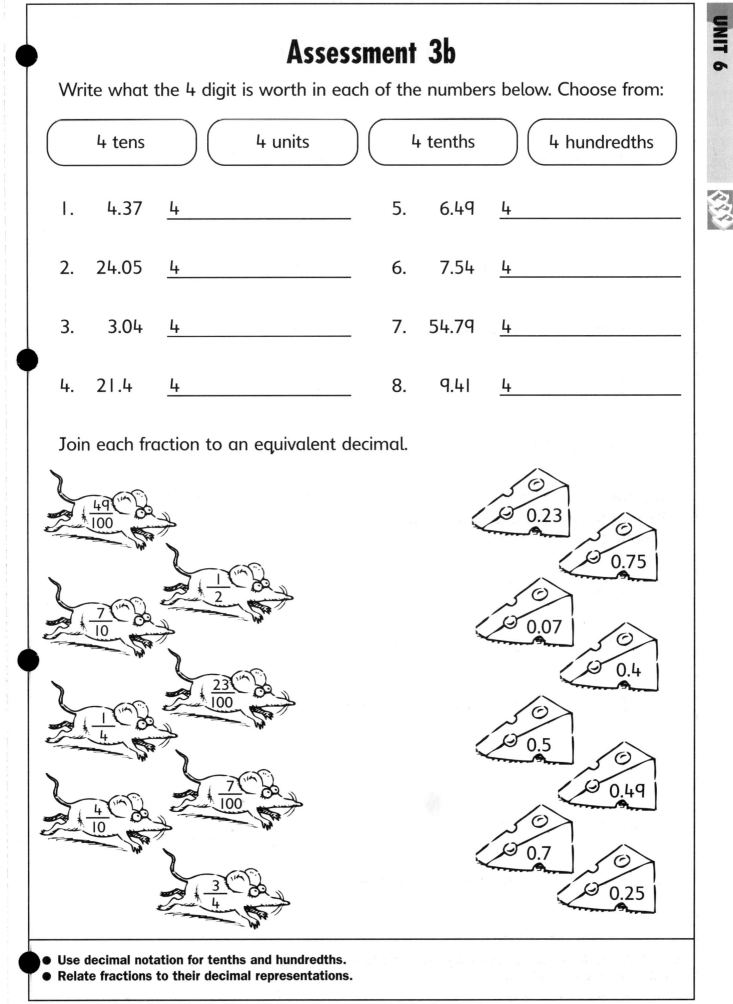

$\frac{49}{100}$ $\frac{1}{2}$ $\frac{7}{10}$ $\frac{23}{100}$ $\frac{1}{4}$ $\frac{7}{100}$ $\frac{4}{10}$ $\frac{3}{4}$

0.23 0.75 0.07 0.4 0.5 0.49 0.7 0.25

● **Use decimal notation for tenths and hundredths.**
● **Relate fractions to their decimal representations.**

UNITS 7-8

ORGANISATION (10 LESSONS)

	LEARNING OUTCOMES	ORAL AND MENTAL STARTER	MAIN TEACHING ACTIVITY	PLENARY
LESSON 1 +2	• Use, read and write standard metric units (l, ml), including their abbreviations, and relationships between them. Convert larger to smaller units (l to ml). • Know imperial units (pint, gallon). • Suggest suitable units and measuring equipment to estimate or measure capacity. • Record estimates and readings from scales to a suitable degree of accuracy.	PAIRS TO 100 IN THREES: Generate pairs of numbers to total 100 and say the addition. PAIRS TO MAKE 1: Generate pairs of decimal numbers to total 1.	ESTIMATING CAPACITY: Estimate and measure the capacity of different containers. Convert measures of capacity from l to ml.	Compare the capacity of different-shaped containers. Convert values in litres to approximate values in pints.
LESSON 3	• Understand, measure and calculate perimeters of rectangles and regular polygons.	PAIRS TO MAKE 1000: Generate pairs of multiples of 50 to total 1000.	POLYGON PERIMETERS: Measure lengths and calculate perimeters.	Given the perimeter of a regular polygon, find the length of a side.
LESSON 4 +5	• **Understand area measured in square centimetres (cm²).** • **Understand and use the formula in words 'length × breadth' for the area of a rectangle.**	NUMERAL CARDS: Respond to multiplication questions. MULTIPLICATION BINGO: Repeat from Lesson 2, Unit 5.	INTRODUCTION TO AREA: Find area of a rectangle on squared paper. Given area and one side length of a rectangle, find other side length.	Given area and length of a rectangle, find width. Find area of composite shape made from two rectangles.
LESSON 6 +7	• **Use all four operations to solve simple word problems involving numbers and quantities** based on 'real life' and measures, using one or more steps.	GROUP BINGO: Respond to division questions using a set of answers. FOLLOW ME: Repeat from Lesson 5, Unit 8 of Term 1.	WORD PROBLEMS: Write questions about measures, given answers. Solve two-step word problems about measures.	Convert l to ml and vice versa. Go through the problems and discuss any difficulties.
LESSON 8	• Solve a problem by representing and interpreting data in tables, charts, graphs and diagrams, for example: bar line charts, vertical axis labelled in 2s, 5s, 10s, 20s or 100s.	FOLLOW ME: Repeat from Lesson 5, Unit 8 of Term 1.	BIRTHDAY DATA: Collect information and display it as a chart.	Discuss what the chart shows.
LESSON 9	• Solve a problem by representing and interpreting data in tables, charts, graphs and diagrams, for example: bar line charts, vertical axis labelled in 2s, 5s, 10s, 20s or 100s. • Find the mode of a set of data.	SPEED PAIRS: Generate pairs of decimals that total 1 against time.	MOST COMMON RESULT: Find the mode and range of a set of scores.	Look at a graph of the data to see the mode and range.
LESSON 10	• Solve a problem by representing and interpreting data in tables, charts, graphs and diagrams. • Find the mode of a set of data.	PAIRS TO MAKE 1000: Repeat from Lesson 3, using a number line.	FINDING THE MODE: Work in groups to collect data and find the mode.	Discuss findings.

ORAL AND MENTAL SKILLS: Know by heart all multiplication facts to 10 × 10. Derive quickly or continue to derive quickly: all two-digit pairs that total 100; decimals that total 1; pairs of multiples of 50 with a total of 1000; division facts corresponding to tables up to 10 × 10.

Lessons 1, 3, 4, 6, 8 and 9 are shown in detail. Lessons 2, 5, 7 and 10 follow on from what has already been taught.

LESSON 1 +2

RESOURCES

A range of containers (of different heights, widths and shapes); sand, rice or lentils; measuring jugs.

PREPARATION

Put a number of different containers (about 6 for each group of 4 to 6 children), a container of sand, rice or lentils (or water if nothing else is available) and a number of measuring jugs on each table. For Lesson 2, the same (or other) containers need to be marked with their capacity in litres.

VOCABULARY

Litres, millilitres, pint, gallon, metric, imperial, full, empty, hold.

LEARNING OUTCOMES

ORAL AND MENTAL STARTER
● Derive quickly or continue to derive quickly: all two-digit pairs that total 100; decimals that total 1.
MAIN TEACHING ACTIVITY
● Use, read and write standard metric units (l, ml), including their abbreviations, and relationships between them. Convert larger to smaller units (l to ml).
● Know imperial units (pint, gallon).
● Suggest suitable units and measuring equipment to estimate or measure capacity.
● Record estimates and readings from scales to a suitable degree of accuracy.

ORAL AND MENTAL STARTER

PAIRS TO 100 IN THREES: Ask the children to sit in groups of 3. The first child says a number, the next says how many more to make 100 and the third says the addition, eg '34 and 66 make 100.' Continue round the room.

MAIN TEACHING ACTIVITY

ESTIMATING CAPACITY: Tell the children they are going to estimate and measure the capacity of different containers. *What unit of measurement do we use to measure capacity? Millilitres, litres, pints, gallons.* Say that they are going to measure using metric units: millilitres and litres. *How many millilitres make 1 litre? 1000.* Write '1000ml = 1l' on the board. Show the class a litre measure; fill it to the litre mark with sand (or equivalent); then pour the sand out so the children can see it, and say that this is a litre. Show the class half a litre or 500ml.

Hold up a container. *What do you think the capacity of this container is? Would it be better to use litres or millilitres to measure its capacity?* Take a range of estimates and write them on the board. Pour sand into the container and then pour it from the container into the measure; draw on the board what the scale on the side of the measure looks like and where the sand comes up to. Ask what the measure shows. *Whose estimate was closest?* Repeat with at least two other containers.

The groups estimate and measure the capacity of the containers on their tables.

DIFFERENTIATION

Differentiate by outcome.

PLENARY

Look at containers that are wide and shallow and containers that are tall and thin. Discuss which ones will hold the most and why.

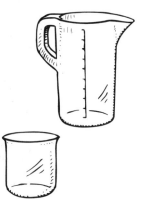

LESSON 2

For the **Oral and mental starter**, play PAIRS TO MAKE 1: say a 1-place decimal number between 0 and 1; the children tell you how much more is needed to make 1. For the **Main teaching activity**, extend Lesson 1. Write some amounts in litres on the board, eg 1 litre, 1.5 litres, $2\frac{1}{4}$ litres. Ask what these are in ml. Remind the children that 1 litre = 1000 millilitres.

Give them a range of containers; they write down the capacity of each in litres, then in millilitres. More able children can convert values given to two decimal places, eg 2.35l. Less able children can convert whole and half litres to millilitres. In the **Plenary**, tell the children that a pint is a bit more than half a litre. Convert the amounts on the board to their approximate value in pints.

LESSON 3

RESOURCES

String; rulers; regular 2-D shapes.

PREPARATION

Draw a rectangle on the board.

LEARNING OUTCOMES

ORAL AND MENTAL STARTER
● Derive quickly or continue to derive quickly pairs of multiples of 50 that total 1000.
MAIN TEACHING ACTIVITY
● Understand, measure and calculate perimeters of rectangles and regular polygons.

ORAL AND MENTAL STARTER

PAIRS TO MAKE 1000: Tell the children you are going to say a multiple of 50, and they must say how much more is needed to make it up to 1000. Give different multiples to different groups.

MAIN TEACHING ACTIVITY

POLYGON PERIMETERS: Tell the children they are going to calculate the distances round different shapes. Hold up a rectangle and point to the edges. *The distance around the edge of a shape is called the perimeter.* Wrap a piece of string around the edge and show how long the string is. *How could I measure it without a piece of string?* Encourage children to measure the length and the width. Write these measurements on the board. *There are two sides that length* (point to the length), *and two sides that length* (point to the width). *What is the total perimeter?* Look at a square; discuss how you could work out the perimeter quickly. Try other regular polygons.

The children each choose a regular 2-D shape, draw round it and find the perimeter using a ruler.

DIFFERENTIATION

More able: Look at some shapes that have more than one side length, eg trapezium, rhombus. Can they write a formula for the perimeter in words?
Less able: Do a number of squares before moving on to other shapes.

PLENARY

Ask perimeter and length questions, eg *If the perimeter of a square is 28cm, what is the length of each side? If the perimeter of a regular pentagon is 50cm, what is the length of each side?* Discuss the methods used.

LESSON 4 +5

RESOURCES

Numeral cards (one set per child); squared paper; photocopiable page 125.

PREPARATION

Draw a grid of squares on the board (at least 10 × 10).

VOCABULARY

Area, covers, surface, square centimetres (cm²), square metres (m²), square millimetres (mm²).

LEARNING OUTCOMES

ORAL AND MENTAL STARTER
● **Know by heart all multiplication facts up to 10 × 10.**
MAIN TEACHING ACTIVITY
● **Understand area measured in square centimetres (cm²). Understand and use the formula in words 'length × breadth' for the area of a rectangle.**

ORAL AND MENTAL STARTER

NUMERAL CARDS: Children hold up numeral cards in response to quick-fire multiplication questions. Use a range of vocabulary, eg *product of, multiplied by, times, lots of*.

MAIN TEACHING ACTIVITY

INTRODUCTION TO AREA: Tell the children they are going to find out how to find the area of a rectangle. Draw a rectangle 6 × 4 squares on the board. Explain that the area is the surface that is covered by the shape, and that it is measured in units squared: *This rectangle is 6 units long by 4 units wide. To find the area, we can count the squares or we can multiply 6 by 4. There are 4 rows, each with 6 squares in, so there will be 24 units squared altogether.* Count the squares to check. Repeat, asking the children to imagine that the units are centimetres or metres. Do several examples.

Each child draws 10 different rectangles on a sheet of squared paper, then swaps with a partner and finds the area of each of the rectangles.

DIFFERENTIATION

More able: Draw some rectangles that have half squares at the end of a row, eg $5 \times 4^1/_2$. Less able: Start with five rectangles. Provide multiplication squares to support the calculation of the areas, if necessary.

PLENARY

Draw some rectangles on the board. *If we know the area of this rectangle is 28cm², and its length is 7cm, what is its width?*

LESSON 5

For the **Oral and mental starter**, repeat MULTIPLICATION BINGO from Lesson 2, Unit 5. For the **Main teaching activity**, repeat the Plenary of Lesson 4. The children then complete photocopiable page 125. More able children can try shapes with sides to half-centimetres. Less able children can refer to multiplication tables. In the **Plenary**, go over the sheet. Draw a composite shape of two rectangles (see figure right). Discuss how its area might be found.

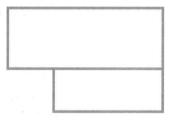

LESSON 6 + 7

RESOURCES

Photocopiable page 126; numeral cards (one set per group); 'follow me' cards (page 67).

PREPARATION

Copy photocopiable page 126. Give out the upper half; keep the lower half for Lesson 7. Copy photocopiable page 67 onto card and cut up for Lesson 7.

LEARNING OUTCOMES

ORAL AND MENTAL STARTER
● Derive quickly or continue to derive quickly division facts corresponding to tables up to 10 × 10.
● **Know by heart all multiplication facts up to 10 × 10.**

VOCABULARY

Area, perimeter, capacity, centimetres squared (cm^2), metres squared (m^2), pints, litres, millilitres, full, empty.

MAIN TEACHING ACTIVITY
● **Use all four operations to solve simple word problems involving numbers and quantities** based on 'real life' and measures, using one or more steps.

ORAL AND MENTAL STARTER

GROUP BINGO: Groups of three or four children pick five numeral cards and place them face up on the table. Ask division facts questions; if a group has the answer, they turn over the card. The first group to turn over all its cards wins.

MAIN TEACHING ACTIVITY

WORD PROBLEMS: Tell the children they are going to look at word problems that focus on measures. Write on the board: *The answer is 500ml.* Ask the children to discuss in pairs what the questions could be. After a couple of minutes, take some ideas and discuss. Repeat for another answer: *The answer is 24cm².* Ask the pairs to write a question involving measures. Take some examples to solve as a class.
The children work through the first half of photocopiable page 126.

DIFFERENTIATION

More able: Write some questions and swap with a partner.
Less able: Work as a group with teacher support.

PLENARY

Look at the questions on the photocopiable sheet (page 126) involving capacity. Work through them and discuss how the answer might be written in litres, millilitres or both (eg $1^1/_2$ litres = 1.5l = 1500ml = 1 litre and 500ml).

LESSON 7

For the **Oral and mental starter**, repeat FOLLOW ME from Lesson 5, Unit 8 of Term 1. Can the class beat its previous best time? For the **Main teaching activity**, extend some questions from Lesson 6 (photocopiable page 126) to two-step problems, eg *3 glasses hold 400ml of water each. How much do they hold altogether? If the glasses are filled from a jug containing 2 litres of milk, how much milk will be left in the jug?* Work through them as a class. The children then work through the second part of page 126. Less able children can continue with one-step problems. In the **Plenary**, go through the problems. Which were the most difficult? Why?

RESOURCES

Squared paper.

PREPARATION

Draw a pair of axes and a table, both labelled with the months of the year and frequency on the board (see figure below).

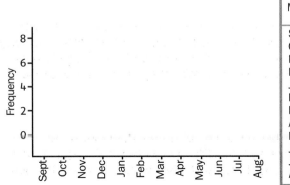

Month	Number of birthdays
Sept	
Oct	
Nov	
Dec	
Jan	
Feb	
Mar	
Apr	
May	
Jun	
Jul	
Aug	

LEARNING OUTCOMES

ORAL AND MENTAL STARTER
● **Know by heart all multiplication facts up to 10 × 10.**
● Derive quickly or continue to derive quickly division facts corresponding to tables up to 10 × 10.

MAIN TEACHING ACTIVITY

● Solve a problem by representing and interpreting data in tables, charts, graphs and diagrams, for example: bar line charts, vertical axis labelled in 2s, 5s, 10s, 20s or 100s.

ORAL AND MENTAL STARTER

FOLLOW ME: As for Lesson 7. Can the children beat their previous best time?

MAIN TEACHING ACTIVITY

BIRTHDAY DATA: Tell the children they are going to collect information to find out when their birthdays are, and whether most of the class will be 10 years old by the end of March. *How could we collect and record this information?* Discuss possibilities. Use a tally chart, asking a child to come up and record the tallies. Discuss how to show this in graph form. Remind the children about labelling axes, and say that the frequency usually goes on the vertical axis. *What would be an appropriate scale on the vertical axis?* (2s, 5s, 10s etc.) Ask individual children to come up and draw some of the bars.

The children make their own bar chart from the data, and use it to work out how many people in the class will be 10 by the end of March.

DIFFERENTIATION

More able: Write some questions that can be answered using the bar chart they have drawn.
Less able: Can complete a chart that has the axes and the first bar drawn.

PLENARY

Discuss what the children's bar charts show.

RESOURCES

Number cards with 1-place decimals between 0.1–0.9 (one set per child); stopwatches; squared paper.

PREPARATION

Make sets of decimal number cards (see above).

LEARNING OUTCOMES

ORAL AND MENTAL STARTER
● Derive quickly or continue to derive quickly decimals that total 1.
MAIN TEACHING ACTIVITY
● Solve a problem by representing and interpreting data in tables, charts, graphs and diagrams, for example: bar line charts, vertical axis labelled in 2s, 5s, 10s, 20s or 100s.
● Find the mode of a set of data.

ORAL AND MENTAL STARTER

SPEED PAIRS: The children work in pairs, one with a stopwatch and one with two sets of decimal cards shuffled together. The first child times the second: How many cards can they turn over, saying what must be added to each to make 1, in a minute? (So if they turn over 0.6, they say 0.4.) The child with the stopwatch keeps a tally. They swap roles and repeat.

MAIN TEACHING ACTIVITY

MOST COMMON RESULT: Tell the children they are going to use the data they have collected to find out the most common score and the difference between the highest and lowest scores. Ask a child to scribe on the board; ask each child in turn for his or her best

VOCABULARY

Count, tally, sort, data, graph, represent, chart, bar chart, tally chart, table, frequency table, label, title, axis, axes.

VOCABULARY

Count, tally, sort, data, graph, represent, chart, bar chart, tally chart, table, frequency table, label, title, axis, axes, most common, range, mode.

LESSON 9

score in 'Speed pairs'. Tell the children they are going to find the mode of this set of data (*the mode is the most common value*) and the range (*the range is the difference between the highest and lowest scores*). Discuss how they might do this, eg count up the number of children who had each best score and write down the frequency – how often that best score comes up.

Ask the children to group their data (see below) and display it in graph form.

DIFFERENTIATION

More able: Decide how to label the vertical axis (in 2s, 5s, 10s etc). They could go on to find the mode and range of the worst scores.
Less able: Label the vertical axis with teacher guidance.

PLENARY

Look at a graph of the data. *Which bar shows the mode? What is the range?* Look at other sets of data to determine the mode and range.

LESSON 10

LEARNING OUTCOMES	**ORAL AND MENTAL STARTER** ● Derive quickly or continue to derive quickly: pairs of multiples of 50 with a total of 1000. **MAIN TEACHING ACTIVITY** ● Solve a problem by representing and interpreting data in tables, charts, graphs and diagrams. ● Find the mode of a set of data.
RESOURCES	String, pegs, large number cards with multiples of 50 on.
ORAL AND MENTAL STARTER	PAIRS TO MAKE 1000: Hang up the string to make a number line. Peg 0 at one end and 1000 at the other. Show a number card to the class. *Where should it go on the line?* Ask a child to peg it up. Use this to help work out how many more it is to 1000.
MAIN TEACHING ACTIVITY	FINDING THE MODE: Tell the children they are going to collect their own data and find the mode. Discuss appropriate data to collect (eg shoe size, hand span), then let the children work in groups.
DIFFERENTIATION	Differentiate by outcome.
PLENARY	Discuss the data collected and what it shows.

Missing side

Find the length of each missing side.

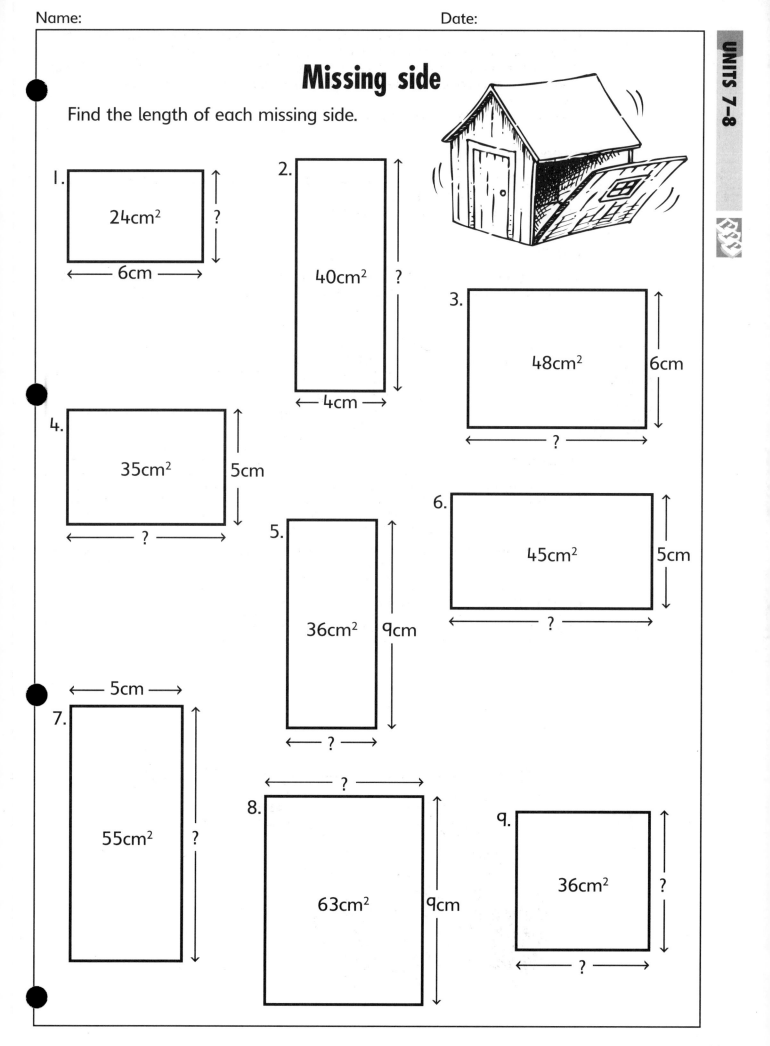

1.
24cm² ?
← 6cm →

2.
40cm² ?
← 4cm →

3.
48cm² 6cm
← ? →

4.
35cm² 5cm
← ? →

5.
36cm² 9cm
← ? →

6.
45cm² 5cm
← ? →

7.
← 5cm →
55cm² ?

8.
← ? →
63cm² 9cm

9.
36cm² ?
← ? →

Measurement problems

One-step problems

1. Find the area of a room 3 metres long and $2\frac{1}{2}$ metres wide.

2. A bottle contains one litre of lemonade. 350ml is poured into a glass. How much is left in the bottle?

3. Sally needs 15 litres of paint to decorate the outside of her house. One tin of paint contains $1\frac{1}{2}$ litres. How many cans of this size will she need to paint the house?

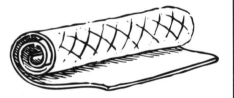

4. A school playground is 100 metres long and has an area of 6000m². What is its width?

5. A car takes 30 litres of petrol. A lorry holds 120 litres of petrol. How many times could the car be filled using the petrol in the lorry?

6. A litre of orange squash needs 4 litres of water to dilute it. How many litres of water would be needed to dilute $3\frac{1}{2}$ litres of orange squash?

Two-step problems

1. Carpet costs £10 per square metre. How much would it cost to carpet a floor 6m long and 4m wide?

2. A jug holds $1\frac{1}{2}$ litres of water. 8 such jugs are filled from a barrel that contains 20 litres of water. How much water is left in the barrel?

3. Maria wants to tile the floor in her kitchen and dining room. Her kitchen is 3 metres by 4 metres, and her dining room is $3\frac{1}{2}$ metres by 4 metres. What is the total area of the floor that needs to be tiled?

4. A car runs on unleaded petrol, which costs 70p a litre. It takes 40 litres of petrol to fill the car's tank. John hands over £30 to the garage attendant. Is this enough money? Explain your answer.

UNITS 9-10

ORGANISATION (10 LESSONS)

	LEARNING OUTCOMES	ORAL AND MENTAL STARTER	MAIN TEACHING ACTIVITY	PLENARY
LESSON 1	• Add several numbers (eg multiples of 10 such as 40 + 50 + 80). • Check the sum of several numbers by adding in the reverse order.	+ AND – GAME: Hold up number cards to answer questions.	MULTIPLES OF 10: Add several multiples of 10 mentally.	Extend to adding multiples of 100.
LESSON 2	• Add or subtract the nearest multiple of 10, then adjust. • Check with an equivalent calculation.	THE NEXT TEN: Make a number up to the next ten.	ROUND AND ADJUST: Add or subtract near-multiples of 10.	Extend to adding or subtracting near-multiples of 100.
LESSON 3 + 4	• Partition into H, T and U, adding the most significant digits first. • Use informal pencil and paper methods to support, record or explain additions and subtractions. **Extend written methods to: column addition of two integers less than 10 000;** addition of more than two integers less than 10 000.	ADDING 2-DIGIT NUMBERS: Use numeral cards to show answers. APPROXIMATE ANSWER: Select numbers to make an approximate total.	ADDING LARGE NUMBERS: Use an informal written method for adding 3- or 4-digit numbers. Column addition of several 4-digit numbers.	Lead into the standard written method. Give approximate answers to 4-digit additions.
LESSON 5	• Extend written methods to addition of a pair of decimal fractions, both with one or both with two decimal places. • Use informal pencil and paper methods to support, record or explain additions and subtractions.	PAIRS TO MAKE 10: Generate pairs of decimal numbers to total 10.	ADDING DECIMALS: Use an informal written method to add decimal numbers.	Check using a calculator.
LESSON 6	• Use informal pencil and paper methods to support, record or explain additions and subtractions. • Check with the inverse operation when using a calculator.	PAIRS TO 100 BINGO: Crossing off answers to subtraction questions.	NUMBER LINE DIFFERENCE: Find the difference between two numbers, using a blank number line. Check with a calculator.	Use estimation and knowledge of odd/even numbers to judge whether a subtraction may be correct.
LESSON 7 + 8	• Use informal pencil and paper methods to support, record or explain additions and subtractions. **Extend written methods to column subtraction of two integers less than 10 000.** • Check with the inverse operation when using a calculator.	SUBTRACTION FROM TENS: Subtract from multiples of 10 to make a target number. APPROXIMATE DIFFERENCE: Select numbers with a given approximate difference.	WRITTEN SUBTRACTION: Develop a written method with partitioning. Use the standard written method (decomposition).	Lead into the standard written method. Explain the method.
LESSON 9	• Use informal pencil and paper methods to support, record or explain additions and subtractions. Extend written methods to subtraction of a pair of decimal fractions, both with one or both with two decimal places. • Check with the inverse operation when using a calculator.	PAIRS TO MAKE 10: Generate decimal numbers to total 10.	SUBTRACTION OF DECIMALS: Use informal and standard written methods. Check using calculator.	Talk through any difficulties.

LEARNING OUTCOMES		ORAL & MENTAL STARTER	MAIN TEACHING ACTIVITY	PLENARY
LESSON 10	● **Use all four operations to solve simple word problems involving numbers and quantities** based on 'real life' and money, using one or more steps. **Explain methods and reasoning.** ● Choose and use appropriate number operations to solve problems, and appropriate ways of calculating: mental, mental with jottings, written methods, calculator.	WHAT IS THE QUESTION? Combine given numbers, using any operations, to make target numbers.	WORD PROBLEMS: Solve problems in pairs. Explain methods.	Talk through methods and any difficulties.

ORAL AND MENTAL SKILLS: Know by heart addition and subtraction facts for all numbers to 20 (Year 4 revision). Use known number facts and place value for mental addition and subtraction. Estimate by approximating (rounding to the nearest 10 or 100), then check result. Derive quickly or continue to derive quickly: decimals that total 10; all two-digit pairs that total 100. Choose and use appropriate number operations to solve problems.

Lessons 1–3, 6, 7 and 9 are shown in detail. Lessons 4, 5, 8 and 10 follow on from what has already been taught.

LESSON 1

RESOURCES

Number cards 1–20 (one set per pair of children); multiples of 10 cards (see below); numeral cards (one set per child).

PREPARATION

Write the multiples of 10 (from 10–100) on cards (playing card size).

LEARNING OUTCOMES

ORAL AND MENTAL STARTER
● Know by heart addition and subtraction facts for all numbers to 20.

MAIN TEACHING ACTIVITY
● Add several numbers (eg multiples of 10, such as 40 + 50 + 80).
● Check the sum of several numbers by adding in the reverse order.

ORAL AND MENTAL STARTER

+ AND – GAME: Ask each pair of children to choose any six cards from their set of number cards 1–20. Set problems; the children respond using the cards they have. Eg *Hold up three cards that have a total of 20... three cards that have a sum of more than 20... two cards that have a difference of 5.* For each one they can do, they get a counter. The first pair to collect five counters wins.

MAIN TEACHING ACTIVITY

MULTIPLES OF 10: Tell the children they are going to add three or more multiples of 10. *What is a multiple of 10? What will it always end in?* Ask three children for a multiple of 10 and write them on the board. Ask the children to add them up and discuss strategies with their partner. Take feedback; look for strategies such as pairs that make 100 or starting with the largest number.

Shuffle the multiple of 10 cards and ask a child to pick a card. Repeat twice. Stick the cards on the board with addition signs between to form a number sentence, eg 60 + 20 + 40 =. Ask for the answer and a method. Swap the cards around. *What will the answer be now? Why? Because when you add numbers, the order doesn't matter.* Repeat with four multiples of 10.

The children pick three numeral cards to generate multiples of 10 (eg if they pick 3, 4, 5, the number sentence will be 30 + 40 + 50 =). How many can they do in a given time?

DIFFERENTIATION

More able: Add a higher number of multiples of 10 as appropriate.
Less able: Work with the teacher. Given a multiple of 10, say how much more is needed to make 100. Then add three 2-digit multiples of 10 (including a pair of numbers that make 100) to complete number sentences written by the teacher.

PLENARY

Write some 3-digit multiples of 100, eg 600 + 400 + 300 =. *How can we use what we have learnt to help us find the total of these multiples of 100?*

LESSON 2

RESOURCES

Sets of 2-digit number cards; photocopiable page 135.

PREPARATION

Separate the 2-digit number cards into 30–50, 51–70 and 71–99.

VOCABULARY
Add, subtract, nearest, round, multiple of 10, next ten, after.

LEARNING OUTCOMES

ORAL AND MENTAL STARTER
● Know by heart addition and subtraction facts for all numbers to 20.
MAIN TEACHING ACTIVITY
● Add or subtract the nearest multiple of 10, then adjust.
● Check with an equivalent calculation.

ORAL AND MENTAL STARTER

THE NEXT TEN: Give the class a 2- or 3-digit number. They respond by saying how many there are to the next ten (eg for 37, the answer is '3'). Discuss their methods.

MAIN TEACHING ACTIVITY

ROUND AND ADJUST: Tell the children they are going to add or subtract a 2-digit number to or from another number by rounding it to the nearest multiple of 10, then adjusting. Write 36 + 29 = on the board. Ask the children how they would do this. Encourage the response: 'Add 30 and subtract 1.' Work through the example and check using an equivalent calculation, eg add 20 and add 9. Repeat with 46 + 38 = and the subtractions 67 – 49 = and 73 – 37 =.

The children each pick a card from the set numbered 51–70, and write the number in the space provided on photocopiable page 135; then they answer each question.

DIFFERENTIATION

More able: Use cards 71–99 to bridge 100 with additions.
Less able: Use cards 30–50 to avoid bridging 100.

PLENARY

Work through some examples and equivalent calculations. Then do some examples using near-multiples of 100, eg 236 + 99 = or 257 – 98 =. Discuss strategies.

LESSON 3 +4

RESOURCES

A pack of 2-digit number cards; numeral cards (one set per pair of children).

PREPARATION

Make sure each pair of children have a set of numeral cards.

LEARNING OUTCOMES

ORAL AND MENTAL STARTER
● Use known number facts and place value for mental addition.
● Estimate by approximating (rounding to the nearest 10 or 100), then check result.
MAIN TEACHING ACTIVITY
● Partition into H, T and U, adding the most significant digits first.

VOCABULARY

Add, total, sum, thousands, hundreds, tens, units, 3-digit number, 4-digit number.

● Use informal pencil and paper methods to support, record or explain additions and subtractions. **Extend written methods to: column addition of two integers less than 10 000;** addition of more than two integers less than 10 000.

ORAL AND MENTAL STARTER

ADDING 2-DIGIT NUMBERS: Ask a child to choose two 2-digit number cards from the pack. Write the numbers on the board to form a number sentence, eg 28 + 34 =. Ask pairs of children to find the answer together, discussing how they did it – then, when you say *Go!*, they hold up their answer. Repeat several times.

MAIN TEACHING ACTIVITY

ADDING LARGE NUMBERS: Tell the children they are going to add 3-digit and 4-digit numbers, using pencil and paper when they need to. Ask two children for a 3-digit number. Write them on the board to form a number sentence, eg 267 + 156 =. Read this together. Tell the children they need to add the hundreds first: *200 add 100 is? 300*. Say that you are going to write 300 down to remember it. Repeat with the tens and units, so the addition reads: 267 + 156 = 300 + 110 + 13 =. Ask the children to talk to their partners about what the answer might be. Take an answer. Repeat with another pair of 3-digit numbers, then with pairs of 4-digit numbers.

The children work in pairs, generating additions by picking numeral cards. When they have done several 3-digit number examples, they can go on to 4-digit numbers.

DIFFERENTIATION

More able: Start with 4-digit numbers.
Less able: Start with 2-digit numbers, then go on to 3-digit multiples of 10.

PLENARY

Write an addition down in column form (see figure below). Say that you are going to add the units first. *5 and 8 is 13.* Write the '1' ten under the tens column. *30 and 60 is 90 and another 10 is 100.* Write the '1' hundred under the hundreds column. *400 and 200 and the extra 100 is 700.* Repeat with another example, stressing the value of the digits when adding them, eg *30 and 60 make 90,* not *3 and 6 make 9* for the numbers in the tens column:

$$
\begin{array}{r}
435 \\
+ \ 268 \\
\hline
\end{array}
$$

LESSON 4

For the **Oral and mental starter**, play APPROXIMATE ANSWER: Ask the children for 3-digit numbers; write ten suggestions on the board. The children find three that add together to give a total of about 1000. Repeat with other approximate totals, then differences. For the **Main teaching activity**, revise the Plenary of Lesson 3. The children use numeral cards to generate examples for practise. More able children can concentrate on 4-digit numbers, while less able can start with 2-digit addition, and move on to 3-digit addition with help. In the **Plenary**, write some 4-digit additions on the board; ask for quick answers to the nearest 1000 and 100.

LESSON 5

LEARNING OUTCOMES	**ORAL AND MENTAL STARTER** ● Derive quickly or continue to derive quickly: decimals that total 10. **MAIN TEACHING ACTIVITY** ● Extend written methods to addition of a pair of decimal fractions, both with one or both with two decimal places. ● Use informal pencil and paper methods to support, record or explain additions and subtractions.
RESOURCES	1-place decimal number cards between 0 and 10, eg 6.4, 7.2; calculators.
ORAL AND MENTAL STARTER	PAIRS TO MAKE 10: Hold up a decimal card. Ask class or groups to say together how many to the next whole number, eg 6.4 = '0.6'. Repeat several times. Then to say how many to make ten, eg 7.2 = '2.8'. Repeat several times.
MAIN TEACHING ACTIVITY	ADDING DECIMALS: Write two 1-place decimals on the board, eg 5.7 and 3.8. Ask for an approximate total. Read the number sentence. *How many units altogether? 8. How many tenths? 15. 15 tenths is 1 unit and 5 tenths, so the answer is 9.5 or 9 and 5 tenths.* Repeat several times, stressing the value of each digit according to its position. Do some examples.
DIFFERENTIATION	More able: Move on to 2-place decimals, with initial teacher guidance. Less able: Start with 1-place decimals <1, eg 0.5 + 0.6 Use pictorial representations to help.
PLENARY	Check answers using a calculator; encourage the children to read the display aloud.

LESSON 6

RESOURCES

Numeral cards (one set per child); paper; calculators.

PREPARATION

Draw a blank number line on the board. Write some 2-digit numbers elsewhere on the board, eg 34, 44, 54, 27, 37, 47, 57, 36, 46, 56, 23, 33, 43, 53.

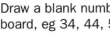

VOCABULARY

Subtract, take away, count up, difference, next ten, next hundred, how many more to, larger

LEARNING OUTCOMES

ORAL AND MENTAL STARTER
● Derive quickly or continue to derive quickly two-digit pairs that total 100.
MAIN TEACHING ACTIVITY
● Use informal pencil and paper methods to support, record or explain additions and subtractions.
● Check with the inverse operation when using a calculator.

ORAL AND MENTAL STARTER

PAIRS TO 100 BINGO: Ask the children to write five of the 2-digit numbers from the board on a piece of paper. Explain to the children that you are going to say a number; they must work out how much would be left if the number said were taken away/subtracted from 100. If they have that number on their paper, they can cross it out. Continue saying numbers and discussing methods until someone has crossed out all his or her numbers.

MAIN TEACHING ACTIVITY

NUMBER LINE DIFFERENCE: Tell the children that they are going to subtract one number from another by finding the difference between them. Point to the blank number line. Write 180 at one end and 230 at the other. *To find the difference between these two numbers, we are going to count up first to the next hundred and then beyond. What is the next hundred after 180? 200.* Write 200 on the number line:

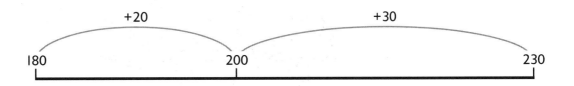

Ask: *How many from 180 to 200? 20.* Write +20 above the number line as shown. *How many from 200 to 230? 30.* Write +30 above the number. *What's the difference between 180 and 230 altogether? 20 add 30 is 50, so the difference is 50 altogether.* Repeat the process with other pairs of numbers, eg 275 and 346, 257 and 362. Each time, count to the next ten and then the next hundred.

Working in pairs, the children generate pairs of 3-digit numbers using numeral cards. Where possible, they should put consecutive digits in the hundreds column; for instance, if the numbers chosen are 2, 5, 6, 3, 8, 1, they can put 256 – 183 or 638 – 521, so they do not have to bridge a second hundred. They should find the difference between the numbers, using a blank number line to show the process, then check using a calculator.

DIFFERENTIATION

More able: Work with 4-digit numbers, finding the next ten, hundred and thousand.
Less able: Work with 3-digit multiples of 10.

PLENARY

Write some 3-digit subtractions horizontally on the board, with answers. The children work in pairs to decide which answers may be correct and which cannot be. Discuss how they know. Encourage the use of estimation and differences between odd and even numbers.

LESSON 7 + 8

RESOURCES

Calculators, textbooks or worksheets with 3-digit subtractions.

PREPARATION

Write some 3-digit subtractions vertically on the board, eg

269	354	283	438
– 146	– 238	– 192	– 353

LEARNING OUTCOMES

ORAL AND MENTAL STARTER
● Use known number facts and place value for mental subtraction.
● Estimate by approximating (round to the nearest 10 or 100), then check result.
MAIN TEACHING ACTIVITY
● Use informal pencil and paper methods to support, record or explain additions and subtractions. **Extend written methods to column subtraction of two integers less than 10 000.**
● Check with the inverse operation when using a calculator.

VOCABULARY

Subtract, take away, count up, difference, partitioning, multiples, inverse.

ORAL AND MENTAL STARTER

SUBTRACTION FROM TENS: Ask the children to work with a partner, writing down as many subtractions from a 2-digit multiple of 10 that have an answer of 19 or 21 as possible (eg 90 – 71, 80 – 59). After about 2 minutes, brainstorm possibilities and discuss patterns.

MAIN TEACHING ACTIVITY

WRITTEN SUBTRACTION: Tell the children they are going to subtract a 3-digit number from another 3-digit number using a written method based on partitioning. Look at the first question on the board and read it together: *269 subtract 146.* Write next to the subtraction the numbers partitioned into hundreds, tens and units:

$$
\begin{array}{rcrcccc}
269 & = & 200 & + & 60 & + & 9 \\
- 146 & - & 100 & + & 40 & + & 6 \\
\hline
 & & 100 & + & 20 & + & 3 \\
\end{array}
$$

Calculate answers and recombine: 123.

Repeat with the next subtraction, this time encouraging the children to partition the numbers:

$$354 = 300 + 50 + 4$$
$$238 = 200 + 30 + 8$$

Say that instead of using negative numbers, which will happen if 8 is subtracted from 4, it is easier to partition 354 into 300 + 40 + 14 (*three hundred and forty fourteen*): still the same number, but partitioned in a different way. Calculate the answer and recombine. Repeat with the other two subtractions.

The children work through some examples from a textbook or worksheet.

DIFFERENTIATION

Less able: Work initially with 2-digit numbers.
More able: Do examples which require exchanging from two columns – hundreds to tens, tens to units.

PLENARY

Explain how to check using the inverse operation on a calculator: add the answer to the number that was taken away (the smaller number). *Do you get the number you started with?* The children can check some of their answers.

Introduce the standard written method for subtraction (decomposition). Explain using one of the previous examples, eg 354 – 238. Explain that the method is the same as before, just written in a shorter form. The number at the top is still changed into *three hundred and forty fourteen.*

LESSON 8

For the **Oral and mental starter**, APPROXIMATE DIFFERENCE, ask the children for 3-digit numbers; write ten suggestions on the board. The children find two numbers that have a difference of about 200, 350 etc. Discuss methods. For the **Main teaching activity**, go through several subtractions using the standard written method (decomposition); make connections with the expanded written method of Lesson 7, and make sure the value of the digits is clear when the numbers are read out. The children work through some other examples from textbooks. More able children can work with 4-digit numbers, less able children with 2-digit numbers. In the **Plenary**, ask children to come up and talk through a subtraction they have done, explaining their method.

RESOURCES

Numeral cards (one set per pair); photocopiable page 136.

PREPARATION

Give each pair of children a set of numeral cards. Write some decimal subtractions on the board, eg

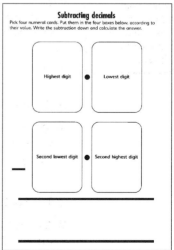

3.4	4.2	6.73	3.24
– 1.6	– 2.7	– 3.92	– 2.18

LEARNING OUTCOMES

ORAL AND MENTAL STARTER
● Derive quickly or continue to derive quickly decimals that total 10.

MAIN TEACHING ACTIVITY
● Use informal pencil and paper methods to support, record or explain additions and subtractions. Extend written methods to subtraction of a pair of decimal fractions, both with one or both with two decimal places.
● Check with the inverse operation when using a calculator.

ORAL AND MENTAL STARTER

PAIRS TO MAKE 10: Tell the children you are going to say a decimal number, and they have to say how much more needs to be added to make 10. Start with simple number (eg 4.0) and go on to more difficult ones, eg 7.5, 9.2. They respond as a class. Give particular groups some examples for them to respond to as a group. Discuss methods.

MAIN TEACHING ACTIVITY

SUBTRACTION OF DECIMALS: Work through the examples on the board, asking the class to read out each question first. Do the first one using the expanded written method (partitioning) first, as in Lesson 6. Then work through the same example using decomposition, making links with the expanded written method. Work through each problem as a class, asking children to tell you what to do next and why.

Show the children how to use photocopiable page 136 to generate questions, putting numeral cards in the places shown. The children work in pairs to generate and work out subtractions. When they have done 10 questions, they can swap with a partner and check with a calculator using inverse operations.

DIFFERENTIATION

More able: Use the space at the bottom of page 136 to answer questions without using the written method, with teacher guidance.
Less able: Use the expanded written layout initially.

PLENARY

Go over any difficulties or misconceptions. Stress the importance of reading numbers and making estimates.

LESSON 10

LEARNING OUTCOMES	**ORAL AND MENTAL STARTER** ● Choose and use appropriate number operations to solve problems. **MAIN TEACHING ACTIVITY** ● **Use all four operations to solve simple word problems involving numbers and quantities** based on 'real life' and money, using one or more steps. **Explain methods and reasoning.** ● Choose and use appropriate number operations to solve problems, and appropriate ways of calculating; mental, mental with jottings, written methods, calculator.
RESOURCES	Some prepared word problems.
ORAL AND MENTAL STARTER	WHAT IS THE QUESTION? Write four single-digit numbers, two 2-digit numbers, and some 2- and 3-digit numbers that can be made using those numbers on the board. In pairs or threes, the children work out how to make the answers using the numbers available and any operations. Discuss their methods.
MAIN TEACHING ACTIVITY	WORD PROBLEMS: Write three or four number problems involving 'real-life' contexts or money on the board. Read through them together. Discuss what operations are needed. The children work in pairs, writing down a method and solution. Work through each problem as a class, giving pupils opportunities to come to the board and explain. The children work through more examples.
DIFFERENTIATION	More able: Do two-step problems. Less able: Only do one-step problems.
PLENARY	Discuss which problems the children found most difficult and why. Encourage children to come up and talk through how they found solutions, jotting on the board to show their workings.

Add or subtract near multiples of 10

Pick a 2-digit number card and write the number in the first space in the number sentence, then calculate the answer.

1. _____ + 19 = _____   2. _____ – 9 = _____

3. _____ + 19 = _____   4. _____ – 19 = _____

5. _____ + 18 = _____   6. _____ – 8 = _____

7. _____ + 21 = _____   8. _____ – 18 = _____

9. _____ + 29 = _____   10. _____ – 11 = _____

11. _____ + 28 = _____   12. _____ – 19 = _____

13. _____ + 31 = _____   14. _____ – 17 = _____

15. _____ + 39 = _____   16. _____ – 18 = _____

17. _____ + 32 = _____   18. _____ – 21 = _____

19. _____ + 38 = _____   20. _____ – 27 = _____

21. _____ + 37 = _____   22. _____ – 28 = _____

Subtracting decimals

Pick four numeral cards. Put them in the four boxes below, according to their value. Write the subtraction down and calculate the answer.

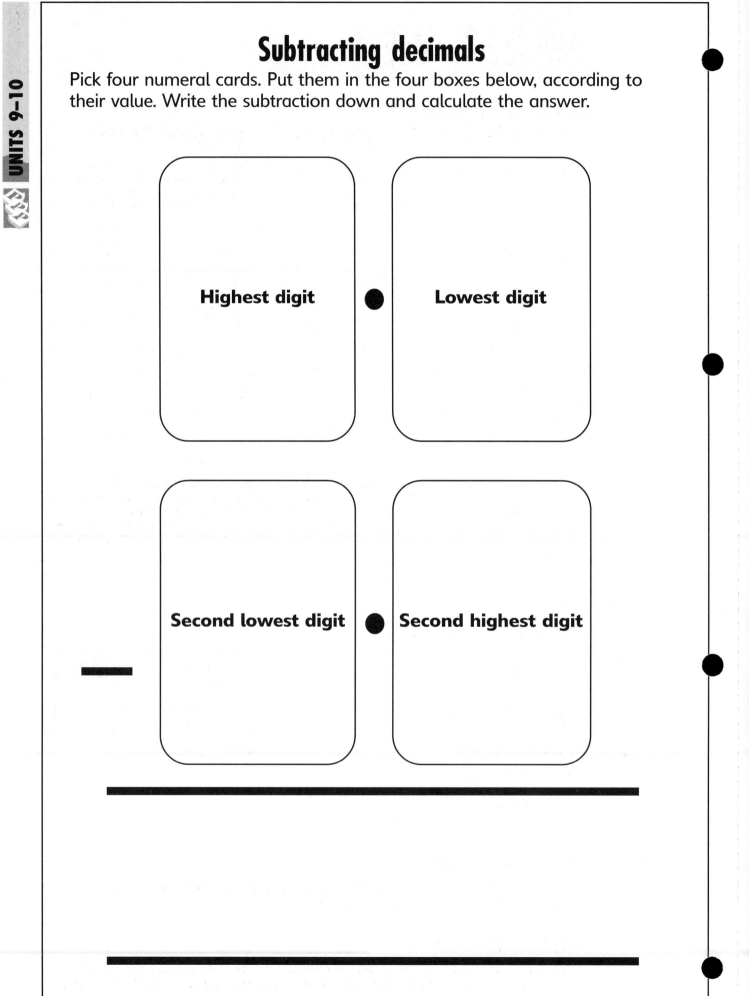

Highest digit

Lowest digit

Second lowest digit

Second highest digit

UNIT 11

ORGANISATION (5 LESSONS)

	LEARNING OUTCOMES	ORAL AND MENTAL STARTER	MAIN TEACHING ACTIVITY	PLENARY
LESSON 1	● Know squares of numbers to at least 10 × 10.	NUMERAL CARDS: Hold up answers to multiplication fact questions.	SQUARE NUMBERS: Draw squares to represent square numbers.	Look at larger square numbers, including squares of multiples of 10.
LESSON 2 +3	● Know and apply tests of divisibility by 2, 4, 5, 10 or 100. ● Explain methods and reasoning, orally and in writing. ● Make and investigate a general statement about familiar numbers by finding examples that satisfy it; explain a generalised relationship in words.	COUNTING IN MULTIPLES: Chant multiples, then answer quick questions about the 2, 4, 5 and 10 times tables. STAND UP: Repeat from the Plenary of Lesson 2.	RULES OF DIVISIBILITY: Play a divisibility game using 2-digit numbers. Investigate divisibility of 3-digit numbers by integers to 10.	Identify given numbers as divisible by 2, 4, 5 or 10. Check findings using divisibility tests.
LESSON 4 +5	● Recognise multiples of 6, 7, 8, 9 up to the 10th multiple. ● Solve mathematical problems or puzzles, recognise and explain patterns and relationships, generalise and predict.	GROUP COUNTING: Count up and down in steps of 6, 7, 8 and 9.	INVESTIGATE MULTIPLES: Look for patterns in multiples of 4, 5, 6, 7, 8, 9. Find out which numbers have the most factors.	Discuss patterns in the multiples. Discuss findings.

ORAL AND MENTAL SKILLS: Know by heart: multiplication facts up to 10 × 10. Know and apply tests of divisibility by 2, 4, 5, 10 or 100. Recognise and extend number sequences formed by counting from any number in steps of constant size. Recognise multiples of 6, 7, 8, 9 up to the 10th multiple.

Lessons 1, 2 and 4 are shown in detail. Lessons 3 and 5 follow on from what has already been taught.

RESOURCES

Interlocking cubes; squared paper.

PREPARATION

Draw a table on the board (see figure right). Leave it blank apart from the headings.

Rows	Columns	Number squared
1	1	1
2	2	4

LEARNING OUTCOMES

ORAL AND MENTAL STARTER
● **Know by heart: multiplication facts up to 10 × 10.**
MAIN TEACHING ACTIVITY
● Know squares of numbers to at least 10 × 10.

VOCABULARY

Square number, squared, multiplied, rows, columns.

ORAL AND MENTAL STARTER

NUMERAL CARDS: Ask quick-fire multiplication facts questions. The children hold up numeral cards to answer. Discuss different methods.

MAIN TEACHING ACTIVITY

SQUARE NUMBERS: Hold up one cube. *We are going to look at square numbers. This is a square number: it has 1 row and 1 column, and is made up of a total of 1 cube.* Fill in the first row of the table on the board (as shown on page 137). Take four interlocking cubes to make a square. Hold it up and say: *2 rows and 2 columns make 4 cubes altogether.* Fill in the second row. *How many cubes do you think there will be in the next square number?* Take a range of answers. *Why do you think 9? Because 3 × 3 is 9.* Ask a child to come up and fill in that row of the table, and to draw a 3 × 3 square on the board.

The children fill in the table to 10 × 10 in their books, and draw squares to represent each square number (eg a 4 × 4 square with 16 written in it).

DIFFERENTIATION

More able: Those who complete the table can investigate the pattern in the difference between successive square numbers (it goes up in steps of consecutive odd numbers). Less able: Use interlocking cubes to build up square numbers.

PLENARY

Complete the rest of the table as a class. The children should check the results against their own answers. Go on to look at larger square numbers (multiples of 10), for example 20 × 20 or 50 × 50.

LESSON 2 +3

RESOURCES

10-sided dice; photocopiable page 141; numeral cards (one set per child).

PREPARATION

Make enough copies of photocopiable page 141 – part A for core, part B for less able. Draw two tables like the one shown below on the board.

Divisible by 2	Divisible by 4	Divisible by 5	Divisible by 10

LEARNING OUTCOMES

ORAL AND MENTAL STARTER
● **Know by heart: multiplication facts up to 10 × 10.**
● Recognise and extend number sequences formed by counting from any number in steps of constant size.
● Know and apply tests of divisibility by 2, 4, 5, 10 or 100.

MAIN TEACHING ACTIVITY
● Know and apply tests of divisibility by 2, 4, 5, 10 or 100.
● Explain methods and reasoning, orally and in writing.
● Make and investigate a general statement about familiar numbers by finding examples that satisfy it; explain a generalised relationship in words.

ORAL AND MENTAL STARTER

COUNTING IN MULTIPLES: Count up and back down in multiples of 2, 4, 5 and 10 as a class. After each set of multiples, ask questions relating to that times table, eg *How many 2s make 12? What are 5 fours?* Aim questions at particular groups or individuals.

MAIN TEACHING ACTIVITY

RULES OF DIVISIBILITY: Tell the children they are going to find out how to recognise whether a number is divisible by another number. *If a number is divisible by 2, it means 2 can go into it exactly, leaving no remainder.* Ask the class to chant in twos again; as they chant, write the numbers on the board up to the 10th multiple. *What do you notice about those numbers? They are even: they all end in 0, 2, 4, 6 or 8.* Ask for other examples of multiples of 2. Repeat the process for numbers divisible by 5, 10 and 4. *What do you notice about numbers divisible by 5? They all end in 5 or 0. What do you notice about numbers divisible by 10? They all end in 0. What do you notice about numbers divisible by 4? They are all even, and if you halve the number you will still get an even number.*

Look at the tables on the board. Tell the children they are going to play a game against you. *I am going to roll two 10-sided dice and make a number that fits into one of these columns. For example, if I rolled 1, 6, I could make 16 or 61. Which columns could I put 16 in? Divisible by 2 or by 4. I am going to put it in the divisible by 4 column, because fewer numbers are divisible by 4.* Give the dice to a child to roll; the class decide what number to make and where to put it on the grid on the board. Repeat several times, with you and the class each taking turns.

When the children are clear, set them off on the task. They work in pairs with a grid each (see page 141), taking turns to generate a 2-digit number using two 10-sided dice and writing it in their grid. If they have filled up a column or can't put a number anywhere, they miss a go. The first child to complete the grid wins.

DIFFERENTIATION

More able: Roll 3-digit numbers and decide where they should go.
Less able: Use the grid in Part B of the sheet to look at numbers divisible by 2, 5 or 10.

PLENARY

Give each table a number: 2, 4, 5 or 10. Ask the children to stand up if you say a number which is divisible by their number. Start with random numbers, then count up in ones. Discuss why the twos are standing up a lot. *Which numbers will everyone stand up for? 20, 40, 60 etc. How would we recognise a number divisible by 100?*

LESSON 3

For the **Oral and mental starter**, STAND UP, repeat from the Plenary of Lesson 2. For the **Main teaching activity**, recap Lesson 2. The children then pick 3-digit numbers using numeral cards and investigate which of them are divisible by 2, 4, 5, 10 or 100, using a calculator to check. Less able children can focus on numbers divisible by 2, 5 or 10, more able children on numbers divisible by 3, 6, 7, 8, 9 and 100. In the **Plenary**, discuss the results. *Which number was divisible by the most numbers?* Check using divisibility tests.

LESSON 4 + 5

RESOURCES

A hundred square (1–100) per child; a large laminated hundred square and dry-wipe marker. For Lesson 5, you will also need interlocking cubes in several colours; hundred squares (one per pair) with spaces large enough to put cubes on; numeral cards (one set per child); 2-digit number cards.

PREPARATION

Write multiples of 4 and 5 on the board up to the 10th multiple. Display the large 100 square at child height. For Lesson 5, circle all the multiples of 2 on the large hundred square. Ask the children to spread out the 6, 7, 8 and 9 numeral cards on the table in front of them.

VOCABULARY
Multiple, divisible, count, investigate, pattern.

LEARNING OUTCOMES

ORAL AND MENTAL STARTER
● Recognise and extend number sequences formed by counting from any number in steps of constant size.
MAIN TEACHING ACTIVITY
● Recognise multiples of 6, 7, 8, 9 up to the 10th multiple.
● Solve mathematical problems or puzzles, recognise and explain patterns and relationships, generalise and predict.

ORAL AND MENTAL STARTER

GROUP COUNTING: Tell the children they are going to count up in sixes. Start as a class, then point to particular groups. Say that if you clap your hands, the count will change direction and go down in sixes. Repeat with counts of sevens, eights and nines, starting from 0 each time.

MAIN TEACHING ACTIVITY

INVESTIGATE MULTIPLES: Look at patterns in the multiples of 4 and 5, eg the units in multiples of 5 alternating between 0 and 5; the units in multiples of 4 going up as 4, 8, 2, 6, 0, 4, 8 etc. Ask children to come and circle numbers on the large hundred square that are multiples of 4. *Do they make a pattern?*

The children look at patterns in multiples of 6, 7, 8 and 9, first without using their 100 squares and then looking at the patterns formed on them. Help them to look for patterns in number before they use the squares.

DIFFERENTIATION

More able: Write a description of each pattern found.
Less able: Go straight to looking for patterns on the hundred square.

PLENARY

Discuss the patterns found in the multiples of each number.

LESSON 5

For the **Oral and mental starter**, repeat GROUP COUNTING from Lesson 4. For the **Main teaching activity**, extend Lesson 4: point to the large hundred square with the multiples of 2 circled. Say that you are going to circle the multiples of 3 in a different colour. *Which numbers should I circle? Which numbers are multiples of both 2 and 3? Which other number are they multiples of?* The children work in pairs to find out which numbers are multiples of the most numbers (have the most factors), using hundred grids and interlocking cubes (use a different colour for each factor from 2 to 10). More able children can mark numbers on a hundred grid and decide on their own key. Less able children can use counters of different colours for different multiples, eg red for 2s and green for 3s, then determine which numbers have the most counters on. In the **Plenary**, look at the hundred grids with cubes on. Discuss which numbers have the most cubes, which have no cubes, and why.

Name: _____ Date: _____

Divisibility games

Game 1

Make sure you and your partner have a grid each. Roll the dice to generate a number (either 2- or 3-digit). Can you write the number in one of the columns? Take turns until one of you has completed the grid. If you can't write your number in the grid, miss a turn.

Divisible by 2	Divisible by 4	Divisible by 5	Divisible by 10

Game 2

Make sure you and your partner have a grid each. Roll the dice to generate a 2-digit number. Can you write the number in one of the columns? Take turns until one of you has completed the grid. If you can't write your number in the grid, miss a turn.

Divisible by 2	Divisible by 5	Divisible by 10

UNIT 12: Assess & Review

Choose from these activities. During the group activities, some of the children can work with you on practical tasks, while others complete assessment worksheets 4a and 4b which assess their skills in working with shapes, measures and written methods of addition and subtraction. The specific assessment criteria for the assessment sheets can be found at the bottom of each sheet.

RESOURCES

Plain paper; rulers; pencils; calculators; number cards.

ORAL AND MENTAL STARTER

ASSESSMENT

Can the children derive quickly:
- decimals that total 1
- decimals that total 10
- pairs of multiples of 50 with a total of 1000?

DERIVE QUICKLY: Give the children a quick mental test where the answers are written down. Ask 12 questions: four to test each of the three assessment criteria listed above. Use a range of vocabulary, eg *0.3, how many more to make 1? How much needs to be added to 2.7 to make 10? 1000 subtract 350 leaves what?* Read each question out twice and give the children 10 seconds to answer.

GROUP ACTIVITIES

ASSESSMENT

Can the children:
- **understand area measured in square centimetres (cm²)**
- **understand and use the formula in words 'length × breadth' for the area of a rectangle**
- know and apply tests of divisibility by 2, 4, 5 and 10?
- choose and use appropriate ways of calculating: mental, mental with jottings, written methods, calculator?

AREA: Ask the children to draw three rectangles on a plain piece of paper: one with an area of 24cm², one with an area of 18cm², the third with an area of 36cm². They then swap their work with a partner to check. Can the children explain why the rectangles are drawn correctly or incorrectly (eg by referring to the lengths of the sides)?

DIVISIBILITY: Give each child six 2-digit number cards, including one multiple of 10, one multiple of 5 (that is not a multiple of 10 or 4), one multiple of 4 (but not of 5) and one multiple of 2 (but not of 4 or 5) – eg 60, 35, 16 and 22 – and two other odd numbers that are not multiples of 2, 4, 5 or 10. Make sure that each child in the group has a different set of numbers.

   Ask each child to show a number divisible by 10. Repeat with numbers divisible by 5, 2 and 4. They may show a number they have already shown if appropriate. Now ask with two criteria, eg *divisible by 5 but not by 2*. Repeat several times. Check that the children can select the correct numbers.

CALCULATIONS: Write the following calculations on the board:

30 × 6 =	36 + 29 =	300 ÷ 6 =	216 + 173 =	594 – 432 =
27 × 20 =	347 + 133 =	147 ÷ 7 =	348 – 287 =	374 + 268 =

   Ask the children to find the answers. They can use a full written method, calculate mentally (with jottings) or use a calculator. Discuss with them why they chose a particular method. If they used a calculator, they should explain why they couldn't do it mentally.

Assessment 4a

Find the missing measurement (length, breadth or area) for each of the shapes below. Then calculate the perimeter.

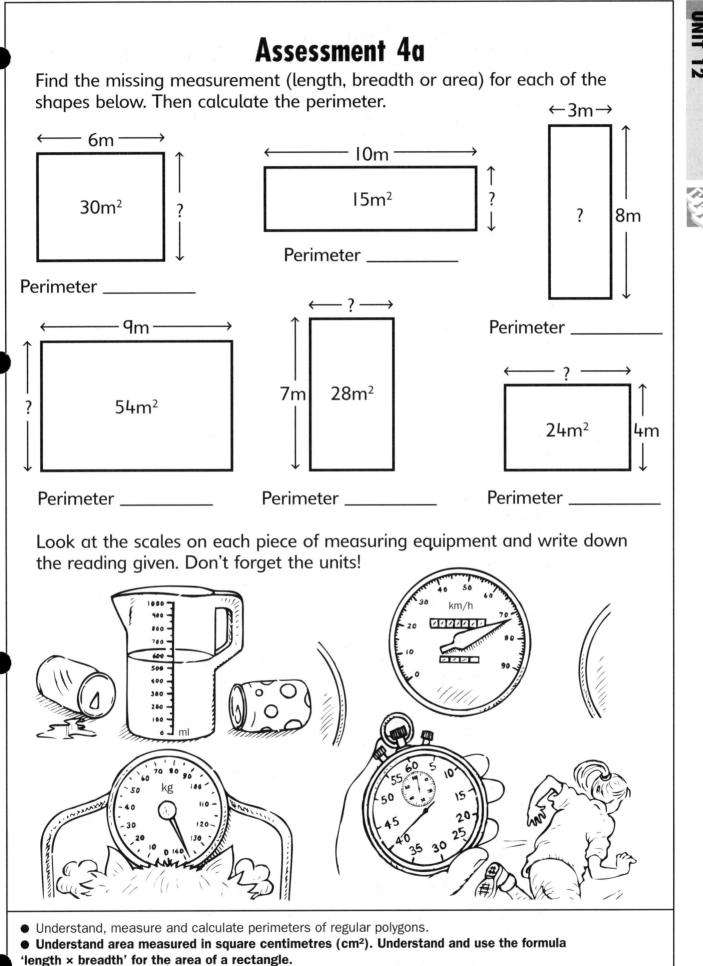

←— 6m —→

30m²   ?

Perimeter _____

←———— 10m ————→

15m²   ?

Perimeter _____

← 3m →

?   8m

Perimeter _____

←——— 9m ———→

?   54m²

Perimeter _____

←— ? —→

7m   28m²

Perimeter _____

←—— ? ——→

24m²   4m

Perimeter _____

Look at the scales on each piece of measuring equipment and write down the reading given. Don't forget the units!

- Understand, measure and calculate perimeters of regular polygons.
- **Understand area measured in square centimetres (cm²). Understand and use the formula 'length × breadth' for the area of a rectangle.**
- Record readings from scales to a suitable degree of accuracy.

Assessment 4b

Complete the calculations below. Jot down how you calculated the answer. The first one has been done for you.

1. 127 + 19 ⟶ 127 + 20 – 1 = 146 _____

2. 236 + 48 ⟶ _____

3. 149 + 63 ⟶ _____

4. 278 + 27 ⟶ _____

5. 136 – 49 ⟶ _____

6. 264 – 47 ⟶ _____

7. 328 – 197 ⟶ _____

8. 526 – 289 ⟶ _____

Complete the calculations below.

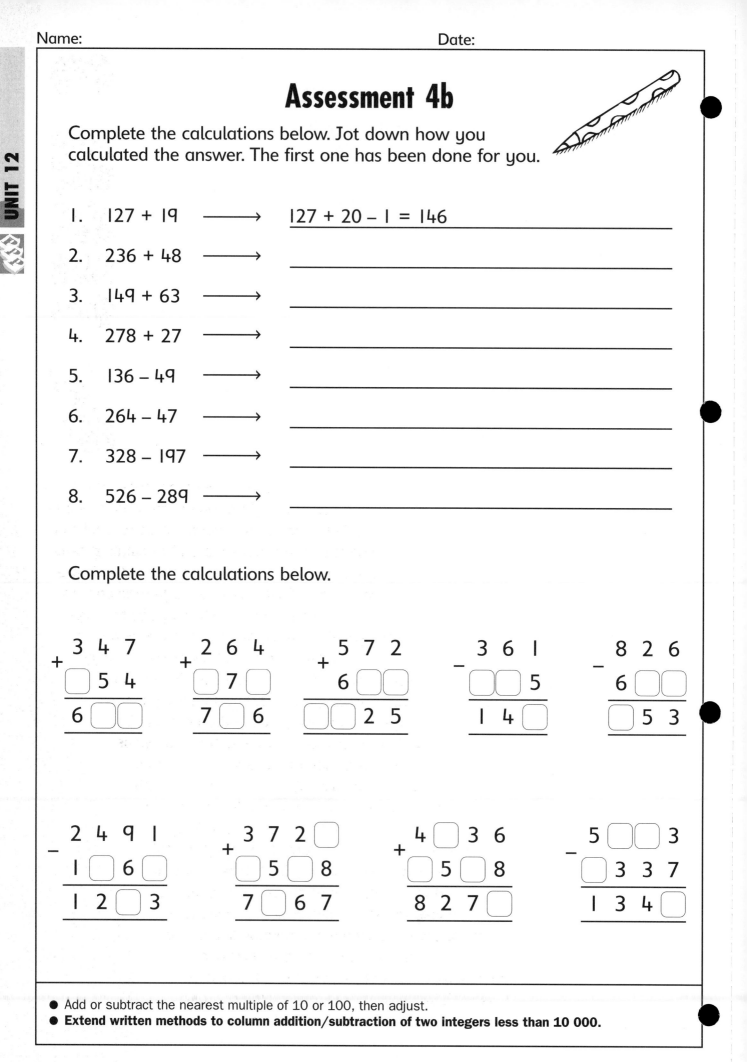

```
    3 4 7          2 6 4          5 7 2          3 6 1          8 2 6
  +  ☐ 5 4       +  ☐ 7 ☐       +  6 ☐ ☐       -  ☐ ☐ 5       -  6 ☐ ☐
  ─────────      ─────────      ─────────      ─────────      ─────────
    6 ☐ ☐          7 ☐ 6          ☐ ☐ 2 5        1 4 ☐          ☐ 5 3
```

```
    2 4 9 1        3 7 2 ☐        4 ☐ 3 6        5 ☐ ☐ 3
  -  1 ☐ 6 ☐     +  ☐ 5 ☐ 8     +  ☐ 5 ☐ 8     -  ☐ 3 3 7
  ───────────    ───────────    ───────────    ───────────
    1 2 ☐ 3        7 ☐ 6 7        8 2 7 ☐        1 3 4 ☐
```

- Add or subtract the nearest multiple of 10 or 100, then adjust.
- **Extend written methods to column addition/subtraction of two integers less than 10 000.**

TERM 3

Work in this term reinforces what has been covered in the previous two terms. Children continue working with numbers up to 1 million, ordering negative numbers and calculating rises and falls in temperature. Written methods are extended to 3-digit by single-digit division with remainders and two-digit by two-digit multiplication, while mental methods continue to be developed. Work includes rounding decimal numbers to the nearest whole number, finding simple percentages and solving simple problems involving ratio and proportion. The work in 'Shape and space' extends previous work on angles to measuring and drawing angles and calculating angles on a straight line. In 'Measures', children will measure and estimate mass and convert kg to g. They will extend their work from Term 1 on using the 24-hour clock and reading timetables. Work on 'Handling data' introduces children to the concept of probability, as well as extending previous work. Children's understanding of the properties of numbers is developed by continuing to look at sequences with steps of a constant size, square numbers, multiples, tests of divisibility and factors.

ENLARGE THIS SHEET TO A3 AND USE IT AS YOUR MEDIUM-TERM PLANNING GRID.

Oral and mental: Read and write whole numbers in figures and words, and know what each digit represents. Round any integer less than 10 000 to the nearest 10, 100 or 1000. **Know by heart all multiplication facts up to 10 × 10.** Use known facts and place value to multiply and divide mentally. Derive quickly or continue to derive quickly: division facts corresponding to tables up to 10 × 10; doubles of all whole numbers 1 to 100; doubles of multiples of 10 to 1000; doubles of multiples of 100 to 10 000; and the corresponding halves. Know what each digit represents in a number with up to two decimal places. Order a set of numbers or measurements with the same number of decimal places. Recognise and extend number sequences formed by counting from any number in steps of constant size, extending beyond zero when counting back, eg count on or back in steps of 0.1. **Relate fractions to division**, and use division to find simple fractions, including tenths and hundredths, of numbers and quantities. **Relate fractions to their decimal representations**: that is, recognise the equivalence between the decimal and fraction forms of one half, one quarter, three quarters... and tenths and hundredths (eg $0.7 = \frac{7}{10}$, $0.27 = \frac{27}{100}$). Express one half, one quarter, three quarters, and tenths and hundredths, as percentages. Begin to understand percentage as the number of parts in every hundred, and find simple percentages of small whole-number quantities. Solve simple problems using ideas of ratio and proportion.

UNIT	TOPIC	OBJECTIVES: CHILDREN WILL BE TAUGHT TO...
1	Place value, ordering and rounding Using a calculator	● Use the vocabulary of comparing and ordering numbers, including symbols such as <, >, =. Give one or more numbers lying between two given numbers. Order a set of integers less than 1 million. ● Use the vocabulary of estimation and approximation; make, explain and justify estimates of large numbers, and estimate simple proportions. ● Round any integer up to 10 000 to the nearest 10, 100 or 1000. ● **Order a given set of positive and negative integers** (eg on a number line, on a temperature scale); calculate a temperature rise or fall across 0°C. ● Develop calculator skills and use a calculator effectively.
2–3	Understanding × and ÷ Mental calculation strategies (× and ÷) Pencil and paper procedures (× and ÷) Money and 'real life' problems Making decisions and checking results, including using a calculator	● Understand the effect of and relationships between the four operations, and the principles (not the names) of the arithmetic laws as they apply to multiplication. Begin to use brackets. ● Begin to express a quotient as a fraction, or as a decimal when dividing a whole number by 2, 4, 5 or 10, or when dividing £.p. ● Use factors. ● Use closely related facts (eg develop the ×12 table from the ×10 and ×2 tables). ● Partition, eg 47 × 6 = (40 × 6) + (7 × 6). ● Approximate first. Use informal pencil and paper methods to support, record or explain multiplications and divisions. **Extend written methods to: short multiplication of U.t by U; long multiplication of TU by TU; short division of HTU by U** (with integer remainder). ● **Use all four operations to solve simple word problems involving numbers and quantities** based on 'real life' and money, using one or more steps. **Explain methods and reasoning.** ● Check with an equivalent calculation. ● Choose and use appropriate number operations to solve problems, and appropriate ways of calculating: mental, mental with jottings, written methods, calculator. ● Use known facts and place value for mental addition and subtraction. ● Check with the inverse operation when using a calculator. ● Develop calculator skills and use a calculator effectively.
4–5	Fractions, decimals and percentages Ratio and proportion	● **Use decimal notation for tenths and hundredths.** ● Know what each digit represents in a number with up to two decimal places. ● Order a set of numbers or measurements with the same number of decimal places. ● Round a number with one or two decimal places to the nearest integer. ● **Relate fractions to their decimal representations**: that is, recognise the equivalence between decimal and fraction forms of one half, one quarter, three quarters... and tenths and hundredths (eg $0.7 = \frac{7}{10}$, $0.27 = \frac{27}{100}$). ● **Relate fractions to division**, and use division to find simple fractions, including tenths and hundredths, of numbers and quantities. ● Express one half, one quarter, three quarters, and tenths and hundredths, as percentages. ● Begin to understand percentage as the number of parts in every 100, and find simple percentages of small whole-number quantities. ● Solve simple problems using ideas of ratio and proportion.
6	Handling data	● Discuss the chance or likelihood of particular events. ● Find the mode of a set of data. ● Solve a problem by representing and interpreting data in tables, charts, graphs and diagrams eg bar line charts, first where intermediate points may have meaning.
7	Assess and review	See the key objectives on the appropriate pages.

Oral and mental: Derive quickly: decimals that total 10; all two-digit pairs that total 100; pairs of multiples of 50 with a total of 1000. Use known number facts and place value for mental addition. Calculate angles in a straight line. Convert larger to smaller units (kg to g). **Know by heart all multiplication facts up to 10 × 10.** Read the time from an analogue clock to the nearest minute. Estimate by approximating (round to nearest 10 or 100), then check result. **Use all four operations to solve word problems involving numbers and quantities** based on 'real life', money and measures, using one or more steps. Know and apply tests of divisibility by 2, 4, 5, 10 or 100. Solve mathematical problems or puzzles. Find all the pairs of factors of any number up to 100.

UNIT	TOPIC	OBJECTIVES: CHILDREN WILL BE TAUGHT TO...
8–10	Shape and space Reasoning about shapes Measures, including problems	● Understand and use angle measure in degrees. ● Identify, estimate and order acute and obtuse angles. ● Use a protractor to measure and draw angles to the nearest 5°. ● Make shapes with increasing accuracy. ● Meaure and draw lines to the nearest millimetre. ● Calculate angles in a straight line. ● Solve mathematical problems or puzzles, recognise and explain patterns and relationships, generalise and predict; suggest extensions asking 'What if...?' ● Make and investigate a general statement about familiar shapes by finding examples to match it. ● Use, read and write standard metric units (kg, g), including their abbreviations, and relationships between them. Convert larger to smaller units. ● Suggest suitable units and measuring equipment to estimate or measure mass. ● Record estimates and readings from scales to a suitable degree of accuracy. ● Use units of time; read the time on a 24-hour digital clock and use 24-hour clock notation, such as 19:53. Use timetables. ● **Use all four operations to solve word problems involving numbers and quantities** based on 'real life', money and measures **(including time)**, using one or more steps, including making simple conversions of pounds to foreign currency. ● Choose and use appropriate number operations to solve problems, and appropriate ways of calculating: mental, mental with jottings, written methods, calculator.
11	Mental calculation strategies (+ and –) Pencil and paper procedures (+ and –) Money and 'real life' problems Making decisions and checking results, including using a calculator	● Add or subtract the nearest multiple of 10 or 100, then adjust. ● Use known number facts and place value for mental addition and subtraction. ● Identify near doubles. ● Develop further the relationship between addition and subtraction. ● Extend written methods to addition or subtraction of a pair of decimal fractions, both with one or both with two decimal places. ● **Use all four operations to solve word problems involving numbers and quantities** based on 'real life', money and measures, using one or more steps. ● Develop calculator skills and use a calculator effectively. ● Choose and use appropriate number operations to solve problems, and appropriate ways of calculating: mental, mental with jottings, written methods, calculator. ● Check with an equivalent calculation. ● Check the sum of several numbers by adding in the reverse order. ● Check with the inverse operation when using a calculator.
12	Properties of numbers Reasoning about numbers	● Recognise and extend number sequences formed by counting from any number in steps of constant size, extending beyond zero when counting back; for example, count on or back in steps of 0.1, 0.2, 0.3... ● Recognise multiples of 6, 7, 8, 9 up to the 10th multiple. ● Know and apply tests of divisibility by 2, 4, 5, 10 or 100. ● Know squares of numbers to at least 10 × 10. ● Find all the pairs of factors of any number up to 100. ● Make and investigate a general statement about familiar numbers by finding examples that satisfy it. ● Solve mathematical problems or puzzles, recognise and explain patterns and relationships, generalise and predict; suggest extensions asking 'What if...?' ● Explain methods and reasoning, orally and in writing.
13	Assess and review	See the key objectives on the appropriate pages.

UNIT 1

ORGANISATION (3 LESSONS)

LEARNING OUTCOMES	ORAL AND MENTAL STARTER	MAIN TEACHING ACTIVITY	PLENARY
LESSON 1 ● Use the vocabulary of comparing and ordering numbers, including symbols such as <, >, =. Give one or more numbers lying between two given numbers. Order a set of integers less than 1 million.	MYSTERY NUMBER: As in Lesson 2, Unit 1 of Term 1, but using 4- and 5-digit numbers.	NUMBER ORDER: Put 4-figure numbers in order and find numbers to fit between them.	Estimate the numbers at given points on a number line.
LESSON 2 ● Use the vocabulary of estimation and approximation; make and justify estimates of large numbers, and estimate simple proportions. ● Round any integer less than 10 000 to the nearest 10, 100 or 1000.	BUILDING NUMBERS: Repeat from Lesson 1, Unit 1 of Term 2.	NEAREST TO? Place 4-digit numbers on a number line. Round them to the nearest 10, 100 or 1000.	Round 5-digit numbers to the nearest 1000.
LESSON 3 ● **Order a given set of positive and negative integers** (eg on a number line, on a temperature scale); calculate a temperature rise or fall across 0°C. ● Develop calculator skills and use a calculator effectively.	ROUNDING NUMBERS: To nearest 100 or 1000. Whole-class response.	NEGATIVE NUMBERS: Calculate differences involving negative numbers.	Position positive and negative numbers on a number line.

ORAL AND MENTAL SKILLS: Read and write whole numbers in figures and words, and know what each digit represents. Round any integer less than 10 000 to the nearest 10, 100 or 1000.

Lessons 1 and 2 are shown in detail. Lesson 3 follows on from what has already been taught.

RESOURCES

Photocopiable page 150.

PREPARATION

Write these numbers on the board:
2435, 2426, 2450, 2420, 2442, 2440, 37 180, 37 168, 37 150, 37 185, 37 770.

VOCABULARY
Greater than, less than, equal to, largest, smallest, between, halfway, first, second, third, fourth, ascending, descending.

LEARNING OUTCOMES

ORAL AND MENTAL STARTER
● Read and write whole numbers in figures and words, and know what each digit represents.

MAIN TEACHING ACTIVITY
● Use the vocabulary of comparing and ordering numbers, including symbols such as <, >, =. Give one or more numbers lying between two given numbers. Order a set of integers less than 1 million.

ORAL AND MENTAL STARTER

MYSTERY NUMBER: As for Lesson 2, Unit 1 of Term 1, but this time focusing on 4- and 5-digit numbers.

MAIN TEACHING ACTIVITY

NUMBER ORDER: Look at the first row of numbers on the board. Tell the children they are going to put these numbers in order. *We are going to put them in ascending order, which means we will put the smallest number first and they will go up in size. Which number is the smallest?* Make sure the children read the number as a whole, not just as a series of digits. When the numbers are written in order, say: *We are going to look at two of those numbers, 2450 and 2440. Which number is larger? 2450.* Write 2440 < 2450. Read this out together. *Can you think of numbers which come between those two numbers.* Take some examples. *Which number comes halfway between? 2445. How do you know?*

Repeat the above process with the second set of numbers, putting them in descending order. Then repeat with a set of 6-digit numbers, for example 471 640, 471 460, 471 563, 472 356 and 472 046.

The children work through photocopiable page 150.

DIFFERENTIATION

More able: Go on to choose two other numbers in each set and find the number halfway between them. Try with a set of 6-digit numbers.
Less able: Work with 3- and 4-digit numbers.

PLENARY

Draw a number line on the board. Write 3400 on one end and 3500 at the other. Point to a position halfway along the number line. *Which number would be here?* Repeat with other numbers and other positions on the line.

RESOURCES

Place value chart (photocopiable page 24); numeral cards (one set per child).

PREPARATION

Put up a copy of the place value chart (photocopiable page 24) so all the class can see it. Draw a blank number line on the board.

VOCABULARY

Estimate, approximate, round, nearest, nearly, roughly, approximately.

LEARNING OUTCOMES

ORAL AND MENTAL STARTER
● Read and write whole numbers in figures and words, and know what each digit represents.
MAIN TEACHING ACTIVITY
● Use the vocabulary of estimation and approximation; make and justify estimates of large numbers, and estimate simple proportions.
● Round any integer less than 10 000 to the nearest 10, 100 or 1000.

ORAL AND MENTAL STARTER

BUILDING NUMBERS: Repeat from Lesson 1, Unit 1 of Term 2.

MAIN TEACHING ACTIVITY

NEAREST TO? Write 1000 at one end of the number line and 2000 at the other. Write 1376 on the board. *Where would you put that number on the number line?* Ask a child to come up and point to a place on the line. Consult the rest of the class: do they agree?

Discuss why the child decided to put it there. *Is the number closer to 1000 or 2000? 1000. Is it closer to 1300 or 1400? 1400. How do you know? Is it closer to 1370 or 1380? 1380. So to the nearest thousand it is rounded to 1000, to nearest hundred it is rounded to 1400, to the nearest ten it is rounded to 1380. Approximately what proportion of the number line comes before 1376? What proportion comes after?*

Change the numbers at either end of the number line to 4000 and 5000. Write 4636 on the board. *Where would you put this number on the number line? What is it rounded to the nearest thousand? What is it rounded to the nearest hundred? What is it rounded to the nearest ten?* Repeat with another example.

The children choose 4-digit numbers by picking numeral cards, position them on a blank number line and round them to the nearest 1000, 100 and 10.

DIFFERENTIATION

More able: Work with 5-digit numbers, rounding to the nearest 1000, 100 and 10.
Less able: Work with 3-digit numbers, rounding to the nearest 100 and 10.

PLENARY

Write 21 364 on the board. Read the number together as a class. *Which two thousands does it lie between? 21 000 and 22 000. Is it closer to 21 000 or 22 000? How do you know?* Repeat with other 5-digit numbers.

LEARNING OUTCOMES	**ORAL AND MENTAL STARTER** ● Round any integer less than 10 000 to the nearest 10, 100 or 1000. **MAIN TEACHING ACTIVITY** ● **Order a given set of positive and negative integers** (eg on a number line, on a temperature scale); calculate a temperature rise or fall across 0°C. ● Develop calculator skills and use a calculator effectively.
RESOURCES	String; pegs; a set of large number cards (–10 to +10); a set of small cards (–10 to +10) per pair; calculators.
ORAL AND MENTAL STARTER	ROUNDING NUMBERS: Say a number for the children to round to the nearest 100 or 1000, responding as a class. Ask individuals for examples of numbers that would be rounded to 2000, 2500 etc.
MAIN TEACHING ACTIVITY	NEGATIVE NUMBERS: Order the large number cards on a string number line. Ask: *If the temperature is –3°C and then rises by 5°C, what is the new temperature?* Half the class work it out on a calculator, half use a number line. Repeat with other examples of temperature rises and falls, switching which children use a calculator each time. Children pick two cards from their set and work out the rise from the lower value to the higher.
DIFFERENTIATION	More able: extend range of numbers, eg –30 to +30. Less able: Use cards –5 to +5.
PLENARY	Draw a blank number line on the board. Write –10 at one end and +10 at the other. Point to places on the line. *Which number comes here?*

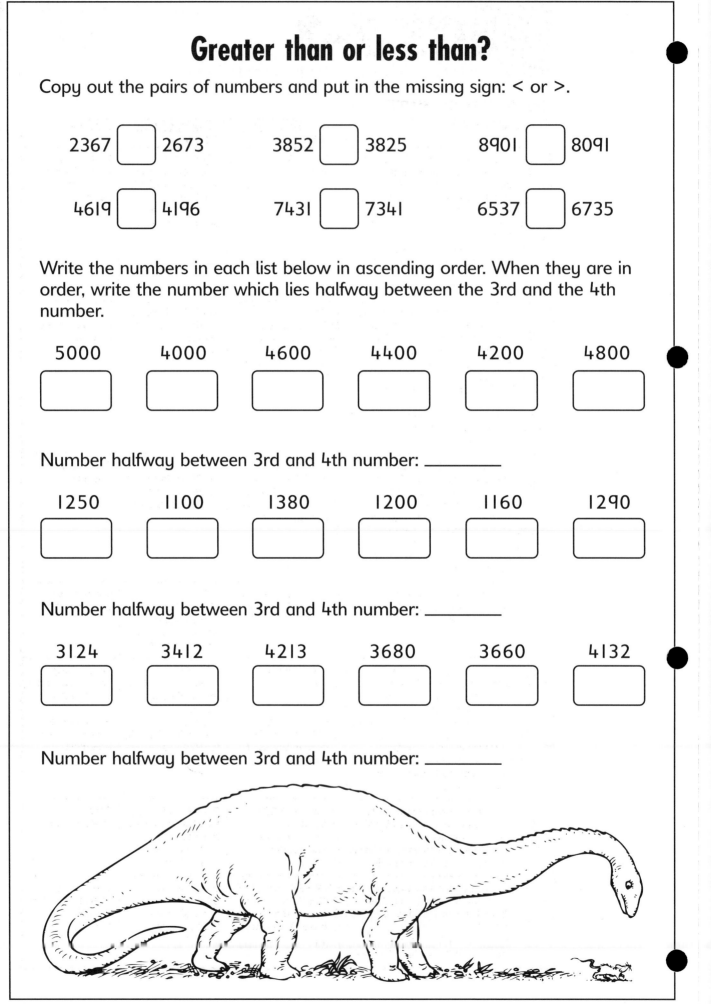

Greater than or less than?

Copy out the pairs of numbers and put in the missing sign: < or >.

2367 [ ] 2673   3852 [ ] 3825   8901 [ ] 8091

4619 [ ] 4196   7431 [ ] 7341   6537 [ ] 6735

Write the numbers in each list below in ascending order. When they are in order, write the number which lies halfway between the 3rd and the 4th number.

5000	4000	4600	4400	4200	4800
[ ]	[ ]	[ ]	[ ]	[ ]	[ ]

Number halfway between 3rd and 4th number: _____

1250	1100	1380	1200	1160	1290
[ ]	[ ]	[ ]	[ ]	[ ]	[ ]

Number halfway between 3rd and 4th number: _____

3124	3412	4213	3680	3660	4132
[ ]	[ ]	[ ]	[ ]	[ ]	[ ]

Number halfway between 3rd and 4th number: _____

UNIT 1

ORGANISATION (10 LESSONS)

LEARNING OUTCOMES	ORAL AND MENTAL STARTER	MAIN TEACHING ACTIVITY	PLENARY
LESSON 1 ● Understand the effect of and relationships between the four operations, and the principles (not the names) of the arithmetic laws as they apply to multiplication. Begin to use brackets. ● Use factors. ● Use closely related facts (eg develop the ×12 table from the ×10 and ×2 tables). ● Check with an equivalent calculation.	FACTOR PAIRS: Repeat from Lesson 1, Unit 2 of Term 2.	EQUIVALENT CALCULATION: Work in pairs to multiply numbers – one partitioning, the other using factors.	Look at different ways of writing the same calculation.
LESSON 2 ● Understand the effect of and relationships between the four operations, and the principles (not the names) of the arithmetic laws as they apply to multiplication. ● Partition, eg 47 × 6 = (40 × 6) + (7 × 6). ● Approximate first. Use informal pencil and paper methods to support, record or explain multiplications.	CHANTING MULTIPLES: As for Lesson 4, Unit 2 of Term 2, but now include multiples of 100.	3-DIGIT × 1-DIGIT: Partition a 3-digit number and use grid layout.	Lead into expanded written method.
LESSON 3 ● **Extend written methods to short multiplication of** U.t by U. ● Choose and use appropriate number operations to solve problems, and appropriate ways of calculating: mental, mental with jottings, written methods, calculator. ● Develop calculator skills and use a calculator effectively.	DOUBLING ROUND THE ROOM: As for Lesson 5, Unit 2 of Term 1, but this time start with multiples of 5.	STANDARD METHOD: Introduce standard written method for U.t × U.	Check using a calculator.
LESSON 4 ● **Extend written methods to: long multiplication of TU by TU.** Check with an equivalent calculation.	FOLLOW ME: Repeat from Unit 8, Lesson 5 of Term 1.	LONG MULTIPLICATION: Use standard written method for long multiplication.	Compare with grid method.
LESSON 5 + 6 ● Approximate first. Use informal pencil and paper methods to support, record or explain divisions. ● Use known facts and place value to multiply and divide mentally. ● Check with the inverse operation when using a calculator. ● **Extend written methods to short division of HTU by U.**	FOLLOW ME: See Lesson 4. DIVISION GROUP BINGO: Repeat from Lesson 6, Unit 3 of Term 2.	REPEATED SUBTRACTION:Use this method for division. Set out repeated subtraction formally for HTU ÷ U.	Check using inverse operation on calculator. Go over some 3-digit ÷ 1-digit examples.
LESSON 7 ● **Extend written methods to short division of HTU by U** (with integer remainder). ● Use known facts and place value to multiply and divide mentally.	COUNTING STICK DIVISION: Use a counting stick to explore related divisions.	DIVISION WITH REMAINDERS: Use repeated subtraction to find remainders.	Check using multiplication.
LESSON 8 ● Begin to express a quotient as a fraction, or as a decimal when dividing a whole number by 2, 4, 5 or 10. ● Check with the inverse operation when using calculator.	HALVING ROUND THE ROOM: As for Lesson 2, Unit 4, Term 1, but with 3-digit multiples of 10.	QUOTIENT AS A DECIMAL: Write remainders as fractions and decimals.	Check using inverse operation on OHP calculator.

LEARNING OUTCOMES	ORAL AND MENTAL STARTER	MAIN TEACHING ACTIVITY	PLENARY
LESSON 9 ● Begin to express a quotient as a fraction, or as a decimal when dividing a whole number by 2, 4, 5 or 10, or when dividing £.p. ● Check with the inverse operation when using calculator.	WHAT IS THE QUESTION? Think of divisions to make a given answer.	MONEY DISPLAYS: Interpret quotients involving money on a calculator.	Look at calculator displays, including ones where rounding is required.
LESSON 10 ● **Use all four operations to solve simple word problems involving numbers and quantities** based on 'real life' and money, using one or more steps. **Explain methods and reasoning**.	DOUBLING ROUND THE ROOM: As for Lesson 5, Unit 2 of Term 1, but starting with 2- or 3-digit multiples of 5.	FOUR RULES PROBLEMS: Solve word problems involving all the four rules.	Pupils explain their approaches.

ORAL AND MENTAL SKILLS: Know by heart all multiplication facts up to 10 × 10. Derive quickly: division facts corresponding to tables up to 10 × 10; doubles of all whole numbers 1 to 100; doubles of multiples of 10 to 1000; and doubles of multiples of 100 to 10 000; and the corresponding halves. Use known facts and place value to multiply and divide mentally.

Lessons 2, 3, 5 and 7–9 are shown in detail. Lessons 1, 4, 6 and 10 follow on from what has already been taught.

LESSON 1

LEARNING OUTCOMES	**ORAL AND MENTAL STARTER** ● **Know by heart all multiplication facts up to 10 × 10**. ● Derive quickly: division facts corresponding to tables up to 10 × 10. **MAIN TEACHING ACTIVITY** ● Understand the effect of and relationships between the four operations, and the principles (not the names) of the arithmetic laws as they apply to multiplication. Begin to use brackets. ● Use factors. ● Use closely related facts (eg develop the ×12 table from the ×10 and ×2 tables. ● Check with an equivalent calculation.
RESOURCES	Numeral cards (one set per pupil).
ORAL AND MENTAL STARTER	FACTOR PAIRS: Repeat from Lesson 1, Unit 2 of Term 2.
MAIN TEACHING ACTIVITY	EQUIVALENT CALCULATION: Look at 34 × 12. It can be written as (34 × 10) + (34 × 2) or as 34 × 4 × 3. Children work in pairs: one child calculates the answer to the first one, the other child works out the second one. Repeat with other examples, as a class. Children do some examples in pairs (one using factors, one using partition), taken from the board: 2-digit numbers multiplied by 12, 16 or 18.
DIFFERENTIATION	More able: Multiply 2-digit numbers by 20, 24 or 28. Less able: Use numbers already broken down into factors (eg 26 × 16 as 26 × 4 × 4).
PLENARY	Look at different ways of writing calculations, eg 27 × 24 = (27 × 20) + (27 × 4) = 27 × 6 × 4 = 27 × 4 × 3 × 2.

LESSON 2

RESOURCES

Arrow cards (for demonstration).

PREPARATION

Write some 3-digit by 1-digit multiplications on the board, eg:

134 × 3   251 × 4   326 × 6

LEARNING OUTCOMES

ORAL AND MENTAL STARTER

● **Know by heart all multiplication facts up to 10 × 10.**

● Use known facts and place value to multiply and divide mentally.

MAIN TEACHING ACTIVITY

● Understand the effect of and relationships between the four operations, and the principles (not the names) of the arithmetic laws as they apply to multiplication.
● Partition, eg $47 \times 6 = (40 \times 6) + (7 \times 6)$.
● Approximate first. Use informal pencil and paper methods to support, record or explain multiplications.

ORAL AND MENTAL STARTER

CHANTING MULTIPLES: Repeat from Lesson 4, Unit 2 of Term 2. This time, divide the class into three groups to chant connected calculations, eg 3×4, 3×40, 3×400.

MAIN TEACHING ACTIVITY

3-DIGIT × 1-DIGIT: Tell the children they are going to multiply a 3-digit number by a single-digit number. Look at the first multiplication on the board: 134×3 . Read it together as a class. *What will the answer be approximately?* Take a range of answers *and* write them on the board. *To calculate the answer, we are going to partition the number into hundreds, tens and units and complete this grid.* Draw a 3 × 1 grid (see figure below) and partition the number. Once it has been partitioned, point to each part again and read the number: *'one hundred and thirty-four'.* Ask questions in order to complete the grid as a class; then find the total of the parts. Repeat with the other calculations on the board.

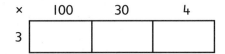

Write more calculations on the board for children to work through.

DIFFERENTIATION

More able: Multiply 4-digit numbers by any single-digit number.
Less able: Concentrate on multiplying 3-digit numbers by 2, 3 or 5.

PLENARY

Take a 3-digit × single-digit example, eg 247×4.
Write it vertically. Complete the calculation using
an expanded form of the standard method (see right).
Repeat with another example.

$$
\begin{array}{r}
247 \\
\times \quad 4 \\
\hline
800 \\
160 \\
28 \\
\hline
988 \\
\end{array}
$$

RESOURCES

U.t × U problems in textbooks; calculators.

PREPARATION

Write three U.t × U multiplications on the board, eg 2.5×7.

LEARNING OUTCOMES

ORAL AND MENTAL STARTER

● Derive quickly: doubles of all whole numbers 1 to 100; doubles of multiples of 10 to 1000.

MAIN TEACHING ACTIVITY

● Extend written methods to short multiplication of U.t by U.
● Develop calculator skills and use a calculator effectively.
● Choose and use appropriate operations to solve numerical problems and ways of calculating: mental, mental with jottings, written methods, calculator.

ORAL AND MENTAL STARTER

DOUBLING ROUND THE ROOM: Repeat from Lesson 5, Unit 2 of Term 1 with whole class in groups. Start with a multiple of 5 and double until a number over 1000 is reached.

MAIN TEACHING ACTIVITY

STANDARD METHOD: Tell the children they are going to multiply a 1-place decimal number by a single-digit number. Work through the multiplications on the board with the class, using the expanded written method from the Plenary of Lesson 2. Introduce the standard written method using the same examples; explain that it is the same method, but is quicker to write down. For example (see calculation right): *6 times 7 tenths is 4 and 2 tenths, so we write the 4 units in the units column and the 2 tenths in the tenths column. 6 times 2 units is 12, add the 4 units we've already got makes 16. So the answer is 16.2.*

$$
\begin{array}{r}
2.7 \\
\times\ 6 \\
\hline
4.2 \\
12.0 \\
\hline
16.2 \\
\hline
\end{array}
$$

The children work through U.t × U questions from textbooks, choosing the method of calculation they prefer to use. Encourage them to explain their methods.

DIFFERENTIATION

More able: Multiply numbers to two decimal places by single-digit numbers.
Less able: Work with the teacher, using expanded method initially. Explain what is happening.

PLENARY

Check some calculations with the class: take a range of answers first, then check these using a calculator.

LEARNING OUTCOMES	**ORAL AND MENTAL STARTER** ● **Know by heart all multiplication facts up to 10 × 10.** ● Derive quickly: division facts corresponding to tables up to 10 × 10. **MAIN TEACHING ACTIVITY** ● **Extend written methods to: long multiplication of TU by TU.** ● Check with an equivalent calculation.
RESOURCES	TU × TU problems in textbooks.
ORAL AND MENTAL STARTER	FOLLOW ME: Repeat from Lesson 5, Unit 8 of Term 1. Can the children beat their previous record?
MAIN TEACHING ACTIVITY	LONG MULTIPLICATION: Go over work from Lesson 3. Write some TU × TU multiplications on the board. Do several examples using the expanded method, emphasising the place value of each digit. Then introduce the standard method. The children work through some examples.
DIFFERENTIATION	More able: Work out some HTU × TU examples. Less able: Work with examples using a grid layout.
PLENARY	Work through some examples using a grid method. Discuss which method pupils prefer and why.

RESOURCES

Division questions from textbooks or worksheets covering 2-digit by 1-digit (no remainders) and 3-digit by 1-digit (no remainders); an OHP calculator.

PREPARATION

Write some 2-digit by single-digit divisions on the board, eg:

57 ÷ 3   68 ÷ 4   84 ÷ 6

VOCABULARY
Multiply, divide, subtract, how many lots of... in, groups of, ten lots of.

LEARNING OUTCOMES

ORAL AND MENTAL STARTER

- **Know by heart all multiplication facts up to 10 × 10.**
- Derive quickly division facts corresponding to tables up to 10 × 10.

MAIN TEACHING ACTIVITY

- Approximate first. Use informal pencil and paper methods to support, record or explain divisions.
- Use known number facts and place value to multiply and divide mentally.
- Check with the inverse operation, using a calculator.
- **Extend written methods to short division of HTU by U.**

ORAL AND MENTAL STARTER

FOLLOW ME: Repeat from Lesson 5, Unit 8, Term 1.

MAIN TEACHING ACTIVITY

REPEATED SUBTRACTION: Tell the children they are going to look at division questions and use repeated subtraction to calculate the answers. Look at the first question on the board: $57 \div 3$. *We could read that as '57 divided by 3' or as 'How many lots of 3 are in 57?'* Ask the children to estimate how many lots of 3 there are in 57. Take a range of answers; encourage them to use what they know (eg *there are 10 lots of 3 in 30, so there are 20 lots of 3 in 60, so 20 will be too many*). Once you have a range of estimates, write the partitioned method on the board:

$$57 \div 3 \qquad \rightarrow \qquad 30 \div 3 = 10$$
$$27 \div 3 = 9$$
$$\text{so } 57 \div 3 = 19$$

Repeat the process with other divisions. Encourage pupils to come and write different stages of the process.

The children work through some 2-digit by 1-digit examples.

DIFFERENTIATION

More able: Go on to 3-digit by single-digit divisions (no remainder).
Less able: Concentrate on dividing multiples of 10 by numbers they are exactly divisible by, for example $60 \div 3$, $80 \div 4$.

PLENARY

Use an OHP calculator to show how to check answers using the inverse operation, eg to check $57 \div 3 = 19$, input $19 \times 3 =$. Ask children what they will need to input to check various answers.

LESSON 6

For the **Oral and mental starter**, repeat DIVISION GROUP BINGO from Lesson 6, Unit 3, Term 2. For the **Main teaching activity**, extend Lesson 5 to using a more formal written method (see example right). Work through some 2-digit by 1-digit divisions, then some 3-digit by 1-digit divisions. The children work through more examples. More able children can focus on 3-digit by 1-digit divisions. Use cubes to demonstrate to a less able group. For the **Plenary**, go over more 3-digit by 1-digit divisions.

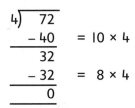

Answer: $72 \div 4 = 18$.

LESSON 7

RESOURCES

A counting stick; 6-sided and 10-sided dice.

PREPARATION

Write some 2-digit by 1-digit divisions on the board, eg:

$$4\overline{)67} \qquad\qquad 6\overline{)83} \qquad\qquad 7\overline{)84}$$

VOCABULARY

Group, divide, how many lots of in, divided into, remainder.

LEARNING OUTCOMES

ORAL AND MENTAL STARTER

● Derive quickly division facts corresponding to tables up to 10 × 10.
● Use known facts and place value to multiply and divide mentally.

MAIN TEACHING ACTIVITY

● **Extend written methods to: short division of HTU by U** (with integer remainder).
● Use known facts and place value to multiply and divide mentally.

ORAL AND MENTAL STARTER

COUNTING STICK DIVISION: Count up the counting stick in 6s as a class. *Each division shows 6 more.* Then count up in 60s. Do divisions by pointing to the relevant parts of the stick, eg ask *What is 12 ÷ 6?* and then use the stick to count the number of sixes; extend to working out 120 ÷ 6 and 120 ÷ 20. Ask related division questions and encourage the children to make connections between them. Repeat with different divisions; the children should look at the stick to help them.

MAIN TEACHING ACTIVITY

DIVISION WITH REMAINDERS: Tell the children they are going to do some divisions, but this time there may be a remainder. Look at the divisions on the board. *Is 67 divisible by 4? No. How do you know? Is 83 divisible by 6?* etc. Ask the children to give an estimate for each answer. Work through the first one together, writing down the remainder using the method as in Lesson 6. Give the children, in pairs, a couple of minutes to work out the answers to the other two divisions, then work through them together.

Generate a division by rolling a 10-sided dice twice for a 2-digit number and rolling a 6-sided dice for the divisor. Write the division on the board and work through it as a class using repeated subtraction.

The children generate their own divisions using 10-sided dice. They start with 2-digit numbers and go on to 3-digit numbers, using the same dice for the divisor (if 1 or 0 is rolled, roll again).

DIFFERENTIATION

More able: Go straight on to 3-digit by 1-digit divisions.
Less able: Use a 6-sided dice to generate the divisor.

PLENARY

Check the answers are correct using multiplication.

LESSON 8

RESOURCES

10-sided dice; sets of number cards 2, 4, 5, 10; calculators; OHP calculator.

PREPARATION

Write some 3-digit multiples of 10 on pieces of card.

VOCABULARY

Quotient,
fraction,
decimal,
remainder,
one decimal
place, divide,
divided by,
groups.

LEARNING OUTCOMES

ORAL AND MENTAL STARTER

● Derive quickly: doubles of all whole numbers 1 to 100; doubles of multiples of 10 to 1000; and the corresponding halves.

MAIN TEACHING ACTIVITY

● Begin to express a quotient as a fraction, or as a decimal when dividing a whole number by 2, 4, 5 or 10.

● Check with the inverse operation when using a calculator.

ORAL AND MENTAL STARTER

HALVING ROUND THE ROOM: As for Lesson 2, Unit 4 of Term 1, but extend to 3-digit multiples of 10 using prepared cards.

MAIN TEACHING ACTIVITY

QUOTIENT AS A DECIMAL: Tell the children they are going to write the answers to division questions as decimals where appropriate, rather than with a remainder. *If we are dividing by 2, the answer will always be a whole number or end in .5.* Divide the class into 3 groups: one group investigates numbers divided by 4, another numbers divided by 5, and another numbers divided by 10. Within each group, the children work in pairs to find out what endings are possible in the answers. Gather the information collected: dividing by 4 gives whole number or ends .25, .5, .75; dividing by 5 gives whole number or ends .2, .4, .6, .8; dividing by 10 gives whole number or .1, .2, .3, .4, .5, .6, .7, .8, .9.

Roll a 10-sided dice twice to generate a 2-digit number and pick a card from a set of 2, 4, 5 and 10 for the divisor. Work through the division, eg 73 ÷ 4 = 18 r1. *1 out of 4 left over is $^1/_4$ or 0.25. So the answer is 18.25.* Repeat with other examples, then let the children work through their own examples independently.

DIFFERENTIATION

More able: Investigate the answers when numbers are divided by 3, 6 or 9.
Less able: Investigate the answers when numbers are divided by 2 or 10.

PLENARY

Use an OHP calculator to show the use of inverse operation to check answers. For the example above: 18.25 × 4 = 73. Try several examples. The children check some of their own answers.

RESOURCES

Calculators.

LEARNING OUTCOMES

ORAL AND MENTAL STARTER

● Derive quickly division facts corresponding to tables up to 10 × 10.
● Use known facts and place value to multiply and divide mentally.

MAIN TEACHING ACTIVITY

● Begin to express a quotient as a fraction, or as a decimal when dividing a whole number by 2, 4, 5 or 10, or when dividing £.p.
● Check with the inverse operation when using a calculator.

VOCABULARY

Product,
multiply,
times, divide,
odd, even.

ORAL AND MENTAL STARTER

WHAT IS THE QUESTION? Write 45 ÷ 9 = 5 and 30 ÷ 6 = 5 on the board. *If I know these, I also know that 450 ÷ 90 = 5, 300 ÷ 60 = 5 and so on.* Write ___ ÷ ___ = 7. Ask the children to work in pairs to think of all possible questions with the answer 7. Give them two minutes, then brainstorm possibilities.

MAIN TEACHING ACTIVITY

MONEY DISPLAYS: Write £66 ÷ 4 = on the board. Ask the children to discuss in pairs what word problems might fit this calculation, eg *Four children are given £66 to share between them. How much do they each get?* Take a range of suggestions. Ask the children to estimate what the answer might be. Work it out on a calculator. *16.5 – How should we read that as an amount of money? £16.50.* Repeat with other examples.

The children generate their own examples by choosing a divisor (2, 4, 5 or 10) and a 2- or 3-figure amount of money (a whole number of pounds) to divide. They should work in pairs, and write the answer as an amount of money.

DIFFERENTIATION

More able: Go straight on to 3-digit numbers; divide by any single-digit number and round answers to the nearest penny with teacher guidance as necessary.
Less able: Divide by 2 and 10 initially.

PLENARY

Go over different calculator displays, eg discuss how 13.2 would be written in pounds. Discuss the work the more able group have been doing.

LEARNING OUTCOMES	**ORAL AND MENTAL STARTER** ● Derive quickly: doubles of all whole numbers 1 to 100; doubles of multiples of 10 to 1000; doubles of multiples of 100 to 10 000. **MAIN TEACHING ACTIVITY** ● **Use all four operations to solve simple word problems involving numbers and quantities** based on 'real life' and money, using one or more steps. **Explain methods and reasoning.**
RESOURCES	Word problems involving all four operations from textbooks or worksheets.
ORAL AND MENTAL STARTER	DOUBLING ROUND THE ROOM: As for Lesson 5, Unit 2 of Term 1, with whole class in groups. Start with a 2- or 3-digit multiple of 5 and double until a number over 10 000 is reached. Can each group guess how many numbers they will need to say?
MAIN TEACHING ACTIVITY	FOUR RULES PROBLEMS: Tell the children they are going to solve some problems. Work through some examples: the children decide in pairs which operation they will need, then discuss and solve the problem as a class. Then the pairs work through given problems, writing down the steps needed to solve them.
DIFFERENTIATION	More able: Use problems with harder numbers. Less able: Use problems with adjusted numbers.
PLENARY	Pairs explain to the class how they approached particular problems.

UNITS 4-5

ORGANISATION (10 LESSONS)

LEARNING OUTCOMES	ORAL AND MENTAL STARTER	MAIN TEACHING ACTIVITY	PLENARY
LESSON 1 • Use decimal notation for tenths and hundredths. • Know what each digit represents in a number with up to two decimal places.	MYSTERY NUMBER: As for Lesson 3, Unit 4 of Term 2, but with 2-place decimals.	DEFEAT THE DECIMAL: Use calculators to look at place value in decimal numbers.	Look at additions involving different magnitudes.
LESSON 2 • **Use decimal notation for tenths and hundredths.** • Know what each digit represents in a number with up to two decimal places. • Order a set of numbers or measurements with the same number of decimal places.	COUNTING DECIMALS: Count decimal numbers in steps of different sizes.	PLACING DECIMALS: Position 2-place decimals on a number line.	Round 2-place decimals to the nearest whole number.
LESSON 3 • **Round a number with one or two decimal places to the nearest integer.**	ORDERING DECIMALS: Order a set of 2-place decimal numbers.	ROUNDING DECIMALS: Round 2-place decimals to nearest integer.	Discuss common mistakes in rounding of decimal numbers.
LESSON 4 • **Relate fractions to their decimal representations:** that is, recognise the equivalence between decimal and fraction forms of one half, one quarter, three quarters... and tenths and hundredths (eg 0.7 = $^7/_{10}$, 0.27 = $^{27}/_{100}$).	DOUBLING ROUND THE ROOM: As for Lesson 5, Unit 2 of Term 1, but using higher numbers.	FRACTIONS TO DECIMALS: Convert, then do reverse.	Look at tenths as hundredths, eg $^7/_{10}$ = $^{70}/_{100}$ = 0.7. Go over fractions of amounts.
LESSON 5 +6 • **Relate fractions to division**, and use division to find simple fractions, including tenths and hundredths, of numbers and quantities.	FRACTION GROUP BINGO: Adapt from Lesson 6, Unit 3 of Term 2. Show answers to fraction questions.	FINDING FRACTIONS: Find non-unitary fractions of given amounts. Make up own fraction 'code' problem.	Solve each other's 'code' problems.
LESSON 7 +8 • Express one half, one quarter, three quarters, and tenths and hundredths, as percentages. • Begin to understand percentage as the number of parts in every hundred, and find simple percentages of small whole-number quantities.	MATCHING ON A NUMBER LINE: Repeat from Unit 4, Lesson 4 of spring term (Main teaching activity). Hold up answers to percentage and fraction questions.	FIND THE PERCENTAGE: Find percentages of numbers using knowledge of fractions. Extend to finding more complex percentages.	Discuss how to find more difficult percentages using known facts. Find 5% of multiples of 10 mentally.
LESSON 9 • Solve simple problems using ideas of ratio and proportion.	FRACTION AND % BINGO: Cross out answers from a list of numbers.	RATIOS IN THE ROOM: Solve ratio problems in real-life contexts.	Explore the connections between ratios and fractions.
LESSON 10 • Solve simple problems using ideas of ratio and proportion.	RATIO RACE: Repeat from Lesson 10, Unit 5 of Term 1.	RATIOS AS FRACTIONS: Convert ratios to fractions.	Convert fractions to ratios.

ORAL AND MENTAL SKILLS: Know what each digit represents in a number with up to two decimal places. Order a set of numbers or measurements with the same number of decimal places. Recognise and extend number sequences formed by counting from any number in steps of constant size, extending beyond zero when counting back. Derive quickly: division facts corresponding to tables up to 10 × 10; doubles of all whole numbers 1 to 100; doubles of multiples of 10 to 1000; doubles of multiples of 100 to 10 000; and the corresponding halves. **Relate fractions to division**, and use division to find simple fractions, including tenths and hundredths, of numbers and quantities. **Relate fractions to their decimal representations**: that is, recognise the equivalence between decimal and fraction forms of one half, one quarter, three quarters... and tenths and hundredths. Express one half, one quarter, three quarters and tenths and hundredths as percentages. Solve simple problems using ideas of ratio and proportion.

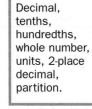

LESSON 1

Lessons 1, 3, 5, 7 and 9 are shown in detail. Lessons 2, 4, 6, 8 and 10 follow on from what has already been taught.

RESOURCES

OHP calculator; calculators; photocopiable page 166; decimal arrow cards (for use with less able children).

PREPARATION

Make one copy per child of photocopiable page 166.

VOCABULARY

Decimal, tenths, hundredths, whole number, units, 2-place decimal, partition.

LEARNING OUTCOMES

ORAL AND MENTAL STARTER
● Know what each digit represents in a number with up to two decimal places.
MAIN TEACHING ACTIVITY
● **Use decimal notation for tenths and hundredths**.
● Know what each digit represents in a number with up to two decimal places.

ORAL AND MENTAL STARTER

MYSTERY NUMBER: As in Lesson 3, Unit 4 of Term 2, adapted for use with 2-place decimals.

MAIN TEACHING ACTIVITY

DEFEAT THE DECIMAL: Tell the children that this lesson is about the value of each digit in a decimal number. Write 3.74 on the board and read it as a class. *How much is the '3' worth – 3 units, 3 tenths, 3 hundredths? 3 units. How much is the 4 worth – 4 units, 4 tenths, 4 hundredths? 4 hundredths. What column is the 7 in?* On an OHP calculator, put in 4.28. *What do I have to subtract to get rid of the 4? 4.* Ask a child to come and subtract 4 on the calculator. *What do I have to subtract to get rid of the 2? 0.2. What will the calculator show if I subtract 0.2?* Ask a child to come and subtract 0.2. *What will I subtract to leave zero?* Repeat, giving children the opportunity to try on their calculators first.

The children work through photocopiable page 166.

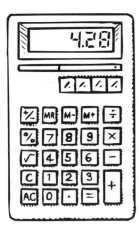
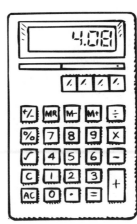

DIFFERENTIATION

More able: Go on to 3-place decimals once they are confident with 2-place numbers.
Less able: Use decimal arrow cards to help them see the place value of digits.

PLENARY

Look at additions, eg 3 + 0.6 + 0.04. *What number does this make? What number does 3.57 + 2 make?*

LESSON 2

LEARNING OUTCOMES	ORAL AND MENTAL STARTER ● Recognise and extend number sequences formed by counting from any number in steps of constant size, extending beyond zero when counting back, eg count on or back in steps of 0.1. MAIN TEACHING ACTIVITY ● Use decimal notation for tenths and hundredths. ● Know what each digit represents in a number with up to two decimal places. ● Order a set of numbers or measurements with the same number of decimal places.
RESOURCES	Number line drawn on board; blank number lines on paper (children could draw these in their books during the lesson).
ORAL AND MENTAL STARTER	COUNTING DECIMALS: Count in steps of 0.1, 0.2 and 0.5. Chant as a class, then round groups. Teacher claps hands to change direction of count (ie count back down the numbers).
MAIN TEACHING ACTIVITY	PLACING DECIMALS: Draw a number line on the board with 1 at one end, 2 at the other and divisions of 0.1 (1.1, 1.2 etc) along the line. Explain that this lesson is about ordering 2-place decimal numbers. Ask children to suggest 2-place decimal numbers between 1 and 2. Write them on the board, then ask children to point to where each would be on the number line. The children write five numbers between two whole numbers, then swap with a partner to mark them on their number line.
DIFFERENTIATION	Less able: Position 1-place decimals on a line with divisions but no labels. More able: Roll three 6-sided dice ten times to generate ten 2-place decimals, then draw a number line and place the numbers on it.
PLENARY	Look at the positions of numbers on the number line; discuss which of two whole numbers each is closest to.

LESSON 3

RESOURCES

String; pegs; large numeral cards; large blank cards; marker pen; eight A4 cards with a 2-place decimal number on each; 10-sided dice (one per pair).

PREPARATION

Hang up a string number line at child height. Peg two consecutive integers (eg 4 and 5) at either end.

VOCABULARY
Round, nearest, nearly, approximately, tenths, hundredths, whole number, between, decimal, one decimal place, two decimal places.

LEARNING OUTCOMES

ORAL AND MENTAL STARTER
● Order a set of numbers or measurements with the same number of decimal places.
MAIN TEACHING ACTIVITY
● **Round a number with one or two decimal places to the nearest integer.**

ORAL AND MENTAL STARTER

ORDERING DECIMALS: Give eight children an A4 decimal number card each. They stand facing the class. Discuss the correct number order as a class, then order the children.

MAIN TEACHING ACTIVITY

ROUNDING DECIMALS: Tell the children they will be looking at how to round decimal numbers to the nearest whole number. Look at the string number line. *Can you give me a 1-place decimal number between 4 and 5?* Write the number on a card and ask a child to peg it at an appropriate place on the line. *Is it closer to 4 or 5?* If the number chosen was 4.5, say that .5 is always rounded up. Repeat with a 2-place decimal number.

Ask the children for any 2-place decimal number between 0 and 10. Write it on a card and show it to the class. *Which two whole numbers does this lie between?* Peg the two whole numbers at the ends of the line; ask a child to come and peg the decimal number at an appropriate place on the line. Discuss which whole number it is closest to. Repeat.

The children work in pairs. They roll a 10-sided dice three times to generate a 2-place decimal number, then write down the number and the number it rounds to (eg 2.39 to 2).

DIFFERENTIATION

More able: Make ten 2-place decimal numbers by rolling the dice, round each number, then use the results to find pairs of decimal numbers that have a rough total of 4 or 7.
Less able: Work with 1-place decimal numbers.

PLENARY

Ask for quick examples of 1- or 2-place decimal numbers that would be rounded to 3 or 8. Examine any misconceptions, eg *What would 3.07 be rounded to? Why?*

LEARNING OUTCOMES	ORAL AND MENTAL STARTER
	● Derive quickly: doubles of all whole numbers 1 to 100; doubles of multiples of 10 to 1000; doubles of multiples of 100 to 10 000. **MAIN TEACHING ACTIVITY** ● **Relate fractions to their decimal representations**: that is, recognise the equivalence between decimal and fraction forms of one half, one quarter, three quarters... and tenths and hundredths (eg $0.7 = {}^7/_{10}$, $0.27 = {}^{27}/_{100}$).
RESOURCES	2-digit number cards, OHP calculator.
ORAL AND MENTAL STARTER	DOUBLING ROUND THE ROOM: Repeat version from Unit 3, Lesson 10.
MAIN TEACHING ACTIVITY	FRACTIONS TO DECIMALS: Say that the lesson is about changing fractions to decimals and vice versa. Write ${}^{34}/_{100}$ on the board. Divide 34 by 100 on the OHP calculator and write 0.34. Ask the children to use this information to convert other fractions of 100 without the aid of a calculator. The children then pick a 2-digit number card, write the number over 100 in fraction form, then write the decimal equivalent. They repeat to make ten decimals, then swap with a partner to convert back to fractions.
DIFFERENTIATION	More able: Work with teacher on writing the fractions of 100 in their simplest form. Less able: Convert tenths to decimals and vice versa initially.
PLENARY	Put 70 ÷ 100 into the OHP calculator. Discuss what it shows: 0.7. *Is this correct?* Discuss the fact that $0.7 = {}^7/_{10} = {}^{70}/_{100}$.

LESSON 5 +6

RESOURCES

Photocopiable page 167; numeral cards (one set per group; one set per child in Lesson 6).

PREPARATION

Write a short coded message on the board, using the same code as on page 167.

LEARNING OUTCOMES

ORAL AND MENTAL STARTER
● Derive quickly division facts corresponding to tables up to 10 × 10.
● **Relate fractions to division**, and use division to find simple fractions, including tenths and hundredths, of numbers and quantities.
MAIN TEACHING ACTIVITY
● **Relate fractions to division**, and use division to find simple fractions, including tenths and hundredths, of numbers and quantities.

ORAL AND MENTAL STARTER

FRACTION GROUP BINGO. Adapt from 'Division group bingo' (Unit 3, Lesson 6, Term 2). Ask questions relating to simple fractions, eg *What is $^1/_4$ of 16? How many fifths are there in $1^2/_5$?*

VOCABULARY

Division, fraction, whole one, half, quarter, third, fifth, sixth, eighth, divided by.

MAIN TEACHING ACTIVITY

FINDING FRACTIONS: Explain that this lesson is about finding fractions of an amount. Write '²/₃ of 18' on the board. *How would you work this out?* Discuss methods. Go over several examples, eg ²/₅ of 20, ⁵/₆ of 24. Look together at the coded word on the board. The children work in pairs to decode it, using the key on photocopiable page 167. Work through it as a class to crack the code.

The children work individually to decode the message on page 167, answering its question on paper.

DIFFERENTIATION

More able: Work with mixed numbers (eg 1²/₃ of 12).
Less able: Use a code with unitary and simple non-unitary fractions (eg ²/₃, ³/₄).

PLENARY

Check that the children have decoded the message. Go over some fractions of amounts. *If I know the answer to a fraction question is 5, what could the question be?*

LESSON 6

For the **Oral and mental starter**, ask FRACTION QUESTIONS: The children hold up numeral cards to show the answers. For the **Main teaching activity**, go over what was learned in Lesson 5. Invite fraction questions for a given answer. The children work in pairs to make up their own coded message, using the same key as before. Differentiate by outcome. In the **Plenary**, decipher a couple of the children's messages together.

LESSON 7 +8

RESOURCES

For Lesson 7: string; pegs; large number cards showing decimals, fractions and percentages (as in Lesson 4, Unit 4 of Term 2); photocopiable page 168. For Lesson 8: blank cards (playing card size); numeral cards (one set per pupil).

PREPARATION

For Lesson 7, hang up the number line at child height. For Lesson 8, write different 3-digit multiples of 10 on five pieces of card.

VOCABULARY
Half, quarter, three-quarters, tenths, hundredths, fraction, decimal, percentage, in every hundred.

LEARNING OUTCOMES

ORAL AND MENTAL STARTER

● **Relate fractions to their decimal representations**: that is, recognise the equivalence between decimal and fraction forms of one half, one quarter, three quarters... and tenths and hundredths (eg $0.7 = ^7/_{10}$, $0.27 = ^{27}/_{100}$).
● Express one half, one quarter, three quarters, and tenths and hundredths as percentages.

MAIN TEACHING ACTIVITY

● Begin to understand percentage as the number of parts in every hundred, and find simple percentages of small whole-number quantities.

ORAL AND MENTAL STARTER

MATCHING ON A NUMBER LINE: Repeat from Main teaching activity in Lesson 4, Unit 4 of Term 2.

MAIN TEACHING ACTIVITY

FIND THE PERCENTAGE: Tell the children that they will be finding percentages of given numbers. Remind them about percentages: *What is 50% as a fraction? Half. How would we find 50% of something? Halve it. What is 25% as a fraction? A quarter. How would you calculate 25% of something? Quarter it – divide by 4.* Repeat for 75% and 10%. Write the numbers 20, 100, 160 and 280 on the board. Children work in pairs to find 50%, 25%, 75% and 10% of each of the numbers.

The children work through photocopiable page 168.

DIFFERENTIATION

More able: Go on to find 5% and 20% of the numbers on page 168.
Less able: Start with 50% and 10%.

PLENARY

Ask the class: *What is 10% of £60? If we know 10%, how can we work out 20% or 30%? What about 15%?*

LESSON 8

For the **Oral and mental starter**, ask FRACTION AND PERCENTAGE QUESTIONS such as *What is 50% of 12?* The children hold up answers,. Discuss the methods used. For the **Main teaching activity**, extend Lesson 7 to using known number facts to calculate more difficult percentages. Take one of the 3-digit multiple of 10 cards and ask the children what 10% of this number is. *How could we use 10% of the number to work out what 20% would be? Double 10%. How could we work out 5%? Halve 10%. How might you work out 15%? Add 10% and 5%.* Calculate 10%, 20%, 5% and 15% of the numbers on the other cards. The children work in pairs, writing six 3-digit multiples of 10 each on different pieces of card, then swap with another pair and work out 10%, 20%, 5% and 15% of each number. More able children can also find 30% and 65%; less able children can work with 2-digit multiples of 10. In the Plenary, discuss how to work out 15% and 35% of a multiple of 10 mentally (by finding 5% and multiplying by 3 and 7 respectively).

RESOURCES

Interlocking cubes, photocopiable page 169.

PREPARATION

Prepare some ratio questions based on the layout of the classroom (see **Main teaching activity** below).

VOCABULARY
Ratio, proportion, in every, for every, fraction, percentage, tenth, hundredth, half, quarter.

LEARNING OUTCOMES

ORAL AND MENTAL STARTER
● Begin to understand percentage as the number of parts in every hundred, and find simple percentages of small whole-number quantities.
MAIN TEACHING ACTIVITY
● Solve simple problems using ideas of ratio and proportion.

ORAL AND MENTAL STARTER

FRACTION AND PERCENTAGE BINGO: The children each write five numbers between 1 and 20 on a piece of paper. Ask questions related to fractions and percentages, eg *What is 20% of 50? What is half of 38?* If a child has the answer, he or she can cross it out. Discuss methods or strategies after each question. Continue until someone has crossed out all five numbers.

MAIN TEACHING ACTIVITY

RATIOS IN THE ROOM: Say that in this lesson, you will be looking at different ratios in the classroom – eg *The ratio of adults to children is 1 to 30. The number of chairs to tables in that group of tables is 6 to 3 or 2 to 1.* Ask someone to explain what that means. *What is the ratio of chairs to tables in that group of tables?* (Point to another group of tables.) *If we added another table, what would the ratio be?*

Ask two boys and a girl to come to the front. *What is the ratio of boys to girls? 2:1.* Write it on the board. Add a girl to the group. *If I want the ratio to be the same as before, how many boys do I need to add?* Continue with different groupings and ratios.

The children work though the problems on the photocopiable sheet.

DIFFERENTIATION

More able: Write some ratios to do with their group or the class, using their own criteria.
Less able: Work with the teacher, using interlocking cubes to show groupings.

PLENARY

Hold up a tower of interlocking cubes, 2 red and 3 yellow. *What is the ratio of red to yellow? 2:3. What fraction of the tower is red?* Explain that there are 5 equal parts in the tower, and 2 out of the 5 are red; therefore two-fifths of the tower is red.

LESSON 10

LEARNING OUTCOMES	**ORAL AND MENTAL STARTER** ● Solve simple problems using ideas of ratio and proportion. **MAIN TEACHING ACTIVITY** ● Solve simple problems using ideas of ratio and proportion.
RESOURCES	6-sided dice; interlocking cubes in 2 colours.
ORAL AND MENTAL STARTER	RATIO RACE: Repeat from Lesson 10, Unit 5 of Term 1.
MAIN TEACHING ACTIVITY	RATIOS AS FRACTIONS: Look at different ratios of cubes, eg red:yellow 2:1, green:blue 1:3. Build the towers. *What proportion of this tower is red? What fraction of this tower is green?* Go straight from a ratio to a proportion, eg *Blue:yellow is 3:5. There are 8 parts in the whole, 3 are blue, so $\frac{3}{8}$ is blue.* The children roll a 6-sided dice twice to generate a ratio, then write it as a proportion in fraction form.
DIFFERENTIATION	More able: Use a 10-sided dice. Less able: Use interlocking cubes to provide an image.
PLENARY	Use cubes to convert fractions to ratios, eg $\frac{2}{3}$ are green. There are 3 parts in total, so 2 are green and the ratio is 2:1.

Decimal numbers

UNITS 4–5

Fill in the missing numbers:

1. $4 + 0.2 =$ _____

2. $5 +$ _____ $= 5.3$

3. _____ $+ 0.6 = 3.6$

4. _____ $+$ _____ $= 2.7$

5. $5.7 - 0.7 =$ _____

6. $6.2 -$ _____ $= 6$

7. $8.1 - 0.1 =$ _____

8. $9.5 -$ _____ $= 9$

Now try these:

9. $3 + 0.2 + 0.04 =$ _____

10. _____ $+ 0.4 + 0.06 = 2.46$

11. $7 +$ _____ $+ 0.08 = 7.38$

12. $6 +$ _____ $+ 0.07 = 6.37$

13. $4 + 0.5 +$ _____ $= 4.51$

14. $9 + 0.3 +$ _____ $= 9.34$

Which numbers would be made by combining the arrow cards below?

15.
  0 . 0 7
  0 . 3
  4
  _____

16.
  1
  0 . 8
  0 . 0 3
  _____

17.
  0 . 0 5
  0 . 6
  2
  _____

18.
  0 . 7
  5
  0 . 0 4
  _____

Name: Date:

Crack the code

A	B	C	D	E	F	G	H	I	J	K	L	M
24	1	14	12	4	22	26	6	20	17	19	13	10
N	O	P	Q	R	S	T	U	V	W	X	Y	Z
8	15	18	5	25	2	16	9	7	3	23	11	21

Decode the secret message below by finding each fraction shown, then using the grid above to write the letters.

$\frac{1}{4}$ of 12	$\frac{2}{3}$ of 9	$\frac{3}{4}$ of 32	$\frac{4}{5}$ of 20

$\frac{2}{5}$ of 50	$\frac{1}{2}$ of 4

$\frac{1}{3}$ of 33	$\frac{5}{6}$ of 18	$\frac{3}{5}$ of 15	$\frac{5}{7}$ of 35

$\frac{2}{3}$ of 12	$\frac{3}{5}$ of 40	$\frac{1}{10}$ of 100	$\frac{2}{5}$ of 10

?

Name: Date:

Same answer

Join up the questions that have the same answer.

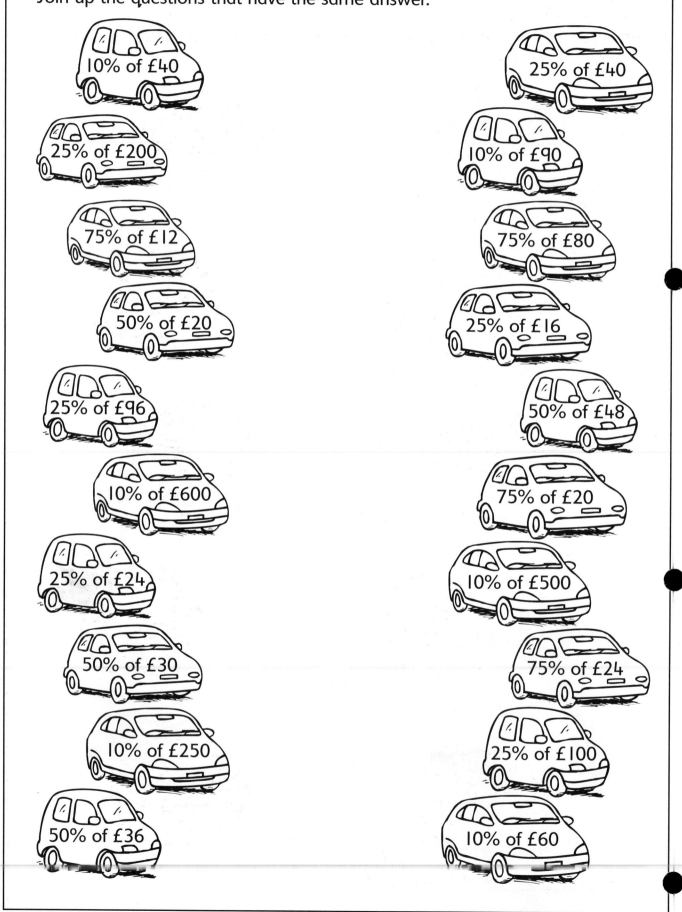

10% of £40

25% of £200

75% of £12

50% of £20

25% of £96

10% of £600

25% of £24

50% of £30

10% of £250

50% of £36

25% of £40

10% of £90

75% of £80

25% of £16

50% of £48

75% of £20

10% of £500

75% of £24

25% of £100

10% of £60

Fruit basket ratios

Look at the ratio statements below. Write in the numbers. The first one has been done for you.

Next to each basket with a ratio, draw fruit in the second basket to keep the ratio the same.

2   for every 1

3   for every 1

___ for every ___

___ for every ___

___ for every ___

UNIT 6

ORGANISATION (8 LESSONS)

LEARNING OUTCOMES	ORAL AND MENTAL STARTER	MAIN TEACHING ACTIVITY	PLENARY
LESSON 1 • Discuss the chance or likelihood of particular events.	NUMERAL CARDS: Respond to multiplication and division questions.	INTRODUCING PROBABILITY: Consider whether events are certain, likely or possible.	Discuss further events.
LESSON 2 + 3 • Discuss the chance or likelihood of particular events. • Solve a problem by representing and interpreting data in tables, charts, graphs and diagrams, eg bar line charts.	CHANTING TABLES: Respond to quick tables questions.	TESTING A SPINNER: Test the fairness of a spinner. Make a prediction and collect data to test it.	Discuss why actual spinners may be biased. Evaluate the predictions. Discuss the data collected.
LESSON 4 + 5 • Find the mode of a set of data. • Solve a problem by representing and interpreting data in tables, charts, graphs and diagrams, eg bar line charts.	DOUBLING ROUND THE ROOM: Repeat from Lesson 5, Unit 2 of Term 1, against the clock.	MODE AND RANGE: Collect data and find mode and range. Find the mode and range of data from a chart.	Discuss answers on photocopiable sheet.
LESSON 6 • Solve a problem by representing and interpreting data in tables, charts, graphs and diagrams, eg bar line charts. • Find the mode of a set of data.	SHOW ME HALF: Show numeral cards to halve a number.	COMPUTER DATABASE: Look at computer graphs and answer questions.	Discuss what was found out. Look at a child's graph: what does it show?
LESSON 7 + 8 • Solve a problem by representing and interpreting data in tables, charts, graphs and diagrams, eg bar line charts where intermediate points may have meaning.	HALVING ROUND THE ROOM: Adapt from Lesson 2, Unit 4 of Term 1.	PULSE RATE: Plot a graph from data. Discuss what it shows. Compare graphs with a partner. Write description of graph.	Discuss some of the descriptions of graphs.

ORAL AND MENTAL SKILLS: Know by heart multiplication facts up to 10 × 10. Derive quickly: division facts corresponding to tables up to 10 × 10; doubles of all whole numbers 1 to 100; doubles of multiples of 10 to 1000; doubles of multiples of 100 to 10 000; and the corresponding halves.

Lessons 1, 2, 4, 6 and 7 are shown in detail. Lessons 3, 5 and 8 follow on from what has already been taught.

RESOURCES

Numeral cards (one set per child); photocopiable page 175.

PREPARATION

Write some (at least five) statements on the board, eg When I leave school, I am going to play football for Manchester United; I will have chips at lunchtime; We will do maths today.

LEARNING OUTCOMES

ORAL AND MENTAL STARTER
● Know by heart all multiplication facts up to 10 × 10.
● Derive quickly division facts corresponding to tables up to 10 × 10.
MAIN TEACHING ACTIVITY
● Discuss the chance or likelihood of particular events.

VOCABULARY

Likely, unlikely, likelihood, certain, uncertain, probable, possible, impossible, chance, good chance, poor chance, no chance.

ORAL AND MENTAL STARTER

NUMERAL CARDS: Ask the children questions related to multiplication and division facts; they show answers on numeral cards.

MAIN TEACHING ACTIVITY

INTRODUCING PROBABILITY: Tell the children they are going to decide how likely it is that different things will happen. *You will need to decide whether an event is certain, likely, unlikely or impossible.* Write the words on the board; ask children for definitions and other words or phrases that might mean the same thing. Look at the five statements on the board. Do the children think they are certain, likely, unlikely or impossible? Why?

The children look at photocopiable page 175 and write each statement in the appropriate column, then add some of their own under each heading.

DIFFERENTIATION

Differentiate by outcome. More able children could also rank the statements in order of likelihood, from the most to the least likely.

PLENARY

Discuss some of the additional events and rank them in order of likelihood.

LESSON 2 + 3

RESOURCES

Card; scissors; hexagon templates (for spinners); used matchsticks or pencils.

PREPARATION

Make a hexagonal spinner: cut out a hexagon from card and divide it into numbered triangles (see figure right).

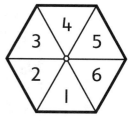

VOCABULARY

Likely, unlikely, likelihood, certain, uncertain, probable, possible, impossible, chance, good chance, poor chance, no chance, fair, unfair, doubt, risk.

LEARNING OUTCOMES

ORAL AND MENTAL STARTER
● **Know by heart all multiplication facts up to 10 × 10.**
● Derive quickly division facts corresponding to tables up to 10 × 10.
MAIN TEACHING ACTIVITY
● Discuss the chance or likelihood of particular events.
● Solve a problem by representing and interpreting data in tables, charts, graphs and diagrams, eg bar line charts.

ORAL AND MENTAL STARTER

CHANTING TABLES: Chant multiples of 6 as a class, then chant back to zero. Ask groups, pairs or individuals quick questions about the 6× table, eg *How many 6s make 42? What are 5 sixes?* Repeat with multiples of 7.

MAIN TEACHING ACTIVITY

TESTING A SPINNER: Tell the children they are going to investigate whether one number is more likely to come up on a spinner than others. Do they think all the numbers have an equal chance, or is one number more likely? Why? Pass the spinner made beforehand round the class, asking various children to spin it. Record the results on a tally chart on the board. After several goes, does it seem that one number comes up more often?

The children work in pairs to make their own spinners and decide which number (if any) is most likely to come up; then spin each spinner 30 times and record the results on a tally chart, then on a bar line graph.

DIFFERENTIATION

Differentiate by outcome.

PLENARY

Discuss why some numbers seem more likely on some spinners, but not on others. *Are the spinners fair or unfair? Why is that?*

LESSON 3

Repeat the **Oral and mental starter** from Lesson 2. For the **Main teaching activity**, look at the results on a graph from an imaginary, biased spinner. Discuss what they show. The children swap their own graphs and spinners with another pair and use the other pair's results to make a prediction, then use their spinner to test the prediction, record the results and compare the graphs. Differentiate by outcome. In the **Plenary**, discuss the accuracy of the predictions and the fairness of the spinners.

LESSON
4
+ 5

RESOURCES

Numerical data, either real or imaginary (see example below); photocopiable page 176.

PREPARATION

Write some data, either from a collected real-life source or imaginary on the board, eg the number of goals scored in ten football matches, for example: 3, 4, 4, 0, 2, 1, 1, 2, 3, 2.

VOCABULARY
Mode, range, most common, least common, popular, highest, lowest, frequency.

LEARNING OUTCOMES

ORAL AND MENTAL STARTER

● Derive quickly: doubles of all whole numbers 1 to 100; doubles of multiples of 10 to 1000; doubles of multiples of 100 to 10 000.

MAIN TEACHING ACTIVITY

● Find the mode of a set of data.

ORAL AND MENTAL STARTER

DOUBLING ROUND THE ROOM: As for Lesson 5, Unit 2 of Term 1. Start with a multiple of 5; how quickly can the class reach a number over 10 000? Repeat.

MAIN TEACHING ACTIVITY

MODE AND RANGE: Explain that this lesson is about finding the most common value in a set of data. *What do we call the most common value? The mode.* Point to the data about football matches on the board. *Decide with your partner which value comes up most often. What is the mode of this set of data?* Take feedback. *How could we check?* Draw up a tally chart or frequency table as a class. *This tells us the most common value is 2, so the mode for this set of data is 2.*

What do we call the difference between the highest value and the lowest value? The range. What is the highest value in this set of data? 4. What is the lowest value? 0. So the range is 4. Collect data from 10 children about the number of siblings (brothers or sisters) they have. Write it on the board. Calculate the mode and range for this data as a class.

The children work in pairs to collect data about shoe sizes, handspans or number of pets from 10 other people in the class, then find the mode and range of each set of data.

DIFFERENTIATION

More able: Decide on their own set of data to collect.
Less able: Work in mixed-ability pairs.

PLENARY

Discuss the information collected. Did all the sets of the same type of data have the same mode and range? Discuss why there may have been discrepancies.

LESSON 5

Repeat the **Oral and mental starter** as for Lesson 4. For the **Main teaching activity**, draw up a bar chart on the board showing number of pets. Discuss how the mode and range can be read from the bar chart. The children work through photocopiable page 176. More able children can look at other bar charts; less able children can concentrate on finding the mode. In the **Plenary**, go through the problems on page 176.

LESSON 6

RESOURCES

Numeral cards (one set per child); computers; data handling software (eg *Find It* (from Appian Way Software; www.appianway.co.uk), *Flexidata* (from Flexible Software; www.flexible.co.uk)); a computer database with information set up in the appropriate program; a worksheet with suitable questions (see 'Preparation' below).

PREPARATION

Go through the information in the database and write questions that the children can answer specifically by looking at some of the graphs the database can generate, eg *On the graph showing the number of legs on minibeasts, what is the mode?* Write about 10 questions referring to different graphs on a worksheet for the children to complete later.

LEARNING OUTCOMES

ORAL AND MENTAL STARTER
● Derive quickly: halves corresponding to doubles of all whole numbers 1 to 100; to doubles of multiples of 10 to 1000; to doubles of multiples of 100 to 10 000.
MAIN TEACHING ACTIVITY
● Solve a problem by representing and interpreting data in tables, charts, graphs and diagrams, eg bar line charts.
● Find the mode of a set of data.

ORAL AND MENTAL STARTER

SHOW ME HALF: Pairs of children hold up numeral cards to show half of a number said. Make connections by asking related questions, eg *What is half of 48? 24. Half of 480? 240. Half of 4800? 2400.*

MAIN TEACHING ACTIVITY

COMPUTER DATABASE: Explain that this lesson is about finding information on a computer database. Ask the children to sit around one computer (or so that they can see a monitor with the computer screen on it). Show them how to move around the data handling program, and discuss what various graphs show. Ask the children what data they would need to look at in order to answer the first question. Repeat with the second question.

The children work through the questions on the worksheet in pairs or threes at each computer. If only one computer is available, some children can do this activity while others do an activity from Lesson 4 or 5.

DIFFERENTIATION

More able: Write their own questions for a partner to answer using the database.
Less able: Work with teacher support.

PLENARY

Go through any difficulties. Work through the answers and how they were found.

LESSON 7 +8

RESOURCES

Graph paper; squared paper; pencils.

PREPARATION

The children, in pairs, should collect information about pulse rates before and after exercise (perhaps during a PE lesson). They take and record their partner's resting pulse rate, run on the spot for 2 minutes and take their partner's pulse rate again, after 2 more minutes, take it again and so on until 10 minutes' exercise has taken place. Before the lesson, draw and label axes for a line graph showing pulse rate against time on the board (see figure above); fill in one pair's set of results.

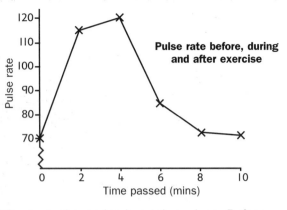

Pulse rate before, during and after exercise

VOCABULARY

Line graph, rise, fall, data, collect, record.

LEARNING OUTCOMES

ORAL AND MENTAL STARTER

● Derive quickly: halves corresponding to doubles of all whole numbers 1 to 100; to doubles of multiples of 10 to 1000; to doubles of multiples of 100 to 10 000.

MAIN TEACHING ACTIVITY

● Solve a problem by representing and interpreting data in tables, charts, graphs and diagrams, eg bar line graphs where intermediate points may have meaning.

ORAL AND MENTAL STARTER

HALVING ROUND THE ROOM: As for Lesson 2, Unit 4 of Term 1. Give the starting group a 4-digit multiple of 100; the groups predict how many goes will be needed to reach an odd number. Repeat several times, keeping it fast.

MAIN TEACHING ACTIVITY

PULSE RATE: Explain that this lesson will focus on bar line graphs. Look at the information on the board and plot the graph together, asking children to come and plot particular points. Discuss what the graph shows. Ask questions about it, eg *What was the pulse rate after 6 minutes? What was it after 9 minutes? When was the pulse rate 80 beats per minute?* The children work individually to plot line graphs of their own data.

DIFFERENTIATION

Differentiate by outcome.

PLENARY

Look at one child's graph. Discuss what it shows: *What do the peaks show? What is happening to the pulse rate when the line goes up?*

LESSON 8

Repeat the **Oral and mental starter** from Lesson 7. For the **Main teaching activity**, use the information and graphs from Lesson 7 to make comparisons. Compare two graphs on the board as a whole class. Then the children work in pairs to compare their graphs, discuss similarities and differences and write a description of each graph. Work with less able children, asking questions to draw out the information and giving them specific questions to answer in their description. In the **Plenary**, read out some descriptions – how accurate are they?

Name: Date:

How likely?

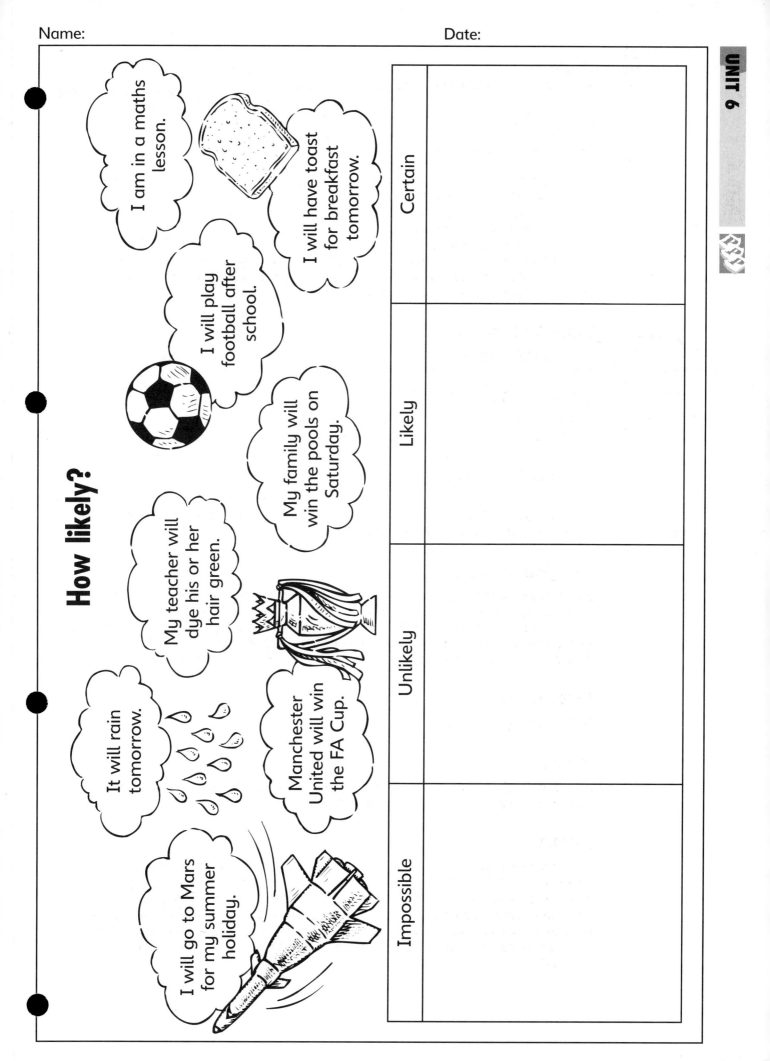

Certain	Likely	Unlikely	Impossible

UNIT 6

Find the mode and range

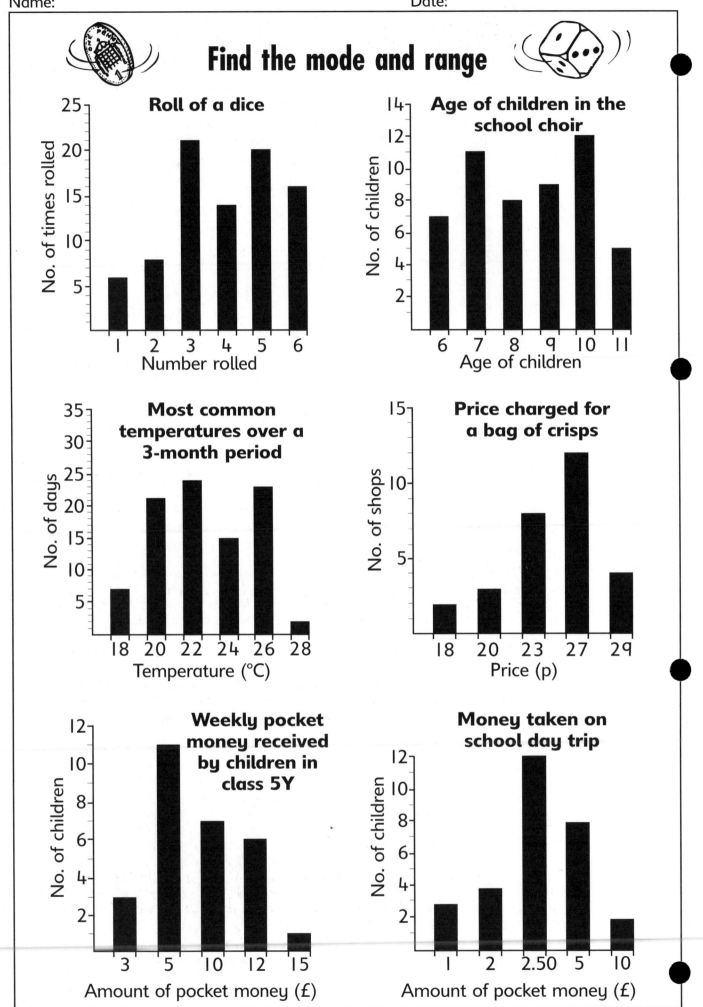

Roll of a dice

Age of children in the school choir

Most common temperatures over a 3-month period

Price charged for a bag of crisps

Weekly pocket money received by children in class 5Y

Money taken on school day trip

Choose from these activities. During the group activities, some of the children can work with you on practical tasks, while others complete assessment worksheets 5a and 5b which assess their skills in handling negative numbers and decimal numbers, and in using written methods for multiplication and division. The specific assessment criteria for the assessment sheets are to be found at the bottom of each sheet.

RESOURCES

Number cards –10 to +10; 2-digit number cards; a set per child of arrow cards (thousands, hundreds, tens and units); numeral cards.

ORAL AND MENTAL STARTER

ASSESSMENT

Can the children:
● derive quickly doubles of all multiples of 10 to 1000 and the corresponding halves
● round any integer less than 10 000 to the nearest 10, 100 or 1000?

SHOW ME: Hold up a multiple of 10 with arrow cards; the children double the number and show the answer with their arrow cards when you say *Go!* Repeat with corresponding halves.

ROUND ME: Write a 4-digit number on the board; the children write down the nearest 1000, 100 and 10.

GROUP ACTIVITIES

ASSESSMENT

Can the children:
● **order a given set of positive and negative integers**
● **multiply a 3-digit number by a 1-digit number, explaining their methods and reasoning**
● **round a number with one or two decimal places to the nearest integer?**

ORDERING NUMBERS: Put a random selection of positive and negative number cards on the table. Ask the children to imagine there is a number line on the table; show them where '0' would be in the middle of the table. Give each child at least two numbers (one positive and one negative) to position on the imaginary number line. As they position the numbers, can they explain the reasons for each decision clearly?

MULTIPLY A 3-DIGIT BY A 1-DIGIT NUMBER: Write these calculations on the board:

$$254 \times 2 = \qquad 320 \times 4 = \qquad 427 \times 7 = \qquad 365 \times 9 =$$

Ask the children to calculate their answers on paper, showing clearly how they worked them out. Ask them to talk through their workings to the rest of the group. Can they explain how they did it? Did they use an appropriate method?

ROUNDING AROUND THE GROUP: Work with a group of four children. The first three children take a card each to make a 2-place decimal number. The fourth child says what (whole) number the decimal number would be rounded to, and explains why. Continue until each child has rounded three numbers.

UNIT 7

Assessment 5a

1. Write these numbers in the appropriate places on the number line.

-2 $+9$ $+2$ -4 $+7$ -1 $+3$ -5

2. Join each of the measurements in the box below to the nearest whole unit.

1.2kg	1.75l	2.17m	2.08l	1.6m	1.47kg
1m	2m	1l	2l	1kg	2kg
1.5l	2.49m	2.32kg	1.25l	1.09m	1.96kg

3. Write three 2-place decimals that could be rounded to the number shown.

2   _____   _____   _____

10   _____   _____   _____

7   _____   _____   _____

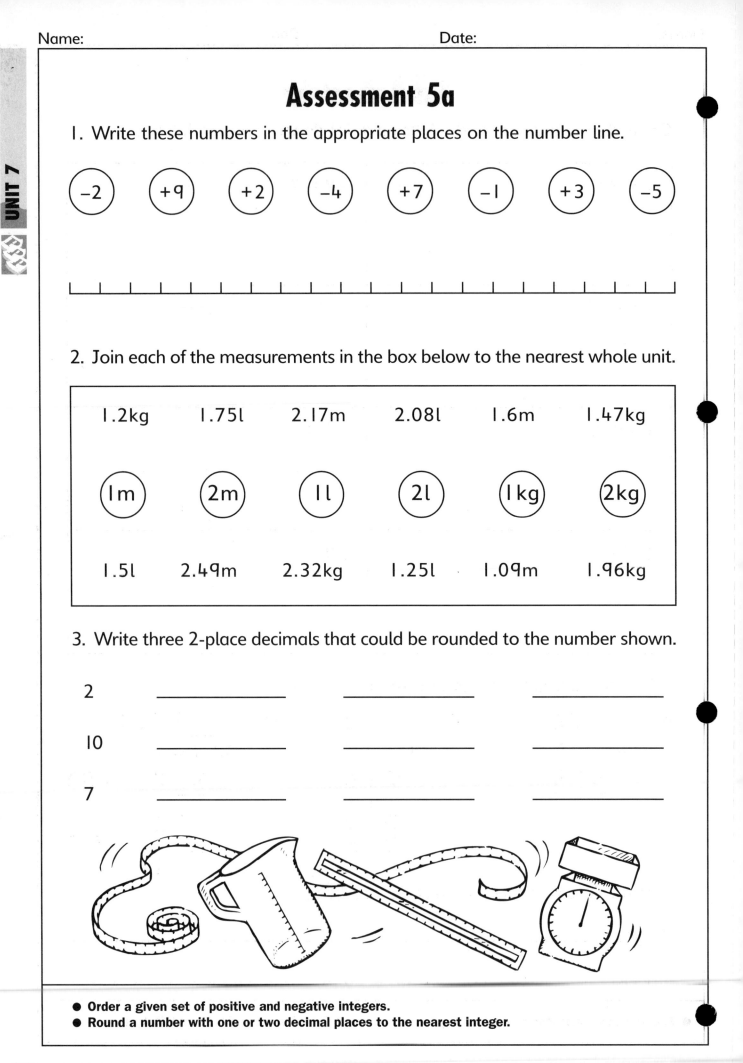

● **Order a given set of positive and negative integers.**
● **Round a number with one or two decimal places to the nearest integer.**

Assessment 5b

Calculate the answers to the following. Jot down your calculations.

2.6 × 4	4.8 × 7
43 × 17	36 × 28
64 × 23	124 ÷ 4
371 ÷ 7	494 ÷ 6

2. Tick the calculations that are correct.

a)
```
        7.6
    ×     9
      6 8 4
         5
```

b)
```
        7 2
    ×   3 3
      2 1 6
      2 1 6
      4 3 2
```

c)
```
          8 5 r 1
    4) 3 4 1
       3 2 0      × 80
         2 1
         2 0      × 5
          1
```

Which calculations are incorrect? _____

Why? _____

_____

● **Extend written methods to short multiplication of** U.t x U, **TU x TU, short division of HTU by U.**

UNITS 8-10

ORGANISATION (15 LESSONS)

LEARNING OUTCOMES	ORAL AND MENTAL STARTER	MAIN TEACHING ACTIVITY	PLENARY
LESSON 1 • Understand and use angle measure in degrees. • Identify, estimate and order acute and obtuse angles.	NUMERAL CARDS: Show number needed to make 100.	NAMING ANGLES: Revise acute, obtuse and right angles.	Draw angles given different criteria.
LESSON 2 +3 • Understand and use angle measure in degrees. • Use a protractor to measure and draw acute and obtuse angles to the nearest 5°.	NUMERAL CARDS: Show number needed to make 180. Say decimal number needed to make 10.	MEASURING ANGLES: Measure angles accurately. Draw angles accurately.	Judge whether estimates of angles may be correct. Draw angles by estimating, then measure.
LESSON 4 • Understand and use angle measure in degrees. • Use a protractor to measure and draw angles to the nearest 5°. • Make shapes with increasing accuracy. • Measure and draw lines to the nearest millimetre.	GUESS THE SHAPE: Repeat from Lesson 1, Unit 5 of Term 2.	ACCURATE SHAPES: Follow instructions to draw regular shapes accurately.	Discuss which shapes were more difficult to draw and why.
LESSON 5 • Understand and use angle measure in degrees. • Use a protractor to measure and draw angles to the nearest 5°. • Calculate angles in a straight line.	NUMERAL CARDS: Repeat from Lesson 2.	ANGLES IN A STRAIGHT LINE: Calculate using known angle facts.	Calculate missing angles in a full turn.
LESSON 6 • Understand and use angle measure in degrees. • Use a protractor to measure and draw angles to the nearest 5°. • Make and investigate a general statement about familiar shapes by finding examples to match it.	NUMERAL CARDS: Show the missing angle in a straight line.	ANGLES IN A POLYGON: Find out the sum of the internal angles in a triangle or quadrilateral.	Identify pattern and extend to pentagon and hexagon.
LESSON 7 • Understand and use angle measure in degrees. • Make shapes with increasing accuracy. • Solve mathematical problems or puzzles, recognise and explain patterns and relationships, generalise and predict; suggest extensions asking 'What if...?'	NAME THE SHAPE: Repeat from Lesson 1, Unit 5 of Term 2.	SHAPES ON COMPUTER: Draw irregular polygons on screen, using LOGO to set angles.	Look at how the shapes were drawn and the results.
LESSON 8 • Use, read and write standard metric units (kg, g) including their abbreviations, and relationships between them. Convert larger to smaller units (eg kg to g). • Suggest suitable units and measuring equipment to measure mass.	NUMERAL CARDS: Repeat from Lesson 3.	INTRODUCING MASS: Estimate weights of objects and suggest suitable units (kg or g).	Convert kg to g.
LESSON 9 +10 • Use, read and write standard metric units (kg, g) including their abbreviations, and relationships between them. Convert larger to smaller units (eg kg to g). • Record estimates and readings from scales to a suitable degree of accuracy.	NUMERAL CARDS: Show mass needed to make up 1kg. Convert kg to g.	HOW MUCH MASS? Estimate and measure mass of objects, using weights. Repeat without using weights.	Discuss estimates of mass: are they reasonable? Solve problems involving times and duration.

	LEARNING OUTCOMES	ORAL AND MENTAL STARTER	MAIN TEACHING ACTIVITY	PLENARY
LESSON 11	● Use units of time; read the time on a 24-hour digital clock and use 24-hour clock notation, such as 19:58.	SHOW ME: Show given times using clock faces.	REVISION OF 24-HOUR CLOCK: Write times in 12-hour and 24-hour clock forms.	Discuss and sum up the children's findings.
LESSON 12 + 13	● Use units of time; read the time on a 24-hour digital clock and use 24-hour clock notation, such as 19:58. Use timetables. **● Use all four operations to solve word problems involving numbers and quantities** based on 'real life', money and measures **(including time)**, using one or more steps, including making simple conversions of pounds to foreign currency.	NUMERAL CARDS: Repeat from Lesson 1. NUMERAL CARDS: Answer multiplication questions involving foreign currency.	PLAN A HOLIDAY: Look at conversion of pounds to foreign currency. Plan dates for holiday.	Groups describe planned holiday. Groups state cost of holiday in pounds and foreign currency.
LESSON 14 + 15	**● Use all four operations to solve word problems involving numbers and quantities** based on 'real life', money and measures **(including time)**, using one or more steps. ● Choose and use appropriate number operations to solve problems, and appropriate ways of calculating: mental, mental with jottings, written methods, calculator.	PAIRS TO 1000: Say what number is needed. PROBLEMS BINGO: Turn over cards which answer word problems.	PROBLEM SOLVING: Solve problems involving time, money and measures.	Check answers on a calculator. Go over any difficulties.

ORAL AND MENTAL SKILLS: Derive quickly: decimals that total 10; all two-digit pairs that total 100; all pairs of multiples of 50 with a total of 1000. Use known number facts and place value to add mentally any pair of two-digit whole numbers (Year 4 revision). Describe and visualise 2-D shapes (Year 4 revision). Calculate angles in a straight line. Convert larger to smaller units (eg kg to g). **Know by heart multiplication facts up to 10 × 10. Use all four operations to solve word problems involving numbers and quantities** based on 'real life', money and measures. Read the time from an analogue clock to the nearest minute (Year 4 revision).

Lessons 1, 2, 4, 7–9, 12 and 14 are shown in detail. Lessons 3, 5, 6, 10, 11, 13 and 15 follow on from what has already been taught.

RESOURCES

Photocopiable page 190; numeral cards (one set per child).

PREPARATION

Draw some acute, obtuse and right angles on the board.

LEARNING OUTCOMES

ORAL AND MENTAL STARTER
● Derive quickly all two-digit pairs that total 100.
MAIN TEACHING ACTIVITY
● Understand and use angle measure in degrees.
● Identify, estimate and order acute and obtuse angles.

ORAL AND MENTAL STARTER

NUMERAL CARDS: Say a 2-digit number. Pupils hold up numeral cards to show how many more are needed to make 100. Discuss strategies.

MAIN TEACHING ACTIVITY

NAMING ANGLES: Tell the children they are going to name different types of angle. *What is an angle? It is a measurement of turn. What types of angle can you think of? Right angle, acute angle, obtuse angle. What does a right angle look like?* Ask a child to come and point to one on the board. *Are there any others? How many degrees are in a right angle? 90°. What sort of angle is smaller than a right angle? An acute angle.* Ask a child to come and point to one. *What type of angle is larger than 90° but smaller than 180°? An obtuse angle.* Indicate examples of obtuse angles.

The children complete photocopiable page 190.

DIFFERENTIATION

More able: Use an angle measurer to measure the angles.
Less able: Use a right angle template to compare the angles with right angles.

PLENARY

Ask the children to draw an acute angle just smaller than a right angle, then an obtuse angle just smaller than two right angles. Talk about the need to measure angles accurately.

LESSON 2 +3

RESOURCES

Photocopiable page 190 from Lesson 1; protractors; board protractor; numeral cards (one set per pair); sharp pencils; rulers; blank paper.

PREPARATION

Draw some angles on the board (as for Lesson 1).

VOCABULARY

Angle, right angle, turn, obtuse, acute, is a greater angle than, smaller angle than, straight line, degrees, protractor, measure.

LEARNING OUTCOMES

ORAL AND MENTAL STARTER
● Use known number facts and place value to add mentally any pair of two-digit whole numbers.
● Derive quickly: all two-digit pairs that total 100; decimals that total 10.

MAIN TEACHING ACTIVITY
● Understand and use angle measure in degrees.
● Use a protractor to measure and draw acute and obtuse angles to the nearest 5°.

ORAL AND MENTAL STARTER

NUMERAL CARDS: Pairs of children each have a set of numeral cards. Say a 2- or 3-digit number less than 180; the children show how many more are needed to make 180. Discuss strategies; encourage the use of known facts.

MAIN TEACHING ACTIVITY

MEASURING ANGLES: Explain that this lesson is about measuring angles, and that it is important to be able to measure and draw angles accurately. *What unit do we measure angles in? Degrees. How many degrees are in a right angle? 90°.* Look at one of the angles drawn on the board. *What sort of angle is this: acute, right or obtuse? Will it measure more than 90° or less than 90°? Will it be much more or less than 90°?* Encourage the children

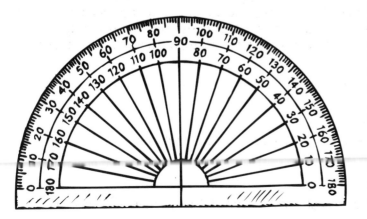

to use what they know about acute and obtuse angles. Show them a protractor. *This is a protractor; it is used for measuring angles.* Use the board protractor to show how to measure an angle; stress the need to line up the protractor correctly. Look at other angles on the board. Ask children to estimate them, then measure them using the board protractor.

Look at the first angle on photocopiable page 190 from Lesson 1. Ask the children to measure it using their protractor. Compare with a partner and feed back to the class. The children measure all the angles on the sheet.

DIFFERENTIATION

More able: With teacher guidance, go on to draw angles to the nearest 5°.
Less able: Can be given a range that each angle lies within.

PLENARY

Draw some angles on the board; write an estimate next to each one, some of them incorrect. Discuss which ones could be correct and which ones are clearly wrong, and why.

LESSON 3

For the **Oral and mental starter**, give groups 1-place decimals between 0 and 10; they say together how many more are needed to make 10. Give different groups connected numbers (eg 1.7, 3.7, 5.7) to make connections clear. Start with a different group each time. For the **Main teaching activity**, demonstrate how to draw angles accurately using a protractor. Encourage children to demonstrate. Write ten angles on the board (eg 35°); the children draw them, then swap with a partner to measure. More able children can draw angles to the nearest degree (eg 107°), less able children can draw angles that are multiples of 10°. For the **Plenary**, ask children to draw given angles on the board by estimating; then ask others to check with the board protractor. Which one is the closest?

RESOURCES

Protractor; board protractor; rulers; sharp pencils; blank paper; shape templates.

PREPARATION

Write on the board:

Square	– length of sides 5.5cm, angles 90°
Equilateral triangle	– length of sides 7.4cm, angles 60°
Regular pentagon	– length of sides 4.2cm, angles 108°
Regular hexagon	– length of sides 5.8cm, angles 120°

VOCABULARY

Angle, right angle, turn, obtuse, acute, a greater angle than, a smaller angle than, straight line, degrees, protractor, measure, triangle, square, rectangle, pentagon, hexagon, octagon, millimetre, centimetre.

LEARNING OUTCOMES

ORAL AND MENTAL STARTER
● Describe and visualise 2-D shapes.
MAIN TEACHING ACTIVITY
● Understand and use angle measure in degrees.
● Use a protractor to measure and draw angles to the nearest 5°.
● Make shapes with increasing accuracy.
● Measure and draw lines to the nearest millimetre.

ORAL AND MENTAL STARTER

GUESS THE SHAPE: Repeat from Lesson 1, Unit 5 of Term 2.

MAIN TEACHING ACTIVITY

ACCURATE SHAPES: Tell the children they are going to use information about length of sides and size of angles to draw shapes accurately. *We know that a square has 4 equal sides and 4 right angles: angles of 90°.* Demonstrate how to use a ruler and protractor to draw a square with 30cm sides. Repeat for an equilateral triangle with 25cm sides.

The children draw the four shapes described on the board, swap with a partner and check by measuring.

DIFFERENTIATION

More able: Also draw an octagon.
Less able: Draw sides to nearest half-centimetre; leave out pentagon.

PLENARY

Discuss which shapes were the easiest and the most difficult to draw. Why was this?

LESSON 5

LEARNING OUTCOMES	**ORAL AND MENTAL STARTER** ● Use number facts and place value to add mentally any pair of two- digit whole numbers. ● Derive quickly all two-digit pairs that total 100. **MAIN TEACHING ACTIVITY** ● Understand and use angle measure in degrees. ● Use a protractor to measure and draw angles to the nearest 5°. ● Calculate angles in a straight line.
RESOURCES	Photocopiable page 191; numeral cards (one set per pair).
ORAL AND MENTAL STARTER	NUMERAL CARDS: Repeat from Lesson 2.
MAIN TEACHING ACTIVITY	ANGLES IN A STRAIGHT LINE: Tell the children they are going to use their knowledge of the size of turn in a straight line to find a missing angle. Draw a straight line on the board, then draw and label an angle on the line (see right).  Discuss how you can use the straight line and known angle to calculate the other angle. Do several examples. The children work through photocopiable page 191.
DIFFERENTIATION	More able: Draw angles from straight lines and label one angle. Swap with a partner to calculate the missing angle. Less able: Use a calculator if necessary to work out the missing angle.
PLENARY	Discuss how to calculate missing angles from a full turn.

LESSON 6

LEARNING OUTCOMES	**ORAL AND MENTAL STARTER** ● Calculate angles in a straight line. **MAIN TEACHING ACTIVITY** ● Understand and use angle measure in degrees. ● Use a protractor to measure and draw angles to the nearest 5°. ● Make and investigate a general statement about familiar shapes by finding examples to match it.
RESOURCES	Photocopiable page 192, protractors, board protractor, numeral cards (one set per child).
ORAL AND MENTAL STARTER	NUMERAL CARDS: Say an angle; the children show how many more degrees are needed to make a straight line.
MAIN TEACHING ACTIVITY	ANGLES IN A POLYGON: Draw 2 triangles and 2 quadrilaterals on the board and measure each of the internal angles. Ask the children to investigate the sum of the internal angles of a triangle and a quadilateral by measuring the angles in the shapes on photocopiable page 192.
DIFFERENTIATION	More able: Go on to investigate the sum of the internal angles in a pentagon. Less able: Concentrate on triangles.
PLENARY	Discuss what has been discovered. *What is the sum of the angles in a triangle? 180°. A quadrilateral? 360°. A pentagon? 540°. Can you see a pattern? The sum increases by 180° for each side. Can you predict the sum of angles in a hexagon?*

LESSON 7

RESOURCES

Computers; LOGO type software (eg screen turtle); shape templates.

PREPARATION

Make sure there is a list of LOGO commands for each computer, eg RT for right turn.

LEARNING OUTCOMES

ORAL AND MENTAL STARTER
● Describe and visualise 2-D shapes.
MAIN TEACHING ACTIVITY
● Understand and use angle measure in degrees.
● Make shapes with increasing accuracy.
● Solve mathematical problems and puzzles, recognise and explain patterns and relationships, generalise and predict; suggest extensions asking 'What if...?'

ORAL AND MENTAL STARTER

NAME THE SHAPE: Repeat from Lesson 1, Unit 5 of Term 2.

MAIN TEACHING ACTIVITY

SHAPES ON COMPUTER: Tell the children they will draw shapes using the computer. Show them how they might draw a square by using and repeating commands. Show them how you would draw a non-equilateral triangle, using knowledge of the sum of the internal angles in a triangle – but remind the children that the drawing programme works with external rather than internal angles. You may need to use trial and improvement when deciding on the lengths of the sides.

The children work in pairs or threes to draw irregular polygons using the software: triangles, quadrilaterals and pentagons. Encourage them to ask and investigate questions, eg *What would happen if I tried an angle of 70°?*

DIFFERENTIATION

More able: Go on to hexagons, heptagons and so on.
Less able: Follow instructions given by the teacher.

PLENARY

Discuss the commands used and the results achieved.

LESSON 8

RESOURCES

Photocopiable page 193; sets of weights (50g, 100g, 250g, 500g and 1kg); scales.

PREPARATION

Put a set of weights on each table.

LEARNING OUTCOMES

ORAL AND MENTAL STARTER
● Derive quickly decimals that total 10.
MAIN TEACHING ACTIVITY
● Use, read and write standard metric units (kg, g) including their abbreviations, and relationships between them. Convert larger to smaller units (eg kg to g).
● Suggest suitable units and measuring equipment to measure mass.

ORAL AND MENTAL STARTER

NUMERAL CARDS: Repeat from Lesson 3.

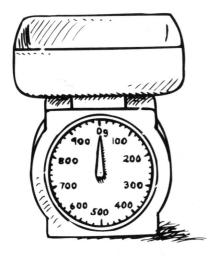

MAIN TEACHING ACTIVITY

INTRODUCING MASS: Tell the children they are going to suggest suitable units to weigh things in and compare objects to see which are lighter or heavier. *What unit of measurement do we use to measure mass or weight? Grams, kilograms, tonnes, pounds, ounces.* Say that this lesson will concentrate on grams and kilograms. *How many grams are in a kilogram? 1000.* Write on the board: 1kg = 1000g. Ask the children to feel the weights on the table. Ask one child from each group to find something in the room that weighs about 100g. Weigh each item; the group that was closest scores a point. Repeat for 250g, 500g and 1kg. Which group has the most points?

Hold up various items, eg a pencil, a large book, a bag of crisps. Discuss whether each would be weighed in grams or kilograms.

The children work through photocopiable page 193.

DIFFERENTIATION

More able: Write a list of things it would be sensible to weigh in grams, and a list of things it would be sensible to weigh in kilograms.

Less able: Work through the first part of the sheet with the teacher.

PLENARY

Read out some weights in kilograms; the children write them down in grams.

RESOURCES

Paper bags containing different items (eg cubes, corks, paper clips, fruit, vegetables, sugar, rice); sets of weights (eg 100g, 250g, 500g, 750g, 1kg), numeral cards (one set per pair).

PREPARATION

Put a set of weights on each table. Make sure the bags are safely sealed. For Lesson 10, change the weight in each bag.

VOCABULARY
Mass, weight, kilogram, gram, unit of measurement, convert, smaller, larger, scales, balance.

LEARNING OUTCOMES

ORAL AND MENTAL STARTER
● Derive quickly all pairs of multiples of 50 with a total of 1000.
● Convert larger to smaller units (eg kg to g).

MAIN TEACHING ACTIVITY
● Use, read and write standard metric units (kg, g) including their abbreviations, and relationships between them.
● Record estimates and readings from scales to a suitable degree of accuracy.

ORAL AND MENTAL STARTER

NUMERAL CARDS: Tell the children you have a bag of flour weighing 1kg, but 250g has been removed. How much is left? In pairs, the children hold up numeral cards. Repeat with other multiples of 50g, starting at 1kg each time.

MAIN TEACHING ACTIVITY

HOW MUCH MASS? Tell the children they are going to estimate the weight of various items. Draw a scale on the board from 0kg to 2kg, with divisions every 100g. Draw an arrow pointing to 700g; ask the children what the scale shows. Repeat with other numbers, eg 1400g, 950g. Ask a child to come and pick up one of the bags to be weighed, then make an estimate of its mass. They might want to compare it with the weights available. *Does it weigh more than 500g? Does it weigh less than 1kg?*

The children work in groups to estimate and measure the weight of each bag.

DIFFERENTIATION

More able: Work with fewer weights to compare against.
Less able: Work with teacher guidance.

PLENARY

Look at weights more than 1kg. *How could we write that in grams if we know that 1kg = 1000g?* Convert several weights from kg to g.

LESSON 10

For the **Oral and mental starter**, say a weight in kilograms. The class respond together, saying how many grams it is – eg *2.5kg is 2500 grams*. For the **Main teaching activity**, extend Lesson 9: The children work in groups, making estimates of mass without direct comparison with a weight. Once the first bag has been weighed, it can be used to help with the estimates of others. More able children could estimate the masses of eight or more bags; less able children could estimate the masses of four bags. In the Plenary, write some estimates for the masses of the bags (some of which are clearly wrong) on the board; discuss which may be true, which cannot be true, and why.

LEARNING OUTCOMES	**ORAL AND MENTAL STARTER** ● Read the time from an analogue clock to the nearest minute. **MAIN TEACHING ACTIVITY** ● Use units of time; read the time on a 24-hour digital clock and use 24-hour clock notation, such as 19:53.
RESOURCES	A class set of clock faces with moveable hands; TV listings from newspapers or magazines; a list of 12-hour to 24-hour clock conversions (see 'Differentiation').
ORAL AND MENTAL STARTER	SHOW ME: Ask the children to show times on clock faces, eg *Show me 4:30. Show me quarter to 3. It is now 11:50, show me 20 minutes later.* Include 24-hour clock times: *Show me 18:15.*
MAIN TEACHING ACTIVITY	REVISION OF 24-HOUR CLOCK: Tell the children they are going to write times using the 24-hour clock. Recap 24-hour clock times. The children work in pairs to choose ten TV programmes, writing their start and finish times in the 12-hour and 24-hour clock, and calculating the length of each programme.
DIFFERENTIATION	More able: Look at train timetables and calculate different journey times. Less able: Use a prepared sheet with 12-hour to 24-hour clock conversions.
PLENARY	Ask questions relating to the programmes, eg *How much time would I spend watching TV if I watched _____ and _____?*

RESOURCES

Local train and bus timetables; travel brochures (including flight or ferry crossings); calculators; photocopiable page 194; numeral cards (one set per pair).

PREPARATION

Collect enough local timetables and travel brochures to provide a selection for each table.

VOCABULARY
Conversion, currency, 24-hour clock, timetable, arrive, depart, how long will it take?

LEARNING OUTCOMES

ORAL AND MENTAL STARTER
● Derive quickly all two-digit pairs that total 100.
MAIN TEACHING ACTIVITY
● Use units of time; read the time on a 24-hour digital clock and use 24-hour clock notation, such as 19:58. Use timetables.
● **Use all four operations to solve word problems involving numbers and quantities** based on 'real life', money and measures **(including time)**, using one or more steps including, making simple conversions of pounds to foreign currency.

ORAL AND MENTAL STARTER

NUMERAL CARDS: Repeat from Lesson 1.

MAIN TEACHING ACTIVITY

PLAN A HOLIDAY: Tell the children they are going to plan a holiday. They will need to work out the time for each stage of the journey, and the costs in pounds and in the currency of the country they are travelling to. Give them a few currencies to choose from. Go over how to change one currency to another, eg *If there are 9 francs to £1, how many francs are* there to £2? How would we calculate £50 worth of francs? Multiply 9 by 50. Go over the bus, train and plane timetable information they will need.

Talk through how to fill in photocopiable page 194. The children work in groups to find information and plan a holiday. They will have a further lesson to do this.

DIFFERENTIATION

More able: Extend the holiday to a second destination. Less able: Concentrate on timetables and total cost rather than currency conversion.

PLENARY

Discuss what the groups have done. *How much money have you spent so far in pounds and in francs?*

LESSON 13

For the **Oral and mental starter**, put a set of numeral cards out in the centre of each group's table. Ask questions related to foreign currency, eg *There are 3 marks to the pound. How many marks do you get for £12?* For the **Main teaching activity**, continue Lesson 12 after recapping what information the children need and what they have done so far. In the **Plenary**, groups describe their planned holiday – where they are going, when, and how much it will cost (in both pounds and foreign currency)?

LESSON 14 +15

RESOURCES

Measure, time and money problems from textbooks or worksheets; calculators; a set of number cards 1–20 per group.

PREPARATION

Write five word problems involving measures, time and/or money on the board, eg *A room is 4m long and 2.5m wide. If carpet costs £12 per square metre, how much will it cost to carpet the room? Sugar costs 85p per kilo. From a 20kg bag of sugar, 5 kilos have been removed. How much will the remaining sugar cost?*

<table>
<tr><td>

VOCABULARY

Capacity, millilitres, litres, weight, mass, kilograms, grams, length, height, centimetres, millimetres, metres, kilometres, area, perimeter, metres squared, centimetres squared, money, pounds, pence.

</td></tr>
</table>

LEARNING OUTCOMES

ORAL AND MENTAL STARTER
● Derive quickly all pairs of multiples of 50 with a total of 1000.
● **Use all four operations to solve word problems involving numbers and quantities** based on 'real life', money and measures, using one or more steps.

MAIN TEACHING ACTIVITY
● **Use all four operations to solve word problems involving numbers and quantities** based on 'real life', money and measures **(including time)**, using one or more steps.
● Choose and use appropriate number operations to solve problems, and appropriate ways of calculating (mental, mental with jottings, written methods, calculator) to solve problems.

ORAL AND MENTAL STARTER

PAIRS TO 1000: Give the class a 3-digit multiple of 50; they respond by saying how many more to make 1000.

MAIN TEACHING ACTIVITY

PROBLEM SOLVING: Tell the children they are going to solve a range of problems involving different measures: money, time, length, capacity, weight, area and perimeter. Brainstorm the sort of problems that could be given. Look at the questions on the board. In pairs, the children work out how to do them and what the answers are. Discuss solutions as a class; encourage children to come up and explain their work on the board, using jottings or standard written methods.

The children work out problems from school resources individually, showing their method of working out each problem.

DIFFERENTIATION

More able: Try problems involving at least two steps.
Less able: Stick to one-step problems, with the teacher indicating which operation is required.

PLENARY

Go through several problems, discussing which operation each one requires. Check the answers on a calculator; discuss how amounts of money and time are displayed, eg *7.5 could mean £7.50; 1.25 could mean an hour and 15 minutes.*

LESSON 15

For the **Oral and mental starter**, play PROBLEMS BINGO: Each group chooses five number cards from the set 1–20. Ask questions, eg *A room has an area of 24m² and a width of 4m. What is its length?* If a group has the 6 card, they turn it over. Play until a group has turned over all its cards. For the **Main teaching activity**, go over the work from Lesson 14. Remind the children to show their method of calculation. Work through a couple of examples. The children continue with the problems, then swap with a partner and check using a calculator. In the **Plenary**, go over any difficulties.

UNITS 8–10

Name the angle

Label each angle as **acute**, **right** or **obtuse**.

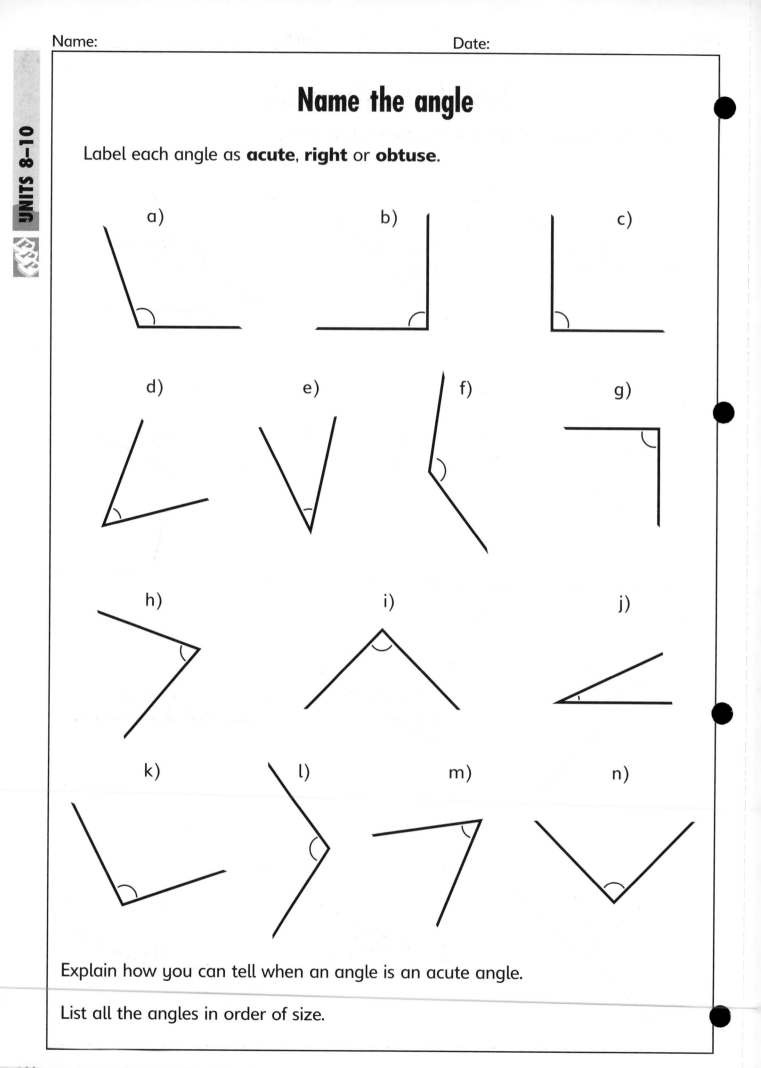

Explain how you can tell when an angle is an acute angle.

List all the angles in order of size.

Name: Date:

Find the missing angle

Use the angle shown to work out the missing angle.

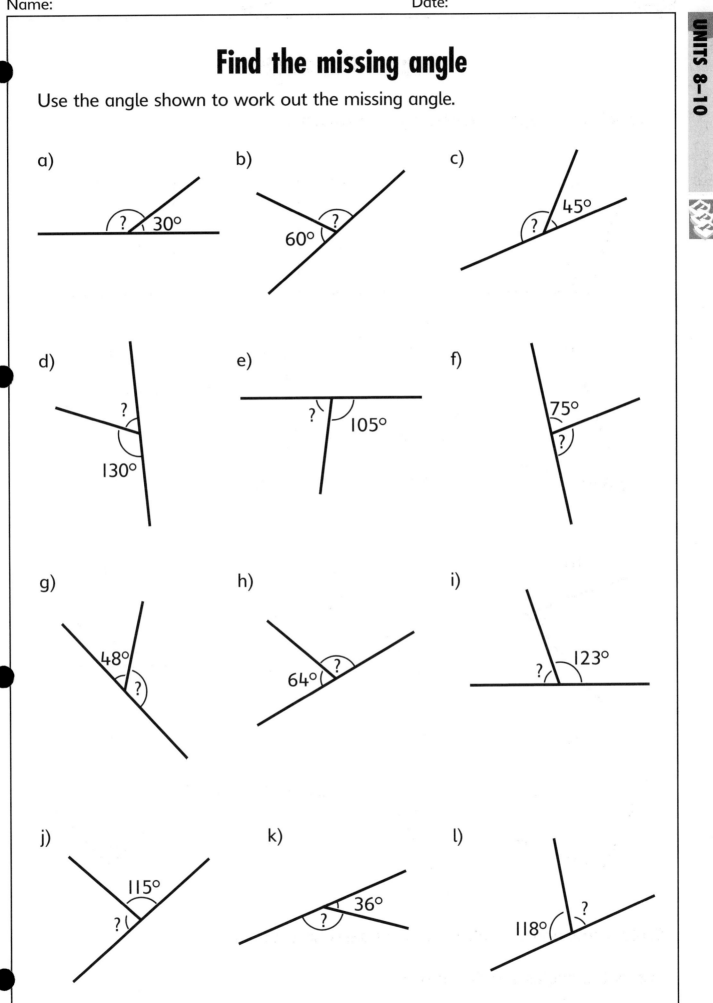

a)

? / 30°

b)

60° ?

c)

45° ?

d)

? 130°

e)

? 105°

f)

75° ?

g)

48° ?

h)

64° ?

i)

? 123°

j)

115° ?

k)

36° ?

l)

118° ?

UNITS 8–10

Angles in polygons

Measure the angles in each triangle.
Find the sum of the angles in each triangle.

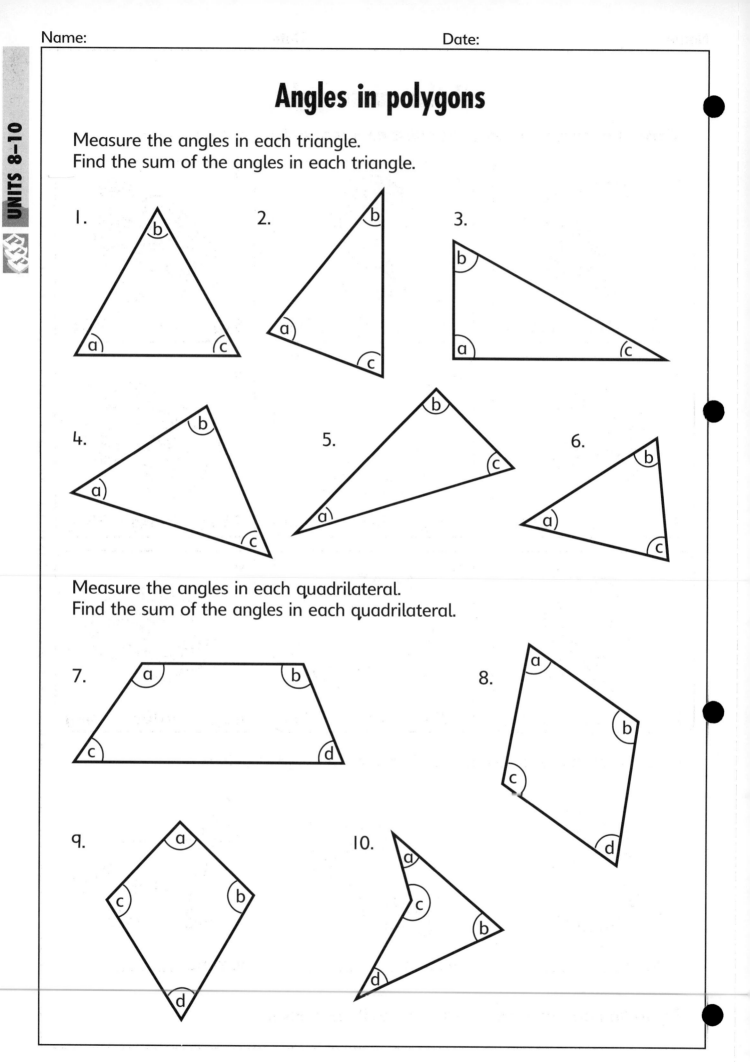

Measure the angles in each quadrilateral.
Find the sum of the angles in each quadrilateral.

Name: _____   Date: _____

Guess my weight

Circle the mass that would be most appropriate for the item shown.

1.
100g   1kg   100kg

2.
35g   3.5kg   35kg

3.
5kg   50kg   500kg

4.
2g   20g   200g

5.
400g   4kg   40kg

6.
250g   2.5kg   25kg

7.
2.5g   25g   250g

8.
200g   2kg   20kg

9.
40g   400g   4kg

Write an estimate for the mass of each of the objects below.

10.

weight: _____

11.

weight: _____

12.

weight: _____

Try to find out the mass of each of the items above.

Planning a holiday

Use timetables and holiday brochures to plan a holiday. Try to complete as many of the questions below as possible.

Travelling from: _____ to: _____

Use an atlas to work out the approximate distance from

home to destination: _____ miles.

Currency of destination: _____

Exchange rate: _____

Time of departure of local bus/train to airport: _____

Time of arrival of local bus/train at airport: _____

Time taken to travel from home to airport: _____

Departure time of flight: _____

Local arrival time of flight: _____

Length of flight (hours and minutes): _____

Cost of bus/train to airport: _____

Cost of flight: _____

Cost of hotel: _____

or

Cost of hotel and flight together
(package holiday): _____

Total cost in pounds: _____

Total cost in foreign currency: _____

ORGANISATION (5 LESSONS)

	LEARNING OUTCOMES	ORAL AND MENTAL STARTER	MAIN TEACHING ACTIVITY	PLENARY
LESSON 1	● Add or subtract the nearest multiple of 10 or 100, then adjust. ● Use known number facts and place value for mental addition and subtraction. ● Check the sum of several numbers by adding in the reverse order.	FIRST OVER TARGET: Count up or down in steps of 10 or 100 from a 2-digit number.	MENTAL ADDITION AND SUBTRACTION: Select best methods for a range of calculations.	Use near multiples of 100 when adding and subtracting.
LESSON 2	● Identify near doubles. ● Use known number facts and place value for mental addition and subtraction. ● Check with an equivalent calculation.	QUICK-FIRE DOUBLES: Groups give doubles of 2-digit numbers.	NEAR DOUBLES: Use near doubles to add nearly equal numbers.	Add three numbers including a near double.
LESSON 3	● Extend written methods to: addition or subtraction of a pair of decimal fractions, both with one or both with two decimal places. ● Develop further the relationship between addition and subtraction. ● Check with the inverse operation when using a calculator. ● Develop calculator skills and use a calculator effectively.	NUMERAL CARDS: Repeat from Lesson 12, Unit 10.	STANDARD METHODS: Add and subtract amounts of money using standard written methods. Check with a calculator using inverse operation.	Judge whether money calculations may be correct.
LESSON 4	● Extend written methods to: addition or subtraction of a pair of decimal fractions, both with one or both with two decimal places. ● **Use all four operations to solve word problems involving numbers and quantities** based on 'real life', money and measures, using one or more steps.	APPROXIMATIONS: Select numbers to make a given approximate total or difference.	PROBLEM SOLVING: Use standard method to solve addition and subtraction word problems.	Look at word problems: which operation is needed?
LESSON 5	● **Use all four operations to solve word problems involving numbers and quantities** based on 'real life', money and measures, using one or more steps. ● Develop calculator skills and use a calculator effectively. ● Choose and use appropriate number operations to solve problems, and appropriate ways of calculating: mental, mental with jottings, written methods, calculator.	PROBLEMS BINGO: As for Lesson 15, Unit 10, but focus on money problems.	MONEY PROBLEMS: Solve word problems, deciding on most appropriate method.	Check solutions using an OHP calculator.

> **ORAL AND MENTAL SKILLS:** Count on or back in steps of tens or hundreds, starting from any two- or three-digit number (Year 3 revision). Derive quickly: all two-digit pairs that total 100; doubles of all whole numbers 1 to 100. Estimate by approximating (round to nearest 10 or 100), then check result. **Use all four operations to solve word problems involving numbers and quantities** based on 'real life', money and measures, using one or more steps.

Lessons 1 and 2 are shown in detail. Lessons 3 and 5 follow on from what has already been taught.

RESOURCES

Photocopiable page 199; a set of 2-digit number cards.

PREPARATION

Adjust copies of photocopiable page 199 for more or less able children.

VOCABULARY

Tens,
hundreds,
multiple,
near multiple,
add, subtract,
sum, total,
difference.

LEARNING OUTCOMES

ORAL AND MENTAL STARTER
● Count on or back in steps of tens or hundreds, starting from any two- or three-digit number.

MAIN TEACHING ACTIVITY
● Add or subtract the nearest multiple of 10 or 100, then adjust.
● Use known number facts and place value for mental addition and subtraction.
● Check the sum of several numbers by adding in the reverse order.

ORAL AND MENTAL STARTER

FIRST OVER TARGET: Divide the class into groups. The first group picks a 2-digit number card from a pack and says the number 10 more than it; the next group says the number 10 more than that, and so on. The first group to go over 100 scores a point. Repeat so that each group has a go at starting. Start with the first group again and count down to a number below zero. Then try counting up in hundreds from a 2-digit number – which group is the first to go over 1000? Which group has the most points?

MAIN TEACHING ACTIVITY

MENTAL ADDITION AND SUBTRACTION: Write 127 + 39 = on the board. Ask the children how they would solve it. Discuss possibilities, eg *round 39 to 40, add on 40 and subtract 1* or *add on 30, then add on 9*. Show how these will give the same answer. Now write   276 – 58 = on the board. Discuss different methods, asking children to jot their methods on the board. Write 320 + 490 = on the board; discuss methods. Compare equivalent calculations and discuss why they are equivalent.

The children work through the questions on photocopiable page 199.

DIFFERENTIATION

Adjust the numbers on the photocopiable sheet for more or less able children.

PLENARY

How would you work out 238 + 998? Encourage the children to round to 1000 and subtract 2.

LESSON 2

RESOURCES

1-place decimal number cards (one set per group).

PREPARATION

Put a set of 1-place decimal cards on each table.

VOCABULARY

Double, near
double,
decimal,
1-place decimal
numbers, two
lots of, add.

LEARNING OUTCOMES

ORAL AND MENTAL STARTER
● Derive quickly doubles of all whole numbers 1 to 100.

MAIN TEACHING ACTIVITY
● Identify near doubles.
● Use known number facts and place value for mental addition and subtraction.
● Check with an equivalent calculation.

ORAL AND MENTAL STARTER

QUICK-FIRE DOUBLES: Ask each child to give you a number between 1 and 100; write the numbers on the board. The first group double the first number, the second group the second etc. Continue round the room until all the numbers have been doubled correctly. How quickly can it be done?

MAIN TEACHING ACTIVITY

NEAR DOUBLES: Write 25 + 26 = on the board. Ask the children to calculate the answer. Discuss the different methods used; focus on the method *double 25 and add on 1*. Tell the children this lesson is about using near doubles to make adding easier. Write 1.5 + 1.6 =. *How would you calculate the answer?* Encourage the method *double 1.5 and add on 0.1*. Check the answer is correct by using an equivalent calculation, eg 1 + 1 + 0.5 + 0.6 =.

Pick a decimal number card (eg 2.7) and write it on the board, plus the next 1-place decimal number: 2.7 + 2.8 =. Remind the children that they can use their knowledge of doubles of whole numbers to help them: *What is double 27? 54. So what is double 2.7? 5.4. So 2.7 add 2.8 is 5.5.* Check with an equivalent calculation. Repeat, starting with a different decimal number.

The children each take a decimal number card to generate a near double calculation.

DIFFERENTIATION

More able: Choose a decimal number, write down the next 1-place decimal, then choose another decimal number to add on, eg 3.4 + 3.5 + 1.7 =.
Less able: Use 2-digit whole number cards.

PLENARY

Write 2.5 + 1.2 + 2.6 = on the board. *How could we use knowledge of near doubles to help us calculate the answer?*

LEARNING OUTCOMES	ORAL AND MENTAL STARTER ● Derive quickly: all two-digit pairs that total 100. **MAIN TEACHING ACTIVITY** ● Extend written methods to: addition or subtraction of a pair of decimal fractions, both with one or both with two decimal places. ● Develop further the relationship between addition and subtraction. ● Check with the inverse operation when using a calculator. ● Develop calculator skills and use a calculator effectively.
RESOURCES	Addition and subtraction questions involving money from textbooks or worksheets; numeral cards (one set per pair); calculators.
ORAL AND MENTAL STARTER	NUMERAL CARDS: Repeat from Lesson 12, Unit 10.
MAIN TEACHING ACTIVITY	STANDARD METHODS: Remind the children how to use the standard algorithms for addition and subtraction. Work through some examples using money; check the solutions as a class, using the inverse operation on a calculator. Stress the importance of reading the display correctly, eg 13.2 means £13.20. The children work through 10 to 20 problems, then check each other's solutions on a calculator.
DIFFERENTIATION	More able: Do calculations with a mixture of 1- and 2-place decimal numbers. Less able: Continue with expanded written method if necessary.
PLENARY	Write some money calculations on the board with answers (some clearly incorrect). *Which could and could not be right?* Include an incorrect interpretation of a calculator display, eg £4.55 + £3.75 = 8.3.

RESOURCES

Photocopiable page 200, an OHP calculator.

PREPARATION

Write twelve 3-digit numbers on the board.

LEARNING OUTCOMES

ORAL AND MENTAL STARTER

● Estimate by approximating (round to nearest 10 or 100), then check result.

UNIT 11

VOCABULARY

Add, sum,
total,
difference,
more than,
less than,
how much
more than,
calculate.

MAIN TEACHING ACTIVITY

● Extend written methods to: addition or subtraction of a pair of decimal fractions, both with one or both with two decimal places.
● **Use all four operations to solve word problems involving numbers and quantities** based on 'real life', money and measures, using one or more steps.

ORAL AND MENTAL STARTER

APPROXIMATIONS: Ask each group to look at the numbers on the board. *You have 20 seconds to find a pair of numbers that have a total of about 500.* Write down the numbers suggested. Check the pairs of numbers on an OHP calculator. *Which pair is closest?* The group whose pair is closest scores a point. Repeat several times with different criteria, eg a difference of about 300.

MAIN TEACHING ACTIVITY

PROBLEM SOLVING: Tell the children they are going to solve money problems involving addition and subtraction. They must calculate their answers using a written method. Ask pairs to think of an addition problem. Choose a pair and write their addition on the board, eg *Sarah has £5.50 and Susan has £6.85. How much do they have altogether?* Read the problem as a class, then write down the vertical algorithm:

$$\begin{array}{r} £6.85 \\ + \ £5.50 \\ \hline \end{array}$$

Calculate the answer. Repeat with a subtraction problem.
   The children work in pairs through the problems on photocopiable page 200.

DIFFERENTIATION

More able: Write other possible questions to go with some of the calculations.
Less able: Work with simpler numbers.

PLENARY

Work through the photocopiable sheet. Ask the class what each question means, and whether it requires you to add or subtract.

LESSON 5

LEARNING OUTCOMES	**ORAL AND MENTAL STARTER** ● **Use all four operations to solve word problems involving numbers and quantities** based on 'real life', money and measures, using one or more steps. **MAIN TEACHING ACTIVITY** ● **Use all four operations to solve word problems involving numbers and quantities** based on 'real life', money and measures, using one or more steps. ● Develop calculator skills and use a calculator effectively. ● Choose and use appropriate number operations to solve problems, and appropriate ways of calculating: mental, mental with jottings, written methods, calculator.
RESOURCES	Calculators; money problems involving all four operations from textbooks or worksheets.
ORAL AND MENTAL STARTER	PROBLEMS BINGO: As for Lesson 15, Unit 10, but focus this time on money problems.
MAIN TEACHING ACTIVITY	MONEY PROBLEMS: Tell the children they are going to solve problems involving all four rules and money. They can decide on the most appropriate way of calculating. Discuss what would not be appropriate, eg adding £5 and £4 on a calculator. The children may decide to use jotting rather than a standard written method.
DIFFERENTIATION	Select different problems at three levels of difficulty.
PLENARY	Check the solutions using an OHP calculator, asking children to come and input their calculations.

Name: Date:

Use what you know

Use rounding to help you work these out.

1.   45 + 39 =

2.   72 + 49 =

3.   137 + 29 =

4.   264 + 79 =

5.   126 + 88 =

6.   213 + 68 =

7.   56 – 29 =

8.   124 – 48 =

9.   241 – 69 =

10. 353 – 58 =

11. 294 – 79 =

12. 227 – 89 =

Solve these. Think about what might help you.

13. 270 + 130 =

14. 430 – 150 =

15. 360 + 220 =

16. 510 – 170 =

17. 260 + 240 =

18. 720 – 360 =

19. 390 + 350 =

20. 600 – 330 =

21. 470 + 460 =

22. 920 – 450 =

23. 380 + 620 =

24. 1000 – 530 =

UNIT 11

Money – addition and subtraction

Write down the methods you use to
work out the answers to these problems.

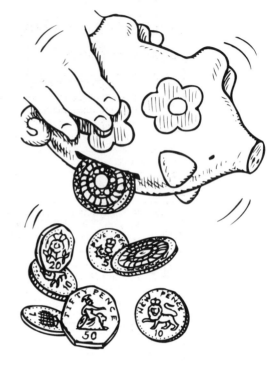

1. Jill gets £7.50 pocket money on
   Friday night. On Saturday morning
   she has £3.65 left. How much has
   she spent?

2. George has £4.65, Daniel has £3.85
   and Shaun has £5.35.

   a) How much have the three friends
   got altogether?

   b) How much more has Shaun got
   than Daniel?

3. Omar has £8.40 in his money box.

   a) Omar wants to buy a book which costs £4.95. If he buys it, how
   much will he have left?

   b) Omar decides not to buy the book, because he is saving for a CD
   which costs £12.95. How much more does he need to save?

4. Tricia buys 2 pens which cost £1.85 each, and a new pencil case which
   costs 95p. How much does she spend?

5. Sally, Jake and Karen are all given some money by their Grandma. It is
   shared out so that Sally gets £5.30, Jake gets £3.75 and Karen gets
   £2.45. How much did their Grandmother give them altogether?

6. In a sale, a book is reduced in price from £12.50 to £8.95. How much
   cheaper is it than before?

7. Kelly has saved up £13.65. She is given another £5.50 as a present, and
   spends £7.39 on a new bag. How much money does she have left?

8. Lara has to buy two presents. One costs £6.79 and the other costs
   £8.45. She has £20 altogether. How much will she have left after buying
   the two presents?

UNIT 12

ORGANISATION (5 LESSONS)

	LEARNING OUTCOMES	ORAL AND MENTAL STARTER	MAIN TEACHING ACTIVITY	PLENARY
LESSON 1	● Recognise and extend number sequences formed by counting from any number in steps of constant size, extending beyond zero when counting back, eg count on or back in steps of 0.1, 0.2, 0.3... ● Explain methods and reasoning, orally and in writing.	CLASS CHANTING: Count up or back in steps of different sizes, going beyond zero.	PATTERNS IN SEQUENCES: Look at patterns of counting in decimals. Explain patterns found.	Discuss patterns found.
LESSON 2 +3	● Recognise multiples of 6, 7, 8, 9 up to the 10th multiple. ● Know and apply tests of divisibility by 2, 4, 5, 10 or 100. ● Know squares of numbers to at least 10 × 10. ● Solve mathematical problems or puzzles, recognise and explain patterns and relationships, generalise and predict; suggest extensions asking 'What if...?'	STAND UP: Repeat from Plenary of Lesson 2, Unit 11 of Term 2. MYSTERY NUMBER BINGO: Turn over cards with answers.	MYSTERY NUMBERS: Find a mystery number from information about it. Write own mystery number clues; swap to solve.	Go through the puzzles. Go through children's puzzles. Discuss and explain findings.
LESSON 4 +5	● Find all the pairs of factors of any number up to 100. ● Make and investigate a general statement about familiar numbers by finding examples that satisfy it.	FACTOR PAIRS: Groups hold up factor pairs for a given number.	FINDING FACTORS: Find out which number from 1 to 100 has the most factors. Investigate numbers which have an odd number of factors.	Discuss findings: is there a pattern?

ORAL AND MENTAL SKILLS: Count on or back in steps of different sizes. Know and apply tests of divisibility by 2, 4, 5, 10 or 100. Solve mathematical problems or puzzles. Find all the pairs of factors of any number up to 100.

Lessons 1, 2 and 4 are shown in detail. Lessons 3 and 5 follow on from what has already been taught.

LESSON 1

RESOURCES
Calculators; OHP calculator.

PREPARATION
Write these instructions on the board:

1. Put a whole number into the calculator.
2. Keep adding 0.1 to the number.
3. Write down the sequence.
4. How many additions until you reach another whole number? Can you explain why?
5. Repeat with sequences that go up in 0.2, 0.3, 0.4 and 0.5.

LEARNING OUTCOMES

ORAL AND MENTAL STARTER
● Count on or back in steps of different sizes.

VOCABULARY

Pattern,
count on,
count back,
sequence,
next.

MAIN TEACHING ACTIVITY

● Recognise and extend number sequences formed by counting from any number in steps of constant size, extending beyond zero when counting back, eg count on or back in steps of 0.1, 0.2, 0.3...
● Explain methods and reasoning, orally and in writing.

ORAL AND MENTAL STARTER

CLASS CHANTING: Start chanting a count; the children join in when they know how it is going, eg *3, 7, 11, 15...* When you clap your hands, they count back down and beyond zero. Then ask groups to chant the numbers. Do a range of different sequences.

MAIN TEACHING ACTIVITY

PATTERNS IN SEQUENCES: Tell the children they are going to investigate patterns in number sequences. Do some counting in steps of 0.1, led by the OHP calculator (using the constant function). Repeat, going up in steps of 0.2 from a decimal number.

Go through the instructions on the board; do the first one together, encouraging the children to think about why there are ten steps of 0.1 from one whole number to the next. The children then work independently on steps of 0.2, 0.3, 0.4 and 0.5.

DIFFERENTIATION

More able: use steps with two decimal places, eg 0.15, 0.35.
Less able: Start with steps of 0.2 and 0.5, supported by the teacher.

PLENARY

Discuss the children's findings. *What patterns did you find? How many steps did you take? Why do you think you needed 5 steps of 0.2?*

RESOURCES

Photocopiable page 205; numeral cards (one set per pair).

PREPARATION

Write three 'mystery number' desciptions on the board, eg *I am a multiple of 6 between 40 and 50, and the sum of my digits is 6; The product of my digits is 2, and I am a multiple of 7; I am an even 2-digit square number over 50.*

VOCABULARY

Multiple,
divisible,
square
number,
puzzle, clue,
times table,
sum, product,
difference.

LEARNING OUTCOMES

ORAL AND MENTAL STARTER
● Know and apply tests of divisibility by 2, 4, 5, 10 or 100.
● Solve mathematical problems or puzzles.

MAIN TEACHING ACTIVITY
● Recognise multiples of 6, 7, 8, 9 up to the 10th multiple.
● Know and apply tests of divisibility by 2, 4, 5, 10 or 100.
● Know squares of numbers to at least 10 × 10.
● Solve mathematical problems or puzzles, recognise and explain patterns and relationships, generalise and predict; suggest extensions asking 'What if...?'

ORAL AND MENTAL STARTER

STAND UP: Repeat from Plenary of Lesson 2, Unit 11 of Term 2.

MAIN TEACHING ACTIVITY

MYSTERY NUMBERS: Tell the children they are going to work out what some mystery numbers are from clues. Go over the vocabulary they need (see list in margin). Look at the first problem on the board (see examples in 'Preparation' above). *What information do we have? It's a number between 40 and 50, it's a multiple of 6. What multiples of 6 are between 40 and 50? 42 and 48. Which of those numbers has digits that total 6? 42.* Work through the other problems.

The children work through photocopiable page 205 in pairs. Encourage them to check by trying different numbers, eg *What if we tried 27; does that fit all the criteria?*

DIFFERENTIATION

More able: After completing the sheet, go on to write their own clues and swap with a partner to work out the mystery numbers.

Less able: Work on simpler problems, eg *I am a number in the 5 times table between 20 and 30. What am I?*

PLENARY

Go through some of the problems on the sheet together. *What do you think the mystery number is? Why?* Discuss methods.

LESSON 3

For the **Oral and mental starter**, play MYSTERY NUMBER BINGO: Pairs select five numeral cards. Give 'mystery number' clues, eg *I'm thinking of a number. If I double it and add 5, the answer I get is 21.* If a pair has the answer, they turn it over. Continue until a pair has turned all its cards over. Discuss methods after each question. For the **Main teaching activity**, go over Lesson 2. Write some 'mystery number' clues as a class. Pairs of children then write five clues and swap with another pair to solve. Stress that each clue should have only one possible answer. More able children can write clues for three-digit numbers. Work with less able children to write and check clues. In the **Plenary**, try out some of the children's clues with the whole class.

LESSON 4 +5

RESOURCES

A large 10 × 10 multiplication grid; numeral cards (one set per child).

PREPARATION

Put up the multiplication grid so the class can see it.

LEARNING OUTCOMES

ORAL AND MENTAL STARTER
● Find all the pairs of factors of any number up to 100.
MAIN TEACHING ACTIVITY
● Find all the pairs of factors of any number up to 100.
● Make and investigate a general statement about familiar numbers by finding examples that satisfy it.

ORAL AND MENTAL STARTER

FACTOR PAIRS: Repeat from Lesson 1, Unit 2 of Term 2.

MAIN TEACHING ACTIVITY

FINDING FACTORS: Tell children they are going to find factors of numbers. *Pairs of factors are whole numbers that can be multiplied together to make a number. The factors of 12 are 1 and 12, 2 and 6, 3 and 4.* Ask the children to work with a partner, looking at the multiplication grid if necessary, to find the factors of 20. *Remember that 1 and the number itself are always factors of a number.* Take feedback on the factors of 20. Try other numbers, eg 28, 39, 52. Remind the children of factors they will not find on the multiplication grid, eg 32 has 16 as a factor.

VOCABULARY

Factor, pair, product, multiply.

The children work in small groups to find out which of the numbers up to 100 has the most factors.

DIFFERENTIATION

More able: Work on numbers to 200.
Less able: Work on numbers to 50.

PLENARY

Which numbers had the most factors? Suggestions might include 36, 48, 72, 96. *What numbers are all these numbers multiples of?*

Number	Factors	Number of factors
1	1	1
2	1, 2	2
3	1, 3	2
4	1, 2, 4	3
5	1, 5	2
6	1, 2, 3, 6	4

LESSON 5

For the **Oral and mental starter**, put a number of sets of numeral cards on each table. Say a number; the group holds up as many different factor pairs as possible. For the **Main teaching activity**, go over Lesson 4. The children then investigate which numbers have an odd number of factors. Start a table together on the board, with the headings: *number, factors, number of factors*. Work through the numbers 1 to 5 as a class. The children work in pairs or small groups to continue the table and try and find out what is special about numbers with an odd number of factors. More able children could write an explanation of why square numbers have an odd number of factors. Less able children could use calculators to check the factors. In the **Plenary**, ask: *Which numbers had an odd number of factors? What is special about 1, 4, 9, 16, 25...?*

Which number am I?

Use the clues to discover each mystery number.

1. I am a 2-digit number between 10 and 20. I am a multiple of 3 and the sum of my digits is 3.

2. I am a 2-digit even number between 20 and 40. The sum of my digits is 6 and I am in the 6 times table.

3. I am the smallest number divisible by both 2 and 5.

4. I am a two-digit odd number less than 100. I am a square number and the sum of my digits is 9.

5. I am a number divisible by 2, 4, 5 and 10. I am greater than 30 and less than 50.

6. I am a two-digit number. The sum of my digits is 9. I am divisible by 5 and smaller than 50.

7. I am a two-digit number less than 40. Among my factors are 8 and 16.

8. I am the first 3-digit number divisible by 2, 4, 5 and 10.

9. I am a two-digit square number. The difference between my digits is 5 and the sum of my digits is 13.

10. I am a two-digit number divisible by 5. The product of my digits is 25.

11. I am a two-digit odd number less than 60 and more than 30. I have 3 and 13 among my factors, and the sum of my digits is 12.

12. I am a cube number, but also a multiple of 9. I am less than 30 and more than 20.

UNIT 13: Assess & Review

Choose from these activities. During the group activities, some of the children can work with you on practical tasks, while others complete assessment worksheets 6a and 6b which assess their skills in working with factors and multiples, solving word problems and using written methods for long multiplication. The specific assessment criteria for the assessment sheets are to be found at the bottom of each sheet.

RESOURCES

Flip chart, 2-digit number cards.

ORAL AND MENTAL STARTER

ASSESSMENT
Can the children:
● use known number facts and place value for mental addition and subtraction
● add or subtract the nearest multiple of 10, then adjust?

QUICK QUIZ: Give the children ten quick questions concentrating on the above skills, eg *What is 53 add 39? What is 72 subtract 28? Add 3.2 and 4.6. Subtract 320 from 650.* Read each question twice and allow the children 10 seconds to write the answer. Run through the answers together, encouraging the children to give a range of methods.

GROUP ACTIVITIES

ASSESSMENT
Can the children:
● **use all four operations to solve word problems involving numbers and quantities** based on 'real life' and money
● recognise multiples of 6, 7, 8, 9 to the 10th multiple
● show knowledge of squares of numbers to at least 10 x 10
● extend their written methods to long multiplication of TU x TU?

WHICH OPERATION? Read some word problems to the group. After each one, they write down the operation they would use in order to solve the problem (+, −, × or ÷). Run through the answers. Can individual children explain why they chose a particular operation?

WORD PROBLEMS: Write some word problems involving capacity, weight, perimeter and/or area on a flip chart. Read each one to the group, then give pairs of children a couple of minutes to solve it. Can the children explain to their partners how they are going to tackle the problem, then come up with an answer?

PROPERTIES OF NUMBER: Children take turns to pick a 2-digit number card. They must decide whether their number is a square number and/or a multiple of 6, 7, 8 or 9. They must explain to the rest of the group why it is or isn't each of these things by identifying suitable criteria. If they can explain it, they score a point for each property of the number – for example, 49 is a square number and a multiple of 7; 54 is a multiple of 6 and 9; so each would score 2 points. Who can be the first to reach 10 points? Check the children's use of vocabulary is accurate.

LONG MULTIPLICATION: Give each child a 2-digit number card (less than 50) and a numeral card, eg 26 and 7. Ask them to multiply the numbers. They can use a written method for any stage of this activity. Then give them a multiple of 10 (up to 50 but not 10), and ask them to find the product of that and their 2-digit number (eg 26 × 30). Ask them to add their numeral card to their multiple of 10 (eg 37) and find the product of the two 2-digit numbers they now have (26 × 37). Discuss how they did it. Now give them two 2-digit numbers (eg 32 and 27) and ask them to find the product. Observe how they calculate the answer.

Assessment 6a

1. On the grid below, circle the numbers:

- divisible by 2 in red
- divisible by 4 in green
- divisible by 5 in blue
- divisible by 10 in black
- divisible by 100 in purple

24	15	3	17	22
200	40	16	19	27
39	62	500	92	25
30	31	104	85	76

Which numbers have the most circles round them? _____

Explain why you think this is. _____

_____

2. Cross out the numbers which are not factors of the number in the box.

| 12 | | 1 | 2 | 3 | 4 | 5 | 6 | 8 | 12 |

| 25 | | 1 | | 2 | 3 | 5 | | 10 | 25 |

| 28 | | 1 | 2 | 4 | 6 | 7 | 8 | 12 | 14 | 28 |

| 44 | | 1 | 2 | 3 | 4 | 6 | 8 | 11 | 22 | 44 |

- Know and apply tests of divisibility by 2, 4, 5, 10 or 100.
- Find all the pairs of factors of any number up to 100.

Assessment 6b

Join each word problem to the correct calculation and work out the answer.

Ashok has £42.35 saved. Kulvinder has £57.65 saved. How much more has Ashok saved than Kulvinder?	£42.35 × 3 =
A computer game costs £42.35. Sally buys 3 games. How much does she spend?	£57.65 ÷ 5 =
Roberto has £42.35 in the bank. He puts in another £57.65. What is his new bank balance?	£57.65 – £42.35 =
5 friends each win £57.65 on the lottery. How much did they win altogether?	£42.35 + £57.65 =
Vimty has £42.35. She wants to buy some cinema tickets at £3 per ticket. How many can she buy?	£42.35 ÷ 3 =
Adam saved the same amount of money for 5 weeks. At the end of 5 weeks he has £57.65. How much has he saved each week?	£57.65 × 5 =

Write a problem to go with each of the answers below.

$12m^2$ _____

_____

127cm _____

_____

650ml _____

_____

● **Use all four operations to solve word problems involving numbers and quantities** based on 'real life' and money.